To Mark
with whom a fine time
is continuing in rhyme —
we're friends

SHAKESPEARE'S

GHOST

With Best Reading Wishes,

[signature]

Portland, Oregon
April 2003

Being

William Shakespeare's
LIFE
OF THE TRAGEDIC & COMICAL
EARL OF OXFORD
The Legend of Edward deVere

Who Secretly Wrote

as

Shakespeare's Ghost

in the words of
William Shakespeare, Edward deVere,
Edmund Spenser, Christopher Marlowe, John Lyly
Anthony Munday, Ben Jonson & Other Elizabethans,
Famous and Anonymous

Now Known As

SHAKESPEARE'S GHOST

AN HISTORICAL MYSTERY NOVEL

BY

JAMES WEBSTER SHERWOOD

OPUS BOOKS
New York
2002

OPUS BOOKS
Grand Central
Five Central Drive
Plandome, New York 11030-1408
FAX: 516-365-8331
www.opusbooks.com

Opus 2
FIRST EDITION
Privately Printed
October, 2000
Second Printing
August, 2002

Library of Congress Card Number: 00-111977

Copyright [C] 2000 by James Webster Sherwood

opus two
ISBN: 0-9661961-1-2   (Pbk.) $25.00

MADE IN THE UNITED STATES OF AMERICA

TO THE READER

Whether this second printing of 'Shakespeare's Ghost' remains a work in progress or becomes my final stamp of thought upon the subject, only you and time will tell. For me, it's been so long a part of what I represent, with forty nine years since I came to study it, I hardly dare to think what being finished might entail. In truth, I've come to count this effort as a dear beginning. You're buying it up in dazzling numbers. I see the future ripe beyond compare. Should I return to it or not, my friend, be sure your thoughts are foremost in my mind, my pleasure in hearing from you tempered only by the hope you will be kind.

Best Reading Wishes,

Jaz

Sherwood Forest
West Glacier, Montana
August 16, 2002

contents

Principle Characters
in order of appearance

Edward deVere, 17th Earl of Oxford, Lord Great
    Chamberlain of England,Viscount Bulbec, Baron
    Sanforth, Scales & Badlesmere, senior peer of
    the realm
Elizabeth I, Queen of England (1558-1603), daughter of
    King Henry VIII & Anne Boleyn
Henry Wriothesley, 3rd Earl of Southampton, the Tudor rose
Mary, Queen of Scots, Elizabeth's cousin, Catholic claimant
    to the throne
Robert Devereux, Earl of Essex, last companion to the
    English Queen
John deVere, 16th Earl of Oxford, godfather to the Queen
Margery Golding deVere, 2nd Countess of Oxford
Sir William Cecil, Lord Burghley, Chancellor of the
    Exchequer, Lord Treasurer, Head of the Domestic
    Security Forces, Principle Minister to the Queen,
    Oxford's Master of Wards & father-in-law
George Gascoigne, soldier, poet, playwright, deVere family
    equerry
Arthur Golding, Oxford's uncle, Latin tutor, translator of
    Ovid & Calvin
Kathrine deVere, Lady Windsor, Oxford's half-sister
Mary deVere, Lady Willoughby d'Eresby, Oxford's sister
Thomas Radcliffe, 3rd Earl of Sussex, Lord Chamberlain,
    Oxford's friend, mentor & role model
Robert Dudley, Earl of Leicester, Lieutenant Governor of the
    Netherlands, Queen's principle advisor, Oxford's foe
Anne Cecil, 1st Countess of Oxford, sister of
Robert Cecil, Lord Salisbury, Secretary of State, Lord
    Treasurer, son of Sir William

William Shaxpere, Gentleman, of Stratford-upon-Avon,
    grain dealer, actor, theatre manager
Elizabeth Trussel, resident of Stratford, Oxford's
    grandmother
Horatio & Francisco deVere, soldiers, Oxford's cousins
Christopher Hatton, Vice Chamberlain, Minister to the
    Queen, courtier
Peregrine Bertie, Lord Willoughby d'Eresby, Ambassador to
    Denmark, Oxford's brother-in-law
Anthony Munday, author, Oxford's 1st secretary
Rowland Yorke, soldier, duelist, Oxford's bodyguard
Lord Henry Howard, son of the Earl of Surrey, Oxford's
    antagonist
Sir Philip Sidney, poet, soldier, courtier, nephew of Robert
    Dudley, Oxford's nemesis
Mary Sidney Herbert, Countess of Pembroke, poet, sister of
    Sir Philip, patron of Ben Jonson, mother of "the Most
    Noble & Incomparable Pair of Brethren" William &
    Philip, Earls of Pembroke & Montgomery
Anne Vavasour, Queen's Maid of Honor, Oxford's mistress,
    mother of Sir Edward Vere, Oxford's second son
Thomas Knyvet, Gentleman of the Queen's Privy Chamber,
    cousin of Mistress Vavasour & Oxford's foe
Emilia Bassano Lanier, court musician, daughter of the
    Bassano family of musicians, "dark lady of The
    Sonnets"
Ben Jonson, poet laureate, playwright, convicted murderer
Elizabeth deVere, Countess of Derby, Oxford's first
    daughter
Bridget deVere, Countess of Berkshire, wife of Francis, 2nd
    Lord Norris of Rycote & Earl of Berkshire, Oxford's
    second daughter

Susan deVere, Countess of Montgomery, wife of Philip
   Herbert, 1st Earl of Montgomery, Oxford's third
   daughter
William Stanley, 6th Earl of Derby, playwright, Oxford's
   son-in-law
Elizabeth Trentham, 2nd Countess of Oxford, Queen's Maid
   of Honor, first Grand Possessor of Shakespeare's
   Sonnets
King James I, King of England (1603-1625)

With 89 Other Members of the Court & Citizens of the
   Countryside of England, France, Italy & Germany

Set Principally in England
In the Time of the Reign of Their Majesties
Queen Elizabeth I & King James I
1550-1625

I

A BACKWARD FOREWORD

We stood before the massive three-quarter-length Ashbourne oil portrait of Mr. William Shakespeare in the spring of 1995. I took my sons to Washington, D.C., and they bargained with me for all-day visits to the Air & Space and Holocaust Museums, in exchange for which I won from them a half-hour tour of the Folger Shakespeare Library.

He gazed down on us, robed and dignified, his great dome and receding hairline familiar to all. In the long, thin fingers of his right hand he clutched a little book, resting it on a human skull. Such sad, clear eyes and sharp features. In this did immortality reside.

The Ashbourne portrait always was believed to be of Shakespeare, until it was X-rayed in 1940 and, identified by the family crest and seals along with the full head of hair and aristocratic neck ruff, under the retouched oil, to be a contemporary of the bard: Edward deVere, 17th Earl of Oxford, Lord Great Chamberlain of England, senior peer of the realm, Viscount Bulbec, Baron Sanforth, Scales & Badlesmere, third in line of succession to the crown, after Queen Elizabeth and her Scots cousin.

I later learned the Ashbourne Portrait formerly was owned by the Earl of Oxford's widow, and passed down to his granddaughter before it came to America and the Folger where all the world identified it as Shakespeare. Strange they painted over him. I wondered. What was Shakespeare to Oxford and he to Shakespeare that Mr. Shakespeare was made to replace so great a nobleman? What could he have done to justify erasing his identity?

I felt a chill.

"Hey, Pop, that book looks like yours at home," said one of my boys.

I nodded and looked at the portrait with the solemn figure holding a book.

According to George Chapman, writing a play in 1613 called 'The Revenge of Bussy d'Ambois', imitating the style of 'Hamlet', that golden book belonged to Edward deVere. It contained his writings.

"And as the foolish Poet that still wrote all his most self-loved verse on paper royall, or parchment ruled with lead, smoothed with the pumice, bound richly up and strung with crimson strings" - there were four such crimson strings of silk in the Ashbourne portrait; it looked the same as described in 'Romeo and Juliet': "That book in many eyes doth share the glory, that in gold clasps locks in the golden story."

What? The Earl of Oxford a writer also? Who on earth ever heard of him - ever? I was entering a world of questions outnumbering answers.

Chapman knew this earl from the 1590's: "I overtook, coming from Italy, in Germany, a great and famous Earl of England, the most goodly fashioned man I ever saw, from head to foot in form rare, and most absolute; he had a face like one of the most ancient honored Romans, from whence his noblest Family was derived. He was, besides, of spirit passing great, valiant and learned, and liberal as the Sun, spoke and wrote sweetly, or of learned subjects, or of the business of public welfare, and 'twas the Earl of Oxford." He was "*never* so blessed as when he wrote and read the Ape-loved (imitated) issue of his brain, and

2

never but joying in himself; admiring *ever.*" I was entering a world of word-play in the infinite landscape of language.

"Yes, boys, that book which existed then exists today," I said and sighed. We went as we'd agreed to the Air & Space and Holocaust Museums where my sons were pleased to find a more exciting afternoon.

At night at home in the silence of my library in the woods on the North Shore of Long Island, as fog brushed at my leaded windows, I settled in alone, taking from the shadows of my safe that secret, silent, hidden treasure which no one but my loved ones knew I owned. Fortified with a Napoleon orange liqueur, the cover of that "book bound richly up" was opened gingerly. Inside, from the first page penned in the most perfectly measured and beautiful hand, was:

Hackney, May 23, 1593. I, Edward Oxenforde, Lord Great Chamberlain of England, attest I have written words with which I state some truths on which I rest. For thirty years I made the story of our time, and those I knew in books of poetry and plays, by name, the detailed chronicle of our days in rhyme. Concealed as masked, where only they who knew the truth would recognize themselves, all tell I did. Truth is truth in everything I writ, yet hid. But truth in truth, untouched by lies, can never be. I put the humblest person in place of me, as the King of France concealed himself to test the maid of Orleans. I am all but dead, by turning mute, swear for the rest of time, that what was true was mine. My word on this, to which I set my silence, which is my only crime.

The text continued with absolute direction that this be concealed from *any eyes with power, for who can protect it will destroy it.*

3

There was a letter folded into the pages, addressed to: The Honourable Lord Henry Wriothesley, 3rd Earl of Southampton, undated:

My Most Noble & Honourable Lord & Master: I was given by your great (illegible) mss. of his plays 'Othello' and 'Two Gentlemen of Verona' for reading before his untimely passing which he said he was revising and wished my advice on certain matters Italian. No greater author was in our age than Lord Oxford nor one who more valued his plays and scholarship than, yours ever in service, John Florio.

John Florio, I later learned, was a tutor of Southampton and the author of the first English-Latin dictionary.

How this book with Florio's crumbling letter to Southampton came to be in my hands is another story. But here ends the first tale of four centuries of failure in the shadow of glory.

II

I came to own the book, which is the subject here, on June 12, 1961, at a kiosk in Paris, France, for which I paid One Nouveau Franc (20 cents equal value). It was at a flea market in the Palais Royale run by a charity called Pour Que l'Esprit Vivre.

I found the book among many cleared from the neglected store rooms and attics of the old aristocracy, contributed without interest or examination of their value, to raise money for this worthy charity.

It was being attended by a young lady who, when I asked her the price, informed me that everything on display was the same; she was attending it in the absence of her mother.

I have conccaled this woeful book, this revelation, ever since. It took me only twenty cents and forty years, perfectly preserved. I hereby warrant that it has been, since that day, the source of my honor, the pride of my heart and the soul of an historic event. The implications are priceless. Truly, I have been made one of the wealthiest men in the world. With a treasure capable of revolutionizing history, time now has come to bring it out.

What we witness on these pages is one of the diamonds of human expression.

Reader, Beware. There are many ideas here which some will label new and speak against. But none are beyond the grasp of fair intelligence or reason. This is a tragedy of unspeakable magnitude, yet all too familiar. It has been my sorrow and frequent joy to have borne some knowledge of it through these years.

Who said, "I'll not trouble thee with words" and then went to his execution? Truth and answers will emerge here, most troubling indeed. I am not sure I bring you happiness. But let us agree that I bring you "News".

(signed) Owen D. Rhodes, owner and book possessor
Archibald Squire, trustee & counsel for above (as witness)

III

In other times, in other minds, the world was viewed with other eyes. One pair studied the Elizabethan Age for fifty four years, not alone as a scholar but only as a man. Those eyes were Edward deVere's.

For on the road from glory to obscurity villains abound, but heroes too. This story is about one hero who made his name the same as truth, for whom there was no greater beauty or meaning or joy than being truthful - and he died for it. And in the ways of that death died truth, not the little crumbs of truth from the tablecloth of history but the idea of truth itself as the foundation of our living. That is what gives this one man's death a poignant meaning. Edward deVere was meant to be forgotten.

We still pay for the loss of his life. Now all are dead who knew him. So there is no excuse for the truth to appear but indifference and bad temper. Yet can there still be hope for truth? This is how he began his career, as a child of nine, with an epic poem:
"My fathers, the earls of Oxford, before the house of lords,
          five centuries stood,
"In honor ready, in valor steady, to serve this England's
          good.
"My father, the 16th earl, in the Forest of Essex showed me
"The ancient, rusted hilt of a sword plunged into the trunk of
          a tree.
"So deep the blade was enveloped and grown over by sap
          and bark

"I marveled at its deathless age as shadows and stillness
        made their mark.
"Only he who is pure of heart can wield this ancient sword
"To which our English honor gives its deathless word.
"'Someday,' my father said, 'When you lay down your steel
        on Essex wood,
"'You'll smile at death, and meet this shade of truth in
        ghostly hood.'"

The censor who would kill his truth has sealed the
grave of Edward deVere. But the silence ends as we speak
here.

My little golden book opens up.

Part One

"I'll not Trouble Thee with Words"

IV

England went through an age of treason under the rule of Queen Elizabeth.

Not much time, eleven years, elapsed following the death of King Henry VIII before the orphaned Princess Elizabeth was called to lead this poor island nation. Her ten-year-old half-brother, King Edward VI, the son of Jane Seymour, King Henry's third wife, wore the crown for only six years before dying at age sixteen. He was followed by a half-sister, Bloody Queen Mary Tudor, who ruled for five more miserable years.

Mary's reign was troubled by her proxy marriage to King Phillip II of Spain, and her reinstatement of the Catholic religion. Her father, Henry VIII had founded the Church of England upon his break with Rome. The boy king Edward continued to maintain this new church, and many in the populace were loath to return to Catholicism under Mary.

When Mary thought she was pregnant, Princess Elizabeth sent her a complete baby wardrobe and sunny letters, first wondering if she should wear mourning for their brother's death, or bright colors for Mary's ascension. Their brother had named Lady Elizabeth "sweet sister Temperance" and so she was, but he also declared her "illegitimate". Mary never recognized her either as the legal daughter of King Henry, her equal. Instead she sent her to The Tower. The Pope proclaimed Elizabeth a bastard, though Henry VIII, himself descended of a bastard son of John of Gaunt, elevated his own bastard son, Henry Fitzroy, to be Duke of Richmond. He gave him precedence over all

11

his heirs, until death cut him off at the age of six. England was divided by factions over its great king's numerous wives and heirs, each rivaling the other for power, until Elizabeth was chosen by vote of the Privy Council.

In the 16th century, what the misty, green fields of farming England wanted of their monarch was everything - a language, a purse, an army, navy, unified faith and law, stability, and national pride to bring it into a world which was being discovered and conquered by Catholic Spain.

Should England lose its challenge, there would be only triumphant Spain which would own two continents, under the Church of Rome.

Transforming a formerly Catholic country into a devoted Protestant nation, Elizabeth would be obliged to rule on life and death. She was to try the highest-ranked Duke of Norfolk, then her cousin, Mary, Queen of Scots, her protege, Robert Devereux, Earl of Essex, and lastly her son for treason. It would come to that, four found guilty and three executed, beheaded. . . Give a penny to the axeman, thank him for his accuracy, then lay the neck down on the block. . . The details would be horrible. There came many other plots, conspiracies and shortened lives over her reign, often with shortened necks. Religion was politics, politics religion. To be a Catholic was treason. To be a Protestant was to be a good citizen.

The queen became known as Gloriana, Diana, a goddess, The monarch, The last word, The absolute. She sought more than death and power.

Through all, Edward deVere was the first to be noted and the longest to remain in her majesty's intimate confidence - for a time much more, though that was erased.

She visited his father, the 16th Earl of Oxford at Hedingham Castle on her first royal progress three years after her coronation.

The good earl, one of England's leading Protestants, had escorted his god-daughter Princess Elizabeth to her coronation at Westminster Abbey in London from Hatfield House where she had been held, like a prisoner waiting for the death of her half-sister. Elizabeth's internment meant waiting possibly for her own death should the English crown be placed upon her cousin Mary Stuart, Queen of Scots, but she had ministers, lawyers, deal-makers working to her advantage. Their names would become legion.

For Elizabeth that wait was like a death sentence. She'd been imprisoned, along with Robert Dudley, in The Tower under sentence of death. She and Dudley were eight when they first met and Dudley protected her, as a young man, even selling land to provide her money for basic expenses. She knew she was a distinct minority choice for the crown when she was escorted at twenty five to her coronation on November 23, 1558, swept "from the prison to the palace."

The 16th Earl of Oxford officiated as Lord Great Chamberlain of England, holding the sword of state, while the Countess of Oxford, Edward deVere's mother, was a Maid of Honor. The earl told his son how he had been raised at the court of Elizabeth's father, King Henry VIII, and his father, the 15th earl, had been King Henry's godfather. Listening with care, young Edward, at the age of eight, swathed in silks and cambric, nodded with eyes wide, clutched by seriousness and the solemnity of Westminster Abbey. This was his first exposure to the pomp and ceremony of a stately occasion. He gazed about its arched and eerie chancels, wondering what part he'd play within its storied confines.

In his golden book, Edward wrote, *She would a tickler be who, being tickled, tempts to tickle me.*

From that point unfolded such tales of things extraordinary, men hear and nod today and marvel at the lies of adjured history.

Would that I could know in a day long gone what weary labors brought me. Dreamed for a pence, done for a life, betrayed on a whim, and everything lost. I'll say what I must. Pray do not mock me. Had I the gift of prophecy, it might have changed my course, but who deters the oracle that foretells what living cost? Read what is mine, and weap. We two alone will sing like birds in the cage. So we'll live, and pray, and sing, and tell old tales of lies made true and truths turned false, and laugh at gilded butterflies, and hear poor rogues talk of court news; and we'll talk with them too - who loses and who wins; who's out, who's in - and assume the mystery of things as if we were God's spies.

I'll tell you about a boy child of a mother who put him out to be raised as an orphan, and then reclaimed him, not as her son but for her lover, and with him bore a son, to whom she promised a kingdom, but saw her evil done, and regretted everything, withdrew that too, and turned away as though of virgin ice made pure in chilled perfection and denial that her life was never lived, by the hour it was over.

And we'll wear out, in an unwalled prison, packs and sects of great ones that ebb and flow by the moon.

V

Gloriana glorious was in her new raiment, with as many as three hundred carts carrying plate, furniture, her bed and hip-bath, entertained with music of the tambour and pipe, plus cornets and trumpets at rest stops. She rode her horse with a velvet saddle, or sat in an open carriage when passing through villages, a thousand men accompanying her progress of twelve miles per day over fifty miles of muck and mud through the verdant summer mists, picking across countryside, where swarms of gnats from undrained ditches and marshes attacked their steaming horses, fording the river Colne into eastern Essex County to the ancestral home of the earls of Oxford.

It had been one of the greatest castles in England, built in 1140 by the first earl, Aubrey deVere, after his grandfather lead the Norman armies in the conquest of 1066 and married Beatrice, William the Conqueror's half sister, and had five sons.

At the battle of Antioch, on the first Crusade in 1098, Aubrey's father's upraised standard refracted a star of light that lit the field after dark and lead to the defeat of the Saracens. From that time on, the five-pointed star became the lasting symbol of deVere nobility.

In 1151 Queen Matilda died at Hedingham. In 1216 King John attacked the castle after the third earl, Robert deVere, signed the Magna Carta. Hedingham was an oasis of medieval chivalry and knights armoured.

In 1561 Queen Elizabeth was the original monarch to use a carriage through the countryside as a tool of political communication, and what better place to pay homage in her first progress bonding with her people, than going to this center of Protestant and liberal thought.

She was, in her own words, the people's sovereign, a simple woman of English ways, none of that foreign affectation about her manner: "mere English," she liked to say and always praised God who brought her through the dangers of threatened death to the people's throne. She lost no opportunity to declare her love for her countrymen, or their strength to keep her crowned.

This moated Norman Castle Hedingham stood five towering stories in ancient splendor on a hill overlooking the sweeping lands and forests of Essex, visible across all East Anglia with the deVere family colors of black and gold unfurled atop its turrets.

It was supported with outbuildings tended by dozens of women - matrons, maids, cooks, keepers, scullery, linen and sewing servants; and men - falconers, huntsmen, grooms, stablemen, ushers, footmen, porters, underbakers, brewers, gardeners, a barber and a scrivener. There were gardens, orchards, a buttery, kitchen, pantry, cowshed, stable, dovecote, barn, dairy, chicken house, pigsty, cheese press house, farmshed and cider mill. Here a stone wheel ground the juice for hot cider on freezing nights in winter. Also nearby were a forge, sawpit, woodyard, bake house, cellar, carpenter's shop and slaughter house. In the orchard were cherry, plum, apple and apricot trees. Castle Hedingham was a community on which survived the surrounding country, and young Lord Edward was its heir.

As the 16th Earl explained to her majesty, "This monument five hundred years hath stood."

16

Upon her arrival at Hedingham, Elizabeth, now twenty-eight, met her "cousin" (as they who were near and dear were fond of calling each other). Edward, a boy of eleven with tawny, tousled hair in long locks hanging down, and sharp, hawk-bright hazel eyes, bent on one knee and gazed unblinking at her, still breathless from practice with his fencing master.

"God save Your Majesty."

He was heir to the oldest title in England, with those of Viscount Bulbec, Baron Sanforth, Scales & Badlesmere already, and showed the fruits of his expanding intellect by offering the phrase in Latin which became the Oxford family motto: *Vero Nihil Verius* (Nothing as True as Truth).

"Some enigma, some riddle; come, thy l'envoy, begin" as the bard wrote in 'Love's Labors Lost'. And so the queen and her young lord began a relationship that lasted for forty two years.

Elizabeth spoke Latin, Italian, French, Spanish, German, Swedish and English. She was avid in her taste for poetry, which she wrote, and theater, on which she doted.

Edward rode his horse each morning, with the huntsmen went hawking afternoons, and only studied in books after evening prayers.

The stage was at its most primitive then, no fixed location to perform, nor developed style of production. What players gave the audiences were "masques" - playing such characters of Virtue and Vice as Greed, Gluttony, Pride, Lust, Rage, Envy and Sloth, Honor, Decency, Innocence and Truthfulness. The actors covered their faces in masks as the classic Greeks had done and their performances were the more valued as they were universal - and anonymous.

Edward preferred to join his father chasing the red stag with bow and arrows.

At Hedingham, the earls of Oxford had the only resident acting company that performed year round in England, as it had throughout the Tudor reign of seventy six years, though other nobles maintained players. The 16th Earl retained his own playwright, John Bale, who wrote 'King John' and other Protestant dramas presented for their guests in the castle's great hall. This was laid out with a proscenium in the center under galleries for musicians.

In Elizabeth's reign, the stage was to reach its fruition as the prime instrument of royal authority, uniting the masses in policy and on matters of history and morality. She thought it the most popular place for development of their growing common language.

That first night of her majesty's visit, Edward took goose quill to paper at his table made from Essex wood, lit by tallow with linen wicks and, inspired by the excitement, wrote, *To My Lord and Father: I shall make my name known to all the world, in praise of our most beautiful queen, whose reign I shall celebrate to eternity - Edward deVere, Viscount Bulbec,* and he sketched his titular crest of a lion brandishing a spear.

In his golden book he noted, *The innocence of dreams, the dreams of innocence, all pure, all beautiful, all fulfilling, with the deep breath of a boy's clear voice, unwretched by the smoke of evil tongues. How dreams would turn to monsters in the long dark night of time.*

Wherever Elizabeth went, entertainment followed. But at Castle Hedingham it was already in full flower with feasts and games and masques and music to dance to for five days and nights. With her great beehive of long blonde and red hair, and flashing blue-gray eyes, she was ravishing, and not afraid to show it. This was her kind of castle - vibrant. These were her kind of people - Protestants. When the Parliament urged her by formal vote to marry, she informed them she was wed already - to her country. And to every available man in its confines, she was the reigning mistress.

"Come Edward, let us stroll by the river. You and your queen shall cross over this arching Roman bridge."

"Yes, Majesty."

"Now shouldn't we have secret names for each other, as I will be your queen for life and you will be the first earl in my land, the Lord Great Chamberlain, responsible to satisfy me in all matters of royal pleasure? You can kneel to me."

"Yes, Ma'am."

"Very good then, my fine and strong young lord, and you are robust. How bright your eyes. I see a wit. And knotted locks. How swarthy your form for a boy. Why, you're a young man already. But I'll let reality wait on wit. What do you do for play?"

"I ride, your Majesty. I go to the hunt at falconing with my father, and hawking with my tutor, Sir Thomas Smith, in the forests of Essex. When Prince Eric of Sweden landed at Harwich my father entertained him. After dinner we went forth hawking and my father showed him great sport, as did I, killing in his sight both pheasant and partridge. I enjoy lessons in fencing, and at times we have bear baiting here. I love the forest and am much practiced in the lists. I would be a knight of the holy grail, though some say chivalry is dead. I content myself with wrestling and archery."

"Do you like tickling, my Ned?"

"Tickling?"

What a strange question indeed.

Following a family tradition at Castle Hedingham, the 16th Earl maintained a group of actors and musicians. The first earl, Aubrey, built churches and withdrew from the world to live a monastic life after the death of his Beatrice.

19

His sons started the first school in the country for the teaching of peasants to read and count.

For the queen's visit, the good 16th earl directed his actors. "Speak the speech and do not saw the air with your hand."

"Do you enjoy the players, Ned?"

"Yes, I love to perform, and devise masks for everyone. I can present a play for your majesty. I love to joust and duel at word play."

"O, I love plays, Ned! Do provide me one! My life's a play, and everything is make believe. Reach me, thrill me, move me with your staged desires and I'll prove you real!"

"What sort? About battles and soldiers?" Tales of proud deVeres, knights and statesmen all, were an inspiration to his young ears absorbed by every telling of the Crusades until Edward thought himself the heir to Sir Lancelot incarnate.

"Why, I'd rather have a play about love, Ned."

"Yes, your majesty. I'll make it about love and battles, then."

"You are my most precious, Ned. You lift my thoughts from the torpor of state matters."

"I will change the world if you so desire - enchanting fools and beguiling kings! And I'll lead armies to conquer the Spanish!"

"And how you'll make me laugh!"

Castle Hedingham was a source of such learning, and contrasting opinions, even one of the late King Henry's theatrical buffoons, Will Somers, was living out his last years there, bringing mirth and remembrance of times past to nights in the great hall round the hearth and playing games and tricks with the boy. He bore him on his back a thousand times.

To the queen Somers bowed and rolled his cap between his palms when time for introductions came. "I kissed your majesty as a baby," he stammered. "In Great King Henry's company."

"And so you shall, sweet Will, again," she laughed.

Surely on the queen's first progress to Hedingham, with Sir William, her chief minister, bustling in attendance like an unamused doorman of political decorum, there were discussions about the Catholic menace mixed with more topical matters of fruit imports from the tropics and sweet wine monopolies, poetry and theater and why there were no significant play makers to take up the literary rebirth initiated by the deVere family cousin, sonneteer Sir Henry Howard, Earl of Surrey, later made so famous.

But as the fire waned to coals in the grate, the good Earl, vibrant and laughing in health, made light of his future and discussed provisions for his heir, that the queen would assume Edward's upbringing were he to die. Wrestlers were invited to perform by the fire as they spoke.

"But you are not at risk?" the queen asked.

"Sound as a rock," the earl's voice boomed. He was forty nine. "But there is always risk," he added, and glanced toward his wife. The Countess of Oxford turned away.

I sneaked and I listened, from the musician's gallery above the great hall, where I peeked down on the gathered few of all I loved on earth, in the red and fading embers of the hearth, and heard such promise of my future loneliness and loss as made me sweat against the stones until I wept, that for my beloved father, who had not left me yet, I vowed then all the world would hear me and take note: he was a deathless prince and in my heart so long as I drew breath. So long as men could hear and voices proudly cry, my father would never die.

21

"But we might create a Court of Wards," said her majesty. "And give Lord Edward a home, upbringing him as befits his station, education. Sir William, you might see to that."

"I'd take him in my house, your majesty, though modest house it is, and raise him with my children," said Sir William. "But mindful ever of his rank and place, he would have every benefit and prospect, spared no amenity to serve him. I would improve our house according to his needs."

"That's settled then. In such event, you will be Master of a Court of Wards," the queen said, rising. "And so good night."

In his golden book, Edward noted: *I slept outside my bed that night. The coldness of the stones was warmer to my heart than all the quilts of Christendom and I felt heated by the rocks.*

Sir William meddled in and promised to take care of everything, that he would see to Edward's welfare, personally, should such a need arise. "Of course I do what you desire, desiring nothing for myself, but your desire done, which is my only desire. I am here to serve your desire, your majesty," said Sir William next morning at table while served with rashers of eggs and tongue and venison and meats, oysters, salmon, rabbits and bacon, lobsters, butter, cream and prawns, all topped by wine, beer, ale and bread, while the queen picked daintily until she found a cherry to pop in her mouth, which she only dipped in cream.

"Then serve me with your silence, Sir William."

To which he answered without a sign of humor, "I am silence itself, and itself is silence, having only silence to serve." He was maddening and all the courtiers knew it. But he was persistent, to a fault, to an egg, to a raindrop. He had a cleft lip; enunciating ponderously, he still sprayed more spit than syllables.

22

"Silence is speech, Sir William." Elizabeth demonstrated the metaphor of the soap bubble to her prospective ward, this queen who was so playful, capricious and inclined to games of the mind. Her metaphor was a warning that some like she and he were privileged to live their lives objectively, outside the bubble of the world, and burdened, they could never hope to penetrate it, at risk of bursting. They were born to their station and so must always remain: insiders outside, and above the rest, joined like a mother and son.

To which Edward gazed across the new-mown grasses of Hedingham's fields, stacked in heaps to dry in the summer heat. He took a torch from Gascoigne's pipe to light a stack to burn. Gascoigne was a family retainer on the deVere estates, an old soldier and amiable tale teller. As they watched the straw go up in flames, Edward declared that only God and man shared the passion and gift of fire. All other living creatures fled from it.

"Why Ned, I think you have the gift of prophecy, my young Turk!"

"Bonfires bring fertility to a family wanting an heir," said Gascoigne.

When the queen nicknamed Edward her Turk she was referring to the chivalrous knight of King Arthur's legend who tilted at jousts in the lists with a mighty spear, and sustained the myth of brave deeds.

"I have the love," Edward answered. "Without love, there can be nothing of meaning."

"Then love is all?"

"Love is blood."

Hers was an August visit, when the green and warmth of the breeze in the fields and play of light on the waters of the Colne were at their highest, days were long, and they could talk of dreams of sprites as they enjoyed the fireflies and stars at night, and the majesty of the northern lights conveyed a celestial performance of gossamer angels dancing over the somber silence of Essex forests.

Country folk had remedies and superstitions for all occasions. A stray dog looking in your eye was a warning of death approaching. All evil's ills were curbed by raven's eggs and magic mandrake juice, spiders swallowed in treacle, snails crushed into a poultice, drinking from a murdered man's skull or stroking warts with a dead man's hand, while eating snakes restored lost youth, a salamander's skin stopped sunburn, and boiling pots in summer heat made the finest jellies from fruit. What was a country kitchen without musk sugar, marigolds, rosewater, pickled fruits, pear cider, mead and sack in gally pots? Honey, vinegar and wine were boiled to whiten teeth. And there were always jumbolds at the buttery door, those fine sweet dry biscuits for nibbling. We call them shortbread now.

When the queen called Edward "Robin Goodfellow", he declared she was a queen of the fairies, a veritable Titania, as his parents looked on bemused by their precocious son, and Sir William coughed and concealed how much he disapproved of their laughter. There was really no harm in it, only childish fancy against which Sir William was powerless to find a fault though he could not formulate a pleasure either; he was only an advisor, after all.

Nor was it mentioned that Her Majesty also gave Robert Dudley a nickname, "Robin Goodnight". As de Quadra, the Spanish Ambassador said, it was "a pretty business to treat with this woman who, I think, must have an hundred thousand devils in her body, in spite of her forever telling me, 'I yearn to be a nun, and to pass my days in prayer in a cell.'"

Elizabeth had nicknames for everyone: Sir Walter Raleigh - Water; Sir Francis Walsingham - Moor; Sir

Thomas Henage - Sanguine; Ambassador Simier - Monkey; the Duke of Alencon - Frog; and another for Robert Dudley - Eyes. Christopher Hatton became Lids, Sheep, Mutton and Bellwether. Her prime minister, Sir William, was the Old Fox, Leviathan and Pondous. It was not merely an age which would favor deceit, but would make of words a web, of thought an illusion, of living an intrigue and of silence - speech. Codes became acts, ciphers the gates to privacy and all was not what it seemed to be, and seeming became all.

I felt a kinship with her majesty, the kind I never felt for another, as though we were of like mind, like flesh. When she embraced me I felt warm, and her tear upon my cheek was hot, and burned me, but I could not wipe it off, for she was my own, and treasured. All that was of her body was mine, and sacred to me.

"O Ned! Dear Ned! At times I've known such fear, to be reminded of it is the same as fear again," she told me. "But you'll know this too. For now, don't be afraid, but love me. Fear will be our enemy. Together shall we slay it!" declared her majesty to me.

Sir William bowed at this display, reminding himself (with sealed lips):

"I am but a servant of Her Majesty, not a personage, not one of the peerage (to crack the wind of the poor phrase) but a pawn for my prince, and I know that nobility has long arms, the better to reach our short lives. I hold my duty as I hold my soul, both to my God and to my gracious Queen. I should neither judge nor act upon my judgment without Her Majesty to guide my act. I serve her in tasks be they great or small."

Edward's gift was that he amused her majesty, and she did the same for him. Theirs was a secret shared, in which none could intervene, though the court would whisper: "Some say Lord Edward is Her Majesty's son. Some say something else. Who but knows?" For when they were together, even in the company of others, they were in a world apart, one of their own by themselves, a bubble of distinct advantage. And Sir William could only watch, and cough into his closed fist.

Edward's father had already raised a daughter in his first marriage, the acerbic-tongued Katherine. She did not like Edward nor consider him her little brother, while the good Earl's second wife, Margery, with a cold and chilly manner toward Edward, thought less of him than of his younger sister Mary.

"I hate him! I loathe him! I detest him!" declared his half-sister Katherine.

"I like him! I enjoy him! I trust him!" replied his younger sister, Mary.

So the boy ignored their squabbles and ran to the silence of a corner to curl up with a book. He seemed isolated by his peers, and alone, which suited him well for the love and company of books, his only true and enduring passion. *My friends are words, their eloquence my sword, my dagger, my lance, and all the tongues of fools I'll stay with a slashing wit!*

The days were more disciplined. For his early education, Lord Edward had gone to the home of Sir Thomas Smith, but he was often in the company of his mother's brother, Uncle Arthur Golding, who translated Protestant Calvinist tomes and taught him Latin and Greek, involving the boy in translations by the age of eight. Now Edward wanted to write a play.

On the last evening of her visit, Edward staged his production for her majesty. His mother barely tolerated these artistic fantasies, but his father smiled indulgently when Edward presented the play in which he took the main parts, and engaged the household servants to be his other

26

actors. Old Will Somers directed the comic bits, while Edward made sure there was a duel, with sword play rehearsed, in a contest over chivalry. John Bale helped in the device. It was a stage piece that contained much action and boyish vigor, with an appropriately heart-breaking turn in the end, upon the sorrows of love.

Following the entertainment, a feast was offered with a boar's head the mark of elegance, set in a garland of laurel and rosemary, a lemon in its mouth, preceded by the spear that killed it, carried by Lord Edward. Many dogs and men in the hunt with nets had cornered the boar, which even in dying was deadly to the animals, until it was speared behind the ear. The feast was crowned with a pie nine feet in circumference, made with twenty four pounds of butter and two bushels of flour, containing geese, rabbits, ducks and pigeons, weighing one hundred sixty five pounds.

When Elizabeth was gone, Edward wrote her and had published his first poem based on that memorable evening's entertainment. With the help of his uncle, he drew his text from a 12th century legend. He called his effort 'The Tragical History of Romeus & Juliet', which he also based on his own experience with Mary Browne, the daughter of the Earl of Montague, blending the love of medieval chivalry with sorrows of his own. Edward wrote a preface describing how he had envisioned this poem as a play, to remind her majesty of their evening's revelry.

The poem was published under a pseudonym, of course, which he and his Uncle Arthur devised to commemorate the life of a young neighbor, drowned at sea.

"That would be a most fitting dedication, to use his name for your poem, Edward - most fitting indeed to his memory, that you give him the authorship."

"I must always give credit, mustn't I, uncle?"

"Such is your station, indeed, nephew. Responsible to all, author to none, for only the Lord in heaven is author of the universe." Uncle Arthur closed his eyes.

Their names combined Edward and his uncle to become Arthur Brooke, as in a stream which a young 'ox' must 'ford'.

"O, I love games with words, uncle!"

Edward deVere continued his study in writing with his uncle who was translating Ovid's 'Metamorphosis' from Latin, a work destined to become one of the most popular books of their age.

"Language is the game of love, I feel," said Edward. "Its words are toyful playthings meant to tease and amuse. I'd rather a jungle of words to juggle than a game of salts, or shoe the mare."

His uncle rolled his eyes and resumed his task as teacher to the talented tyke.

I think of my Uncle Arthur as a wren, that tiny bird of drab and sorrowful taste, his glasses pinched on the end of his nose, his hair drawn back from his pale and clammy pate, a voice more like the chirp of that helpless winged thing than man's which is so full of booming and noise. But he was always mindful of our refuge in books, where mild men grow strong and the death of soldiers transforms the meek with a might reserved for kings. Even Uncle Arthur, forever blowing his running nose, could hear a tale and quiver, only to fill his chest with beating breath and speak the words of war. Though weak in himself, he was by speech made mighty, while his eyes flowed with an angel's tears.

"We shall dedicate Ovid's masterpiece to the Earl of Leicester," said Edward's uncle. "For Leicester is wont to encourage poets to proceed in their painful exercise," he declared.

How differently would I come to see what that Earl of Leicester, Robert Dudley, found most to encourage, and painful, for no man brought me closer to the brink of rage than he, or made me know how dangerous madness could be.

Edward helped the translation by injecting imaginative word spins and ribaldry into its lines. Although Uncle Arthur was pious and proper about such matters as literature, Edward showed little interest in his Calvinist translations, so that Arthur had to engage the young lord with more vibrant material to be found in the Roman poet Ovid.

"But Puritans object to Ovid, don't they, uncle?"

"Indeed, Ovid is deemed libertine, Edward."

"And is Sir William a Puritan?"

"Most devoutly, Edward, for sure."

As the heir to the house, Edward was able to decide what course of study he would pursue most. It was customary then that nobility remain behind the scenes, which included anything they might have studied or written, because the law prevented holding a lord responsible. The public was forbidden from suing royals in court, so a noble's word of honor was assured by his station, never to be compromised by open declaration. An earl could not take credit or be held accountable for anything he did, or wrote or said, except to the queen herself. Uncle Arthur was more a servant who could only suggest and persuade by igniting his nephew's interest in the desired subjects of the day.

"Then I shall translate Ovid, uncle, because it has the force to offend."

Edward's Uncle Sir Henry Howard, Earl of Surrey, invented the English sonnet, which, with the Ovid translation, came to be considered the fountain that launched the age of Shakespeare. Uncle Henry's book, 'Songes & Sonnets' was not published until 1553, six years after his death, which was customary with nobility, to publish not for

29

fame or glory, and surely not for bread, but only for history, just eight years before her majesty's visit to Hedingham. It became one of the first works in English credited to a noble. Edward studied it with an endless fascination and longed to be a poet himself, making lists of words, classified by their rhythm. The book of 'Songes & Sonnets' provided the model from Petrarch for what would soon be his own poetic form and, within his lifetime, the sonnets of Shakespeare.

Here, for the young Lord Edward, with his parents and younger sister, Mary, life on the family estates was full and not yet fraught with danger. . . Sheep and goats and dairy cows mostly, with horses to ride, plus mastiff bandogs and a bear warden for bear baiting - a pastoral rearing, when not enthralled with words. They trained falcons, too, in silk caps with draw tassels and bells on their talons.

"But were it mine to choose, I would serve her majesty as a soldier and lead an army against Spain. I'd conquer all of Europe in honor of our queen," said Edward, and doubled his practice of the sword and on horse, while other children around Hedingham played at blind man's bluff.

It was my desire to know how horses were kept, so I tended them; how fields were planted, so I plowed them; how flowers were bred, so I nurtured them. It was also my interest to listen, for the voices of people are strange, each different, each by a particular emotion raised. I have heard speech in many tongues, no two akin; though some agree in heart or thought or manner; all are different in spirit.

But Edward could vanish if he wanted, under certain conditions.

The freedom of wearing a mask and its sweet oblivion was mandated in a book called 'The Courtier' by Baldasarre Castiglione, the foremost authority on proper behavior in 16th Century Italy. Here was nectar for those to the manner born, offering all, who were in, an out. Castiglione's masterpiece became the passion and the model for Edward's behavior. It was written in dialogue form, like a play of philosophers and moralists, featuring Don Pedro and Lady Julia, Monsieur Lodovic Vives and Master Erasmus, walking in a garden and sitting down to dinner.

The Earl of Oxford at twenty-three would become the patron who published 'The Courtier' in English. Launched with one of the most elegant forwards ever penned or printed (in Latin, no less!) it would become an enduring classic. Largely due to that forward, and his writing and publishing twenty poems, defying the rule of anonymity by signing his own name to the printed word, then founding three London theaters and patronizing them for more than twenty years, history shined on Edward deVere.

Edward's commitment in publishing thirty books led to establishing him in the community of writers and the making of original plays. A dozen of his editions became the standard staples of every English household, on philosophy, medicine, horticulture, manners, literary fashion and poetry, including the first English novel ever published. More than half were remembered by succeeding centuries as "Shakespeare's sources". One even became known as 'Hamlet's Book'.

The deVeres sustained an unbroken line of twenty Earls of Oxford over 561 years. As Lord Macaulay wrote: "the longest and most illustrious line of nobles that England has seen, whose heads brought it honor in the fields of Hastings, Jerusalem, Runnymede, Crecy, Poitiers, Bosworth, and the court of Elizabeth where shone the 17th Earl who had won himself an honorable place among the early masters of English poetry."

I was never concerned for propriety. All my thoughts were consumed by the one desire to know, to absorb, to

31

embrace every aspect of living humanity. This involved the totality of my personal strength, in thought, in daring, in body. If there was a peasant on the road whose load was too great, I relieved him, even as a child, even if all I could offer to carry was his stick. I hungered to hear the voices of each living person, and the tales they could tell. O, the hours spent, which they who watched me called wasted! They were passed in the luxury of admiration and the elixir of preservation. By word and pen did I these hours spend.

Edward at age four was sent to live with his tutor, Sir Thomas Smith, at nearby Saffron Walden in Essex, for learning Latin, Greek, French and Italian. There were twenty servants in the house at Hill Hall and his personal tutor, Thomas Fowle. The students called him "flighty Fowle, unstable Fowle, nervous Fowle, foul Fowle!" and laughed hilariously at this amusement. But pre-eminent of his teachers was Sir Thomas, who was a stickler for accurate words and phraseology, inventor of a new twenty-nine letter alphabet, a new pronunciation for Greek, was an authority on Civil Law, while he sought a better spelling in English, which until that time had no spelling at all. Writing was only phonetic. Sir Thomas was Vice Chancellor of Cambridge by the age of thirty, a renowned humanist, orator, poet and as admired in philosophy as Plato. His passions were gardening, chemistry and medicine.

He was also thought most temperamental and undiplomatic, so he was bettered in government positions by his life-long rival, Sir William. But he revised the Protestant 'Book of Common Prayer', wrote a 'Discourse on the Commonwealth of England', and 'Dialogue on the Queen's Marriage', a play-like conversation between four friends. They were Spitewed, Lovealien, Homefriend and Reason.

Sir Thomas was mercurial, rash, impetuous, insensitive to others and unimpressed by the queen and her court, preferring to write and to study out of nervous anxiety than to pave a career in her favor. He wrote anonymously "to make things happen" rather than to incur fame, and urged the same aesthetic on his pupils. He was respected as the greatest scholar of his age, unequaled in medicine, gardening, astrology, the law and hawking.

His personal style was unaffected and homely, preferring country ways and a hair shirt to courtly manners. "My fault is plainness and that I cannot dissemble enmity or pleasure," he wrote. He preferred thought to action.

Edward recalled him: *"Knowing I loved my books, he furnished me, from my own library, with volumes that I prize above my earldom."*

Sir Thomas always affected himself to be a common man despite his extraordinary learning, never too great he could not play the humble, better a servant than a master, and fond of Edward through the rest of his life, even when the earl was in disgrace. For Edward would not hesitate to make himself the enemy of fame, and pose as great to all who fawned on him, only to explode with a show how they were vain. He cherished his old tutor's wisdom, "flattering none, but to thine own self true, and putting no place in greater esteem than right." Thus was Edward's rustic tutor, like a monk who recalled to him Aubrey deVere, his ancestor.

VI

Following her visit to Castle Hedingham, Elizabeth ordered all future debate in Parliament to be in English, not French, and all laws be written in English, not Latin. The direction of her native England was to be forever English, all English, pure English, "mere English". Like Herself. No longer the kingdom of her father. Formerly for centuries loosely knit and ruled by foreign armies (from Julius Caesar and Roman Legions to French monarchs), the country was entering a new age of national pride and survival among world powers, no matter the challenges, despite the obstacles. Thus five million people lived in ten thousand parishes, a hundred persons per village.

At Hedingham, the deVeres knew well about invaders and occupying forces. Tiberius Claudius Caesar Augustus Germanicus was the first Roman emperor to invade them. Claudius captured their ancestral castle at Colchester, known to posterity as Cymbeline's castle. Stories were often told how Claudius came to power following the murder of his nephew, Emperor Gaius.

"Are kings always killed by their families?" asked Edward.

"Not always," his Uncle Arthur answered. "But fathers always die, sometimes by the will of God, or the evil acts of men."

"Will my father die?"

"One day he will,"

"By his own desire?"

"Not by his will."

34

"But by God's will?"

"His is the only will."

"And suppose I will him to live, for I love my father."

"There is no will that strong, Edward."

The boy became pensive and melancholic, lapsed into periods of long silence, walks by himself, and meditation on the meaning of flowers and trees and animals in the woods, from which no conversation could rouse him.

There was comfort in the rose, and eglantine, of which a gardener told me that the deeper it is rooted in the ground, the sweeter it smells in the flower. I have called her majesty "sweet eglantine". Tulips, lilies, peonies and diverse other flowers soothe me also. I have called her majesty all sorts of names, and others round her, almost to a litany. But none is more sweet or precious than the rose.

"What is your humour, my lord?"

"I am considering the nature of free will - and all will - to desire, to command, to decide as one will, 'to will', to live, to die, to dispose, and how to nill ill-will, and so make nil of will."

"You jest, my lord."

"Not yet, but I will. In this dawning age, our queen will ordain culture. If young men of the nation will be inspired to courtly behavior by her womanly leadership, then the centuries of bloody rule will be replaced by a golden age of enlightenment in which poetry and drama will become the center of civilized attraction, and words will become deeds, and laughter will rule over evil."

A year after Elizabeth's visit to Hedingham, the 16th Earl of Oxford suddenly died there, on August 3, 1562. Within two months Edward's mother remarried and her choice was a commoner who bore the name of history's most notorious assassin, Charles Tyrell, remembered by every school child for his murder of the young princes in The Tower.

Not two months dead and she remarried, turning funeral pyres to wedding wreaths! Edward's feel for the former Lady Oxford, his mother in title, stiffened. It was said that Tyrell had taken his lessons in the school of poison and murdered Edward's father. The great and gallant good earl was cut down at the age of fifty.

Old Will Somers wept at the news and gathered Edward in his great arms to him. "The weight of this sad time we must obey, speak what we feel, not what we ought to say," he whispered.

Edward studied the Countess of Oxford, his mother.

"Look you how cheerfully my mother looks, and my father died within two hours."

"Nay, 'tis twice two months, my lord."

"So long? Nay then, let the devil wear black, for I'll have a suit of sables. O heavens! die two months ago, and not forgotten yet? Then there's hope a great man's memory may outlive his life half a year. But, by 'r Lady, 'a must build churches then, as my ancestor Aubrey did, or else shall 'a suffer not thinking on, with the hobby-horse, whose epitaph is 'For O, for Oxford, the hobby-horse is forgot!'"

"Edward, thou hast thy father much offended."

"Mother, you have my father much offended."

"Come, come, you answer with an idle tongue."

"Go, go, you question with a wicked tongue. How is it with you, lady? A murderer and a villain, a slave that is not twentieth part the tithe of your precedent lord, a vice of kings, a cutpurse of the empire and the rule, that from a shelf the precious diadem stole and put it in his pocket - "

"No more," his mother sobbed.

"A king of shreds and patches - "

"Alas, he's mad," his mother concluded.

36

"Bring me to the test, and I the matter will reword, which madness would gambol from. Mother, for love of grace, lay not that flattering unction to your soul, that not your trespass but my madness speaks. Confess yourself to heaven, repent what's past, avoid what is to come. Forgive me this my virtue. It must of vice beg pardon. I must be cruel only to be kind."

She left her son and married her new commoner, who'd kept the stable and given Edward a horse.

In fact, there is no record they ever met again, this Lady Oxford and her deceased husband's heir, young Edward deVere, Lord Bulbec, Baron Sanforth, Scales and Badlesmere, now the 17th Earl of Oxford and Lord Great Chamberlain to Her Majesty the Queen, Elizabeth I of England, Keeper of the Ewer, Cymbeline's Castle at Colchester and the Forests of Essex. His mother receded in memory. She only mentioned Edward once in a letter, more as to financial arrangements affecting her. So the name of the once-Countess of Oxford, born Margery Golding, second wife and widow of the deceased earl, disappears from history as her little boy rides forth to the great City of London.

"I am going, madam, weep o'er my father's death anew; but I must attend her majesty's command, to whom I am now in Ward."

On September 3, 1562, the twelve-year-old earl, but earl in title only, rode to London directly from his father's funeral at Earl's Colne in Essex, on a day that began in mist and rain, accompanied by one hundred forty horsemen dressed in mourning with the Oxford colors, through London and Chepe to Ludgate and Temple Bar. As the sun burst from the clouds, he took up his new residence at Cecil House in Westminster where he would be tutored by Robert Ramsden, Archdeacon of York, and Sir William's chaplain, along with Sylvius Frisius and Roger Ascham, the queen's

37

own tutor - the best school for statesmen in Elizabethan England, perhaps in all Europe. Nobles were eager for their sons to be educated there, "brought up as the wards be." The new Earl of Oxford was accompanied by his distant relation and companion of the hunt, the old soldier George Gascoigne. They would soon be writing - and publishing - more books, poetry and plays, to the delight - and scandal - of many. They were urged on by Elizabeth who was to show herself both excited, and frightened, by these literary exploits - for plays were regarded as inflammatory and dirty - and by Sir William, an arch Puritan, as the cause of the plague itself.

Who valued words? They did me wrong, that took me out of the grave, and set me aright by the stars on a course to simple justice across the errant heavens. I felt the wrong that was, and was that wrong, even as I was being wronged, a soul in bliss and sin; but I am bound on a wheel of fire, that my own tears do scald like molten lead. Enjoy glass eyes, like a scurvy politician; seem to see the things that can't be seen, and I will show you treason, treachery, and malice, all conniving in a lady's smile.

VII

Elizabeth's closest advisor would remain Sir William Cecil, a secretive, weaseling presence who counted all chits in his ledgers of good and evil, manipulating events to his advantage and hers, until he was known as a camel, her Whale of a man whom she named her Behemoth, her Monster, her Leviathan, and whom all the world called a fox.

Sir William had survived the previous reign of her half-brother, the boy King Edward VI, and her recessionist Catholic half-sister, Queen Mary. He was to devote his shadowy efforts in spying and double-dealing to a single purpose - consolidating authority in the Protestant Reformation's hands, and building up the national treasury, as well as his own personal fortune, both of which were almost empty. About this he had no humor. He was singular of purpose to found a family that would out-last everyone's hereditary wealth.

Sir William had at most eighty men in livery. Twenty served table and each was paid more than five pounds per year. His troubles were with his eldest son, born in his first marriage to Mary Cheke, the daughter of a wine shop keeper in Cambridge, whom he had met and married rashly while at university. Much to his parents' chagrin. Upon her death, Sir William married Mildred Cooke and sent young Thomas to Paris with a tutor, Thomas Windebank, and two servants. Invited to stay with Ambassador Throgmorton, Thomas sold his three horses and asked his father for more money to buy new mounts, as it "was not meet" for his class to walk. Wrote Sir William, "I am here used to pain and troubles but none creep so near my heart as doth this of my lewd son." He signed his letters, "Your father of an unworthy son." The tutor lost all hope of controlling young Thomas and quit. Sir William's family life was calmer with his second wife.

Private land ownership was what distinguished England. The people were yeomen, not tenants. They had an interest in the community more than loyalty to the crown. Their disputes about land were handled by the independent courts of common law. The people with land slowly acquired rights and enforceable contracts, the qualities that make for capitalism. England would create an empire to find customers for its production, not people to enslave.

Sir William's motto was "Cor unum, via una" - one heart, one way, though Edward would see him one day as "Corambis" - double hearted, the minister who was called the reigning uncrowned king of the fickle queen. Sir William thought of the inheritors of crowns and titles as the spoiled, and not worth their salt, while he thought of himself as their keeper, looking down on them with scorn and disapproval. He had no taste for caviar or fun but all was work and treachery, meddling and deceit. Yet his purpose was England's glory, where the common man would prevail and the heir to mud and labor would triumph over titles, with which no Englishman found fault.

But Sir William was not of the noble class, an hereditary lord, given all the trappings of luxury, privilege and power. He was a graduate of Gray's Inn, a lawyer. His father was a landowner in Lincolnshire. His grandfather fought at Bosworth Field in 1485 with Henry Tudor, who became King Henry VII, while his father became a minor functionary at the court of Henry VIII. Sir William's first task was as private secretary to Edward Seymour, the Duke

40

of Somerset, Lord Protector of King Edward VI, during the building of the duke's house by the Thames in London.

It was always said at Sir William's table that one Cecil's service assured the next Cecil's service and what Sir William learned from building Somerset House, by studying pattern books of continental architecture, he would apply to creating two of the greatest homes of the age.

"Then the Cecils will last for generations!" declared Edward.

"The Cecils will out-last," Sir William corrected, and fixed his cold eyes like dead fish on the young lord.

"So all the world will frown with Cecil faces!" Edward and the children laughed.

But Sir William knew that to survive among these nobles, whom he believed were capable of dissipating the nation's resources, would depend on his wits and cunning, and that he kept to himself. "To thine own self be true."

He adopted a Puritanical interpretation of the new Protestant religion and practiced it with rigid self-discipline, resorting even to penning precepts which became maxims he repeated over and over. He wrote for publication often, locking himself up in his chamber, but came out with reams of paper, and nothing published at all. The precepts he used to control his mind and events, and as instruction to his children. "Neither a borrower nor a lender be." He let no thought stray from his absolute control and made notes on everything. "Stretch out thine arm no further than thy sleeve will reach. . Sparing is a rich purse. . Every item shows its grace when it's seen in its proper place."

He made himself a shadow of his queen and for the next forty years of her reign he would identify himself so closely with her interests that not a ray of light would come between them in matters of policy, and he would teach his youngest son to follow the same course. Not his first son, but his other, his last, the dark son and cripple - Robert - who kept secrets and stayed alone away from others, who liked to play with frogs and snails and yellow slugs, isolated in the garden when it rained and mist entwined the shrubs.

Sir William had been the first of this new social breed who wrested history from the hands of heredity. It was his mission after studying at Gray's Inn, and starting as secretary to the Lord Protector, to become minister to John Dudley, the Duke of Northumberland, who succeeded as royal protector of Elizabeth's half-brother, Edward VI. When that situation became a debacle and the young king died of tuberculosis, Cecil shifted as slyly as a slippery eel and gave his allegiance to Bloody Mary for five years. She was so tiny she was restrained from marriage and developed an interest in clock making. As time ticked, she developed her poise by acting in plays at court, specifically the comedies of Terence, until three years had passed. Acting was common among all privileged women who would learn bearing and comportment. Seeing Mary dying of ovarian cancer, and the efforts of others to put scholarly Lady Jane Grey on the throne, Sir William threw in his lot with the notorious, licentious, fickle and libidinous Princess Elizabeth upon whom no one counted.

"She is, therefore, the one whom I alone can count on," he whispered in his bed to his second wife. "She whom none dare trust, I shall make trustworthy, and all will trust in me, even she." Elizabeth was then only fourteen years old. Three years earlier she had translated to English from the French, Marguerite de Navarre's 'Mirror of the Sinful Soul' which was based on the religious movement of the Brethren of the Free Spirit, a libertine group that believed in promiscuity.

Her guardian, Sir Thomas Seymour, was accused of scandalous behavior toward his virginal ward. There was

42

even rumor that he got the princess with child. It was eventually gossiped that Lord Edward might have been the issue of this escapade. Edward deVere! the innocent Earl of Oxford. But Elizabeth would bear many rumors in her time, and be delivered of numerous scandals linking her with men, boys and foreigners, to the shame of her countrymen. But most of them were kept from knowing. The court became a place of secrets, tightly squeezed and closely held, as she assumed a libertine life behind a mask of her own innocence.

Thus Sir William became her protector and took care of these dangerous rumors. He paved the way until Elizabeth became queen, and eventually she would declare: "He that placed me on the throne hath power to keep me on it." In all things dark and final, he was her ruler.

But the scandal did not pass lightly, nor Lady Elizabeth's reputation for promiscuity. It seems that the Lord Admiral, Sir Thomas Seymour, uncle to the boy king Edward VI, her half-brother, desired the princess passionately. He schemed to marry her, something his brother, the king's Lord Protector, discouraged. Any marriage of a royal heir required approval of the Privy Council, the Lord Protector and the king, so Sir Thomas settled for marrying the widow of King Henry VIII, Kathrine Parr, four months after Henry's death, becoming the princess' stepfather instead.

His desire did not dim. While Mistress Parr adored Sir Thomas from youth, in fact having married King Henry only from duty, her affection was not returned by the tall, handsome, thirty-eight year old lecher. Sir Thomas, now responsible for Lady Elizabeth's care, entered her bedchamber in the early morning "in his nightgown" and "bare legged". If the fourteen year old princess was awake he would strike her familiarly on the back and buttocks. If she was in bed, he would open its curtain and "make as though he would come at her," while she "would go further into the bed." When he attempted to kiss her, the princess' maid, Mrs. Kat Ashley, who slept in a corner of the same room, "bade him go away for shame."

Mistress Ashley then pleaded with the princess' stepmother, Kathrine Parr, to restrain her husband, but she thought it a trivial pursuit and joined her husband for tickling the young lady in her bed at Chelsea, and later, in the garden at Hanworth, held Princess Elizabeth while Sir Thomas cut her gown in a hundred pieces. Gossip among the servants, needless to say, was rampant.

When the wife found her stepdaughter in Sir Thomas' arms, however, her patience stopped, Elizabeth was moved out, and all would have ended there, except Kathrine then died in childbirth.

Now scheming Seymour once again was conspiring to marry Elizabeth, his step-daughter, and marry off Lady Jane Grey to the boy king at the same time. But on January 17, 1549, he was arrested, charged with High Treason, and beheaded on March 20. Sir William's cloaked maneuvers were bearing fruit from the closet of his deceit.

Still, Lady Elizabeth was considered complicitous in Sir Thomas' promiscuous behavior, having admitted that she "did bear some affection" for her stepfather. Often she was seen to blush at the mention of his name. Thus was she sent to The Tower for cooling and entered it by the Traitor's Gate where she declared herself pure of sin and innocent to England.

From that stone fortress Elizabeth made virtue her policy and honor her pursuit in all future matters as her eyes gazed on the very ground where her mother was beheaded.

Though she loved to love, she loved honor more, and what she did she hid, for she wore the very raiments of glory, the sun, in her eyes, in her hair, in her lips and fingers. She was Gloriana incarnate. She was my glory, Edward wrote in his golden book.

In these events, involving the youthful and friendless Princess Elizabeth, Sir William acted in her behalf, secretly corresponding with her while craftily working for her enemies. The princess as queen would never forget her early if lowly benefactor. Sir William became Lady Elizabeth's front line of defense in that which was public and private, although he was known to talk too much, despite knowing unlimited stores of her secrets, which he revealed to none, though he seemed to reveal much to many. He whispered to his second wife only, alone at night in their bed, what the kingdom hardly imagined, and which no one said.

When he demanded - and received from her majesty - the head of the Duke of Norfolk for dallying with the Queen of Scotland and inciting the Scots barons to rebellion, Sir William's place in Elizabeth's history was cemented. Her place in the age became marble as the last living duke was beheaded and the Earl of Oxford became her senior royal. But make no mistake, for all his greatness and Protestant fidelity, Sir William was a man with a sense of his own self-righteousness and an unerring eye for the coin. He was as solid as the bank, which he became, while her majesty worked tirelessly to restore her reputation for virtue.

She clung to the ideal when the practice wasn't perfect. She never abandoned her belief in the perfect state, of her people or herself. The perfection was in her mind, which all the realm aspired to mirror. She was our Minerva and the cause of poetry in others.

Whether in fact Edward was truly her out-of-wedlock changeling, Sir William never wholly succeeded at silencing this gossip about her majesty and the adventurous Lord Edward. Some said he had been placed in the custody of the gallant Earl of Oxford and his younger second wife in

45

exchange for Elizabeth's seal of enduring fidelity. The rumor would be whispered from courtier to courtier so long as Elizabeth and Edward lived - in a tangled web of love - never quite laid to rest.

England and its new religion were at war with the world on all sides - with its Scottish neighbors to the north, France and Spain abroad and Ireland to the west. Everywhere rulers were part of the Catholic alliance and regarded this upstart nation, this little island, this band of Britons hatefully, covetously, with an eye to conquest. The talk of Claudius' legacy continued - an England by outsiders preyed-upon.

Only Elizabeth's will stood against them, aided by her faithful lords and ministers. The earls of Oxford and Sussex became foremost in her camp, and Sir William was her minister, though there was little love lost between them. Elizabeth's relations with Sir William relied more on her sense of her need to survive, for without him she might have gone the way of Little Lady Jane Grey, the nine day queen, and her own mother, along with countless more of quality, a good head shorter in the end.

In the darkness of his own family, Sir William spoke of an England where nobles were forgotten and only the will of the people, the will of the common people, would reign supreme. Edward ate his supper in silence and learned to study the devious minister at close range with a distant eye. Dinner was served in the morning precisely at eleven, supper at six in the evening. The first course consisted of sixteen elaborate dishes, followed by fourteen more. Breakfast was also offered at dawn to those who needed.

What Sir William could not control was her majesty's other allegiances. Upon her coronation, having been chosen by vote of the Privy Council, she made a speech to her new counselors, commanding Sir William to be in

46

charge, to tell her the truth no matter how grievous, and the hearts of all to preserve her and the commonwealth. As the queen of hearts she went directly to the people, and in private, directly to the oldest friend she had, indifferent to his approval so long as she sustained his support.

"Where would I be without Sir William? Where would he be without me? Where trust is not born, let it be made."

Shining at Elizabeth's court from the outset was Robert Dudley, soon to be Earl of Leicester. From the early 1560's until his death in 1588, Dudley was loathed (or envied) by everyone at court and yet he was loved (even adored) ((even cherished)) by the queen. Whispering made their affair lascivious, and declared a son born from their undeclared union, named Arthur Dudley who was raised in the country by a gentle family under Robert's direction.

Though Elizabeth could silence speech, whispers would not be suppressed.

A man of loathsome tastes, a brute toward others, a beast to women, Dudley was said to have poisoned his wife before taking up with her majesty in hopes of marrying the queen. He was evil in every point and direction, to the eyes of all who beheld him, but not the queen's.

She was drawn to all levels of life, animals in the clothes of men, those sabled serpents. She prided herself in coquetry and spinning courtiers around her fingers. She made of Dudley her personal poisoner, a murderer on her string, whom she would grant the license to kill whomever she deemed to doom, were that eventuality to come. To go to her court was as a fly to the spider's web.

When Dudley married another behind her back, Lettice Knollys, widow of the Earl of Essex, without her majesty's approval, the queen raged like a madwoman at all who dared address her, so offended was she by Dudley's

47

unfaithfulness. When the new wife came to court better dressed than the queen herself, there was panic in the queen's chambers. Those who could save themselves from their monarch's tirade gasped at her tyranny and wailing. When Lettice acquired a coach more elegant than the queen's, any plans for improving the rock-pitted drain ditches of London and the nearby countryside that passed for roads down which she rode were suspended. There would be no roads until Lettice was off them.

Carriages had only recently been introduced to England and mishaps were as frequent as the outings. In the role of woman scorned, the queen was the very soul of passion - the self-centered object of her own indulgence - and as often ditched by a dumped carriage as any other who rode out. She had several built to an elegant desire, one lined with red leather, one upholstered with black velvet embossed with gold, and all adorned with ostrich plumes. For each she had four horses, plus an additional two spares, with two coachmen and two footmen attending. To go forth was to tumble. To forgive was not in her mind. Once her coach was surrounded by rogues. On investigation, a school of crime for boys was discovered where cutpurses and pickpockets were trained. A law was passed against crime and promised to punish boys who were nyppers and foysters. So her reign would build few roads, but education, the law and language would be her triumph, building words her goal.

To Edward she would say, "I am your Queen, you are my England, my strong-willed Lord Edward, new-made Earl of Oxford. Your ancestors made me, the abbeys, the cathedrals, every country church they built, establishing our faith, our villages and by-ways, by whispers in the fields and cackles in the taverns, Edward. Now I am your queen. I give you Protestant life and meaning. So you will honor me, as I master you."

"Do you call me humble, madam?"

"I call you rash, young man."

"Am I impertinent?"

"You are intemperate."

Such was the woman who was all vanity and flowers, filled with proud promptings and vague promises.

Then she would look another way, to a man from the country, who had no experience with royalty, Walter Raleigh, and give him a pet name, stipends, lands and estates, eventually even a knighthood, but never allow him more than a night to master her.

He was a fool and she indulged him. She suffered fools more lightly. I was not, and she impugned me.

"How can you master me? You are a mistress."

"I am your monarch."

"You are my queen and mother, but I am your son and heir. I am your Phoebus. If you are proud, then I am pride incarnate, and you do not humiliate me."

She kept Dudley in the background as she toyed with prospective foreign consorts which were only a means of keeping a strong hand on international policy. While discussing marriage, she played with Dudley's mind, asking if he thought she might not best be married to young Edward deVere, who was, after all, the peerless peer, and closest to her in social station, the highest ranking earl in the land though seventeen years her junior. The cunning Dudley used the young lord, and answered his arrogance by making away with his inheritance under the eyes of their queen, who did not blink.

"What is Edward's fortune to me, unless it is mine? What good is he, unless he is mine? If I did not have him, he might not even be."

Edward's was the only case of royal wardship set up where Robert Dudley, Earl of Leicester, received the

49

inheritance of lands and Sir William took control of the estates and finances, as executor of Edward's late father's will. Both men picked Edward clean, maintaining him only to loot him for an unmerciful twenty-seven years, until precious little remained to dispossess Edward of, but his talent for speech, which they could not take from him, though try and try they did. Elizabeth's Court of Wards was established because of the need caused by the death of Edward's father. Many wards would follow him under the control of her majesty, but none would exceed him in payment of fortunes surrendered.

Knowing what he knew about Edward's birth, and what all the court so long believed, Dudley did not take his queen seriously on her accounts of prospective marriage, but indulged her coquetry and fickle talk, merely taking her, for when a queen conspires to steal from others it is inevitable that yet others conspire against her.

"And how can you bewail at me?" said Dudley. "You made me your chief poisoner. Beware the poison which you authorize, lest it be yours to finalize."

Elizabeth held Edward's legal custody from his twelfth year until he turned twenty-one and the word at court about their relations, whether mother and son or lovers, continued. He was her possession. He was her toy. She was his fascination. Play with him she did.

"Sometimes it is better I be thought a mother, when a courtier is sufficiently young, thereby silencing gossip that he might be my lover. Only when I am thought of too much as a mother, then it is best I treat him as a lover, thereby silencing some lesser gossip."

Edward's father was barely two years dead when his older half-sister, married to Lord Windsor, challenged Edward's inheritance of his father's earldom and right to his estates, on the grounds his father was not rightfully married to Margery Golding and he was to be presumed a bastard. "Every man can tame a shrew but he that has her." To emphasize this, Lord Windsor broke into the home of Sir Thomas Smith at Saffron Walden, Edward's old tutor, driving Smith and his family from their residence before the aging scholar, armed and with a sheriff, was able to regain his property. People called Kate Windsor a shrew for suing her younger half-brother. It was a claim disproved, with the help of the queen, but only in the course of time, and never completely gone from Edward's life.

Who knows the queen but what she didn't urge my shame herself, and then assume my lame defense, the better to disarm and pluck me, as she seemed to help me. So many sides had she - the phoenix. What a queen was this! Silence is the best ornament of a woman.

The queen put Edward's case in the hands of Sir William. Edward's lands and revenues she gave to the profit of that ubiquitous shadow, her Earl of Leicester, Robert Dudley, he being the beast of the gypsy eyes against whom the dying Sussex warned. The queen's personal companion and closest executor had come to court by freeing himself of an unwanted wife the world would forever suspect him of poisoning. The death of Amy Robsart cursed his reputation but endeared him to his monarch.

"Why Robin, you disposed of a wife to please me? What a grave disposition!"

However, it remained an impediment to marriage with his queen, which prompted her to declare, "I will not marry a subject, and in my house I will have only one Mistress and no Master!" Leicester made everyone associated with Amy's death rich, but the crime could not be silenced, and it clung to his name like leprosy and the shadow would not go away.

51

A darker man Edward would learn to meet, but only by first knowing Leicester.

He circled me. Like a cat he paced. When I said to her majesty, "Good day," he said, "What makes it so?" When I suggested to her grace, "how beautiful the look" of her, he demanded to know what side I looked on her face, if my intent was to flatter for favor or confuse the senses with that favorite drug, charm? When I replied and was stern, he accused me of bullishness. When I was confused and hesitated, he declared me an incompetent. A hairless and beardless twit! When I was slow in answer, he snapped his fingers. When I rushed head-long, he threw up his arms. But never did I mistake his attentions for interest. His only care for me was for his benefit. My estates like stars were twinkling in his eyes.

Leicester's control over Edward's estates resulted in a loss of status and income for Edward who enjoyed no authority over what was rightfully his own, in a lifetime of trying to master his fate, and his estate. Never would he be the granted master, so long as her majesty lived. But the first rule remained: "Know Leicester!" For Leicester seemed to have it all, having the devotion of the queen.

It was a devotion I wished for myself, but what was her devotion but vanity and the love of power. Those who loved her were blind to their love unrequited, for what can a stone love, or fire, or water? It must be, even if that most fickle flee.

"I'll have whom I want - in my bed, in my rooms, in my heart," she said.

"Because she has no heart," said her men, those interchangeable suitors of the night.

History - Edward wrote in the golden book. *What anybody tells everybody about somebody who told nobody! The fabled heart of the foggy night, where everyone is virtuous and anyone is kind, but no one is merciful and nothing is absolute. In truth there is no truth to find, nor lies, nor finalities, and one man's hero is another's devil, someone's saint's a traitor, but all we can do is proceed, unseated by our fates, hostage to desire, and by ourselves made blind, which is unending. Ah, history, it makes me melancholy!*

Edward deVere was not allowed, by the politics of power, to be anything other than accepting, compliant or passive in relating to his monarch. Indeed, he early learned to call her majesty his prince. The queen was a man in everything but sex. By law, by wealth, by position and disposition, this was a she-male animal, a master mistress, and her maids and her men were her playthings, so Edward had a conflict relating to her.

He could be manly, by winning national jousting tournaments where champions displayed their masculine skill and bravery at the lance and horsemanship. But she had the dominant attitude. He could also propel himself over her by literary endeavors at which she was well-trained herself. Or she could crack down like the tyrannous Regina, and banish him to The Tower for humbling. No one existed to countermand her. Everyone was there for her delight.

Edward deVere had his first experience in war on the Earl of Sussex's staff with his own one hundred eighty uniformed officers and men wearing the Oxford livery of black and Reading tawny with golden neck chains, the Blue Boar of the family crest emblazoned on their left shoulders. The rebellion took three thousand conscripts and numerous sorties across the River Tweed, pillaging, slaughtering and burning castles and men by night until the Scottish and their children were afraid ever to offer war to England again.

Edward walked among his troops at night. They did not know him in the shadows but thought him one of them, then talked about him strangely as a stranger. He felt impelled to advise them, but withheld his thoughts, and enjoyed them. "Who goes there?"

"A friend."

"Under what captain serve you?"

"Under Sir Thomas Radcliffe."

"A good old commander and a most kind gentleman."

"I think he is but a man, as I am. The violet smells to him as it doth to me."

"I am afeared there are few die well that die in battle."

"Every subject's duty is the queen's, but every subject's soul is his own." So at night he walked among his men.

When Edward's cousin, the Duke of Norfolk, planned to marry the Queen of Scots, in the foolish belief that he could hold her in religious check, Sir William and Sir Francis Walsingham swept down and entrapped him into a suspicion of treason, conspiring to foment the Catholic rebellion. The two ministers had become the earliest protectors of Elizabeth's supreme authority by their secret service and espionage, their meddlesome double-dealings and betrayals.

Elizabeth questioned the duke herself. Did he plan to marry her cousin? she asked. He lied and denied. He claimed to be a faithful Protestant. He was found out.

One thing no subject dares ever to do, without leaving his life in peril, is to be untruthful to the supreme authority.

Norfolk was condemned. Sir William saw him as a manifest proof of the Catholic resurgence. He demanded Norfolk's head.

Sir William had introduced the rack of torture on which suspects were strapped and stretched and disjointed until they cried out what was wanted. His mercy was in his appetite, for he never ate less than was served, and always took seconds, speaking humbly as though it was God's will: a Puritan heart and hunger.

"Stretch him until he confesses, and gives us the admission we want," said the fox.

"Spare him nothing for his truth, and spare me nothing for lunch." *He became known as the minister for whom nothing was spared, the unsparing Pondous. Great Pondous, Grand Pondous, I say, yet how it devils me, I can not say Good Pondous.*

. Hand to hand combat, with sword and firearms, in the pulpy bog for six months taught Edward the grit of battle, and earned him his monarch's respect. Mud was so deep on the winter roads that horses could sink from sight and leave their riders clamoring. It was Edward's demand to be heard.

The Duke of Norfolk was Oxford's cousin. He must be spared. He can't be dispatched. Certainly compassion compares favorably to a monarch's authority. The queen listens to her dear Edward. She hears his plea of forgiveness at court, and delays the execution.

"She hangs on Edward's every word and dotes on him," the courtiers whisper.

"She lives almost by his looks."

"She gazes on him with a mother's eyes."

"Or a lover's. ."

So the courtiers nod and concur.

Then Sir William demands retribution and revenge as the only punishment the people will understand. He demands decision. Now or never - put down the Catholic Scourge or risk losing the Protestant Tudor throne.

55

"I beg your majesty, ignore Lord Edward's pleas," Sir William urges. "He is a boy and fanciful. His mind leans more to matters of poetry and theater, not on these of weight to our state."

The queen measures Sir William, then Edward, in her eye. "And what say you, Lord Edward?"

The boyish earl is all words and choking. "My queen - good mother - mistress -" He attempts to come up with the phrase but utters nothing complete until his passion brings heart and mind into one expression. "Should those who would die for the crown serve no better than worms? What is a noble worth who instructs us with his nobility? Can the only honor gratitude pay him be the ax?"

"So be it," declares the queen, and at Sir William winks an eye, to which he nods. He knew it all along, and had she not, he would have found a way so that she'd feel persuasion in the wink of an eye.

Edward is bypassed in this decision of authority. Norfolk Beheaded - eight hundred of his fellow traitors hung from trees in their fields, an example that this queen is a monarch who tolerates no revolution against her rule or near her borders, no defiance of the edicts of her Protestant Reform Church.

Edward is taken to bed, cold with shock. The queen is ill for weeks.

Sir William at his dinner table recites the story of his birth, how he was born during that time of the Diet of Worms. Edward, still a ward of the Cecil household, mutters about "a certain convocation of politic worms. Your worm is your only emperor for diet." The other youngsters at the table laugh.

And history will record that at nineteen Edward cries for vengeance against those who would kill his cousin - who, in his turn, being a duke and of the heraldic nobility, submits himself most gently to the executioner's ax, a courtier, a gentleman, for England a glory and a man.

"Am I a coward? Bloody, bawdy villain! O, vengeance! Why, what an ass am I! This is most brave, that I must like a whore unpack my heart with words! Words!" But Edward's cries for vengeance go orphans in the night. "I would rather a soldier be!"

Elizabeth's tastes in vengeance were as passionate and furious as her father's. When this Scottish Rebellion fomented by her cousin was nipped, she ordered those eight hundred hangings of poor sods in their fields, the burning of castles and three hundred villages - a reminder to anyone north of the border who ruled and who would dare offer war to whom. None were so great to defy the heir to King Henry VIII.

She almost had her own head removed as a princess when she was assured of nothing, least of all the crown, and that terror she was not inclined to relive, so the hint of invasion against her was enough to set off her instant wrath.

Sir William was ever-present to remind her.

As the princess who went "from the prison to the palace" she inherited sixty royal houses including five castles on the Thames - Whitehall, Greenwich, Richmond, Hampton Court, and Windsor, plus Lord John Lumley's Nonsuch Castle, Oatlands in Surrey, Otford in Kent, Reading Abbey in Berkshire, Woodstock in Oxfordshire, and Edward's Havering-atte-Bowre in Essex.

"You have an eye for the truth, my Ned, though your passions speak from your heart more than your policy. You have a sovereign soul," Elizabeth told him. "You are a monarch of the mind, but you are more poet than soldier."

Edward began to sign his name with a crown and see himself as heir to her majesty's throne.

"I am Edward VII - monarch of all I've imagined!" he declared and danced and twirled on one foot before the fire which cast his shadow large upon the walls and tapestries of the great hall at Cecil House. No one contradicted him.

VIII

How such a complex woman developed is partly a tribute to circumstance. Elizabeth's father, after all, was sixteen years older than her mother, Anne Boleyn, his second wife, beheaded at twenty nine. The princess had to sit in his presence at dinner and watch him chew his food, ask him kind questions and answer him submissively. She tried to suppress all memories of the mother she lost at age three, while the saliva ran down Henry's chin and he snorted laudanum to ease the pain of his gout. It was her father's lesson in self-control.

Following the king's death in 1547, after a thirty eight year reign, the fourteen year old Elizabeth was sent to be raised by her stepmother. Thomas Seymour went to trial two years after for having molested her, a servant of the house testifying against him. He had been caught in the princess' bedroom, "practicing tickling".

"Tickling?" demanded the inquisitor.

"Yes, the exercise of tickling, sir."

It was a taste that she who was called Diana continued. She also enjoyed other flatteries. The court called her Sylvia and Cynthia.

To become the plaything of an older man, when she was a helpless child of fourteen, made her, as a grownup, become the playmate of younger men, despite her life-long companionship with Robert Dudley. "Amused by all - Faithful to None," could have been her motto. First among her toys was Edward, while Dudley was away from court and angry.

When Dudley was on his knees before her during his investiture as Earl of Leicester, and the sword rested on his shoulder, Elizabeth looked around and then tickled her Robin secretly on the neck. That was when they had fun and laughed. They were in their twenties and not yet doomed. But then came Edward, a diversion of royal distraction. He set a pattern she long would fill with willing, youthful replacements to electrify her Earl of Leicester.

Now see the queen in her fifty fifth year, arriving at the funeral of her long clandestine companion, the man she was forbidden to marry by her own decision of state, her policy to remain single and the bride of her nation. She was inconsolable and distraught almost to a paroxysm of anguish when they buried Dudley, but already in the company of her next companion of the bed, at least for a decade to come, the twenty-one year old Robert Devereux, Earl of Essex, almost thirty four years her junior, and the nephew of Dudley.

One day she would cut Essex off by beheading - definitely a female disposed to flirting with the abyss, neither afraid of a war or a bed or a man less than half her age, and inclined to take on both to be the first to conquer. The virtuous Queen with a taste for virgin boys. Like her father before her, the human race was for savoring, to be devoured. In love or in war - eat or be eaten. In all of this, always, was Edward first - on whom she preyed.

On his death bed, the great Thomas Radcliffe, 3rd Earl of Sussex, had warned against Leicester, the queen's clandestine advisor, a move that could cost a healthy man his life, but immortalized a dying one. This Earl of Leicester was an evil genius who could not be trusted by honorable men. Though he held the queen enthralled, "Beware the gypsy. You do not know the beast as I do. He has a lean and

60

hungry look," said the dying Sussex of that towering tyrant with the poisonous velvet glove.

Be it here remembered, Lord Sussex who gave warning against Leicester had been made Lord Chamberlain after his success in Scotland, and so remained for a dozen years until afflicted with consumption.

As Lord Chamberlain he was in charge of all the theatrical performances at court, which before his advent had been sporadic. After his appointment, a regular season was played annually for the queen between Christmas and Lent, each play by him personally chosen and rehearsed. From Sussex Edward deVere found initial encouragement in the art of the stage.

"Listen to your mentor," Sussex told him. "The life of a soldier is perishing. When the battle's done, death is all he's won. But literature lives forever and its wars in the theater are flourishing."

"The play's the thing," said Edward. "Wherein I'll catch the conscience of the queen."

"And rise to untold heights," said Sussex who then encouraged the queen to vest her interest in drama.

By the close of the decade of the 1570's, Edward was enough versed in stagecraft to assume patronage of the Earl of Warwick's acting troupe of players, and to supervise his own productions at court and on tour to Cambridge University and the countryside.

The theater and literature would teach him politics of the state and stage.

What a man - the sky itself - was Sussex, who for a boy was all, and to a man was everything. He was silent in virtue yet fearless to speak, courteous to a pin and short to none, a gentleman, a soldier, a pillar - and how I leaned toward him, and learned from his least position, wrote Edward in the golden book. *He spoke gently, yet was decisive. He considered all sides, yet maintained his own view. In battle ruthless, in conference merciful, Thomas Radcliffe was an inspiration and signaled to me the battle for the mind. I commend him to the highest honor of memory. He was the founding patron of our dramatic stage and the source of all honorable aspirations. It is to be grieved, the world forgot him. What a fragile thing is reputation. What a bubble, what a flake, what a myth. All that counts is what is, where that which we hold ill can serve the greater cause than good. Even evil becomes a divine persuader in the progress of truth. And the angels are forgot.*

Part Two

"Of a shadow. .a substance. .
"Of a likelihood. . a truth. ."

IX

Edward found his name all the way back to William the Conqueror in history books, five hundred years of fame. His great, great grandfather, the 13th earl, restored Henry VI to his throne in a battle which was yet to be made glorious by Shakespeare's 'Third Part of Henry VI'. And before that was the 11th earl who saved Henry V at Agincourt, and earls who fought at Hastings and Bosworth Field, killed Richard III, and went on the First Crusade. But most beloved, his father, the 16th earl, was noted for his courageous hunting and good deeds.

Stalking a wild boar in France, when he was twenty-eight, the earl dismounted his horse and walked alone down a path away from the others who huddled together with their lances. From the underbrush a great boar charged. The gallant earl drew his "dancing rapier" and killed the animal in a thrust. He said not a word, to the shouts of the many. The Oxford family coat of arms for generations was dominated by the Blue Boar.

The killing amazed the Frenchmen which in turn amazed the good earl. He said, "My lords, what have I done of which I have no feeling? Is it the killing of this English pig? Why, every boy in my nation would have performed it. They may be bugbears to the French. To us they are but servants."

DeVeres were Danes, descended of Vikings and Flemings who traced their family tree back to a direct descendant of Charlemagne, seven hundred fifty years before.   Every generation saw its soldier and titled nobleman. They were owners of vast estates like Wivenhoe, Colne Priory and Hedingham in the rolling hills of Essex County, Bilton and Billesley on the river Avon in Warwickshire, Kensington and Covent Gardens, with Vere House by London Stone.   Then came Fisher's Folly on Bishop's Gate Street, in all including seventy five estates in ten counties, hundreds of thousands of acres.

The queen would give Edward the Manor at Rysing. Together they would enjoy the magnificent Havering-atte-Bowre which oversaw Kent, Sussex and the Thames with its continuous traffic of ships from a summit of hills, where salmon thrived and fishermen lounged as boatmen and parties of revelers rode the tide down to London Bridge before debarking, afraid to pass under one of its nineteen archways and shoot the rapids.

Here Edward drew inspiration. Drawn to the theater, he hoped to make his own mark in a world long used to taking notice of his ancestors. If he could not go to foreign war, he'd bring war to the stage. His family crest was, after all, with the title of Lord Bulbec, a lion shaking a spear.

He would write a play at sixteen called 'Horestes' based on Orestes being ordered by Apollo to avenge his father, Agamemnon's death at the hands of his mother Clytemnestra and her lover, Aegisthus.

"Words, Edward!" Elizabeth commanded. "Give me words - to play with, to charm with, to mutilate and bend their phrase and meaning to my will! My will, remember! What you do is my will."

I'd give her will enough. I vowed her a will to contend with, which she would never will, would she will such a will. "It will be my will!" I swore.

No two minds of the times seemed more attuned than Elizabeth and her Edward in their mutual taste for language.

66

This thrilled her, an enterprise frowned on by those around her, to whom literature was less than a man's sport and unfit for the dalliance of a monarch.

But she awed all present. Wrote Roger Ascham, her tutor, privately to a friend, "It is difficult to say whether the gifts of nature or of fortune are most to be admired in my distinguished mistress. The praise which Aristotle gives wholly centers in her; beauty, stature, prudence and industry. . . She talks French and Italian as well as she does English, and has often talked to me readily and well in Latin, moderately in Greek. When she writes Greek and Latin, nothing is more beautiful than her handwriting. She delights as much in music as she is skillful in it. In adornment she is elegant, rather than showy. . . I am inventing nothing; there is no need."

Now Edward, her challenger, was to be watched and Sir William and his Lady Mildred were put to the task, despite having three children of their own to raise. They maintained a Puritanical, organized and disciplined household in the Strand, a half mile outside the city walls, a few hundred yards from the Thames along Ivy Lane where boatmen for a penny could be hired to ferry their fares to the queen at any one of her residences. Caring for the Cecil children alone was enough. Who would welcome the task of monitoring Lord Edward at Cecil House?

Sir William's oldest boy was uninterested in his father's ministrations. When he went to Paris on his own, he was less than discreet. Sir William paid a friend of his son to spy on the boy. "Not to dishonor him - nothing so rank - but to make his behavior seem the flaws of liberty rather than the virtues of discipline. Make his acts seem the flash of a fiery mind. Slight stains make for better washing, not so? Lead him on to familiar confession, then seal him with a friendly expression - but report to me! To me you report! Here's money!"

Sir William's second child, a daughter, Anne, by his second wife, Mildred, lived in a dream world. But she did what he told her and he always praised her for faithfulness - faithful to him, and none other. His youngest, the son, Robert, was a hunch back, he of the silent counsel.

The Cecils had acres upon acres of beautiful gardens, the largest in Westminster, attended by John Gerard, who would remain with Sir William for the next twenty years. In time, he would write and Edward would publish his definitive, 'Herbal, or General History of Plants'. Sir William's passion for gardens was to extend to the country home he would build in Hertfordshire, which would come to be known as the largest estate in England, Theobalds (pronounced "Tibbalds"), greater than any hereditary nobleman's. To ride its perimeter, the corpulent minister would require a special donkey.

Daily thirty beggars at its gates were fed and hired to tend the gardens, weeding, raking and hoeing while the children played at skittles or hot cockles, the game of a blindfold guessing who touched him, as they would thread the maze.

Here were five inner courtyards, the main hall a total quarter mile long, four corner turrets on towers with gilded vanes, entranceway under a belltower, five galleries lit by many large and spacious windows, roofs almost level for walking, an arboretum so believable that when windows were open birds flew in, landed on the fake leaves and, mistaking them for nature, sang. Above this was in the ceiling an astronomical clock with zodiac signs, suns and stars, and all made to work by an ingenious concealed movement.

Outdoors was a grotto with pictures of wild men and women and covered by the bark of real trees. There was a green gallery painted round the walls with trees representing every county and the coats of arms of the earls, barons and nobles who lived there. The Privy Garden had sixteen cherry trees. The Great Garden enjoyed three levels in nine knots, each seventy feet square, with its own fountain and large, old tree. (Children liked to hide and watch when visitors were shown the central fountain. It sprayed unwary passers.)

The garden was approached through a loggia decorated with genealogies and nearby was a small, round hill with a wood called "Venusberg" entered by a maze leading to the Statue of Venus nude. There were three hedged mazes on the property - one so difficult that few who entered could find their way through it, though the solution was simple enough and easy: come out the way they went in.

Across the Great Garden was a pool where boats could row among the shrubs in spring, two water mills built on rock churned tirelessly, and a summer house for swimmers beckoned with an oval table of red marble reached by crossing a bridge. In the ponds were fish. In the shrubs were cats. In cages monkeys danced, turkeys pranced, with birds of brilliant plumage from Africa, France and the Canaries, while domestic songsters of modest plumage chirped.

It was Edward who would enjoy this, in the company of the gardener, Gerard, though the queen herself made more visits here than to any other palace than her own. She remarked to Sir William upon her first visit, "What a talent you have to build so great a home - with my money." Yet each of her visits cost him two to three thousand pounds (five hundred to seven hundred fifty thousand dollars), and she came at least a dozen times to the estate where young Edward lived.

From Gerard, the children learned of larkspur, passion flower, orange blossom, Christmas rose and laburnum, all first named and described in his definitive book, where the tradition of the English garden was begun.

"Flowers are used for complexion washes and paste," they were told. "Pimples are removed with salt dissolved in lemon juice and patting the face with a linen cloth."

Cecil's children and wards of the court would continue this passion for flowers throughout their lives.

"Now what is henbane, my little ones?" Sir William was invited to question the children and coach them.

"A sticky, hairy, deadly poison of the nightshade family!" they chorused.

"And tell me what is rosemary?"

"The rose of Mary, for remembrance!" they cried.

"And what are pansies?"

"Pansy's for thoughts! And there's the pansies!" cried his own child, Anne, who was just seven and jumped to pick some pansies for her father, running among the hedgerows and down by the moat on the grange. It was all they could do to warn her away from the water. She loved to dance like a sprite in the rain, and to play by the stream, and gaze at herself.

"Careful you don't fall in! Those who play by water-"

Anne ran away from the water. They played blind man's bluff.

"On to geography then. What is the thighbone of the world?"

"Ireland!"

"And the jawbone?"

"France!" they giggled.

Sir William made the children's lessons soberly amusing. Lady Mildred wore a sterner face when she addressed them only in Latin during daylight. At twenty she had translated from Greek.

Their caged monkeys were pointed out as agents of the Devil because of their speed and stealing, volatility and obscene conduct. "They will teach you what the Devil is, to beware!"

Squirrels were kept on leashes for ladies to walk for exercise.

"Now we'll read the parables of Solomon, children!"

"Can't we read Ovid, Plautus and Terence, Sir William?"

"Not safely, Lord Edward. They are not Puritan."

"But aren't they good?"

"We consider them light reading, Lord Edward. Light reading is improper."

"What's the danger in that?"

"The danger of laughter, Lord Edward. If a young woman laughs back at a young man who laughs at her, she giveth herself. In laughter, there is a giving and a taking, and if a woman takes laughter, she selleth herself. Laughter is a sign of a light and dissolute mind."

"But I'm not a woman, Sir William."

"You're inclined to light reading, Lord Edward."

"Which means that Ovid, Terence and Plautus are light."

"Very light, Lord Edward."

"As the sun is light. As a feather is light. And to think, when I was little with my uncle and we translated Ovid, I too was light. Now all that's light's forbidden. I shall be Phoebus, surely."

"But you must beware to be not light, Lord Edward."

"That puts me in mind of a question, Sir William. As a Puritan, what does a thinker think of woman?"

71

Sir William assumed his most sagacious expression. "Why, women should emulate their grandmothers, who did not, in the queen's girlhood, paint their faces, cut short their hair, smoke pipes, dance to excess, gamble at cards, swear great oaths, ride horses astride, wear short skirts, visit public theaters, fall in love with popular actors, mince and twinkle, twitter and giggle, dress like men and act like wantons."

"Ay, that is most Puritan," whistled Edward.

In the city, Cecil House was a towering structure of brick and timber, made imposing with four turrets.

In all, the Cecils housed eighty persons at a cost of fifty pounds ($12,500) a week with another twenty pounds ($5000) to keep their horses; total 3,640 pounds ($910,000) yearly!

In the cause of better knowing Elizabethan finance, this index shows - Income: School teachers (fifteen pounds yearly, being six shillings weekly); Shopkeepers, officials - the middle class (forty to five hundred pounds yearly); Noblemen, merchants (two- to three-thousand pounds yearly). Cost of a loaf of bread, two thirds gallon of beer, one pound of beef, lamb or fish, half pound of butter, one pound of cheese, a ticket to a play (one pence each). In London, a city of two hundred thousand who had no running water and emptied their slop pans out upstairs windows into the streets, a quarter of them were in the forty to five hundred pound bracket. A pound sterling was equivalent to $250 (1999 value).

Sir William did not give Lord Edward an easy passage through the next eight and one half years of hard study and disciplined hours: Up for dancing by 7AM, breakfast, French, Latin, Writing and Drawing studies from 8AM, followed by prayers and more Latin, French and Penmanship until 4:30PM, then more prayers, eat and sleep.

Nor did other powers at court always smile on the education and rise of Lord Edward. Their minions were legion.

Sir William found the young lord perplexing. Meeting him in a hallway he asked, "What do you read, my lord?"

"Words," answered Edward. "Words, words."

Sir William asked, "What is the matter?"

Edward said, "Between who?"

Sir William could make no sense of the young man, except where theater was involved.

Lest we forget the censors who imprisoned playwrights, chopped the writing hand off a pamphleteer, John Stubbes in 1579, and put authors to the run for trivial verbal offenses, let us note that it was the age of the licensed press and the register's copyright office of pre-publication approval. It was also the age of reviving chivalry. When lawyer Stubbes' right hand was removed, he raised the left to take off his hat and bow to the honor of his queen. "God save her majesty!" he cried before fainting away. His crime had been in writing a tract called 'Gaping Gulf' which was not only against the queen's proposed marriage to the Duke of Alencon, but was suspicious of female rule. It proved the power of print in persuading the public by propaganda pertaining to the political process, that the French serpent, seeking a marriage, had "come to seduce the English Eve and ruin the English paradise." Only twenty-five printers were authorized by royal edict in London. Censors reigned, and Sir William was there to remind his young earl of each one. "Books are a danger. They carry fire and plague. Let us beware! Fire and death is their plague!"

"But I will write books one day!" declared Edward.

"And so you shall, my lord - but not for reading. One of your position is not read, Lord Edward. He is only heard."

Youth at Cecil House for Edward was spent in scholarship, where he excelled unopposed.

And as his guardian, Sir William did make a study of expenses and pad the bill according to Edward's heredity. At sixteen, the fashionable young lord was hit for six hundred twenty-seven pounds fifteen shillings in clothing for his first four years at Cecil House, not a penny of it out of Cecil's pocket, but charged to Oxford's estate which was under the thumb of the queen, and her shadow. Edward was never shown the accounts, nor did he ask for a reckoning. He was merely guided, and coddled with bowing and scraping, by all the Cecil servants.

Also, for the first three months of his nineteenth year, he paid fifteen pounds fifteen shillings for the druggist, ten pounds for one pair of black hose, twelve pounds thirteen shillings for the tailor; one pound five shillings for shoes; for hothouse, horse, boat and carriage rental, food and board, wood and coal, thirty pounds sixteen shillings; fifteen pounds ten shillings for a Spanish cape and fine cloths, cambric, Holland and linen; servants and doctors, thirty six pounds five shillings four pence; six pounds per week food for himself at Cecil House, also four pounds six shillings for one velvet hat, one taffeta hat, two velvet caps, a scarf and two pair of garters, silver tipped, a plume of feathers and a hat band, while to a bookseller for books, books and more books, some fifteen pounds. This young lord was made to live like a lord, becoming a very palpable fop. Though he'd object, the seamstress and tailor arrived regularly.

"You must accept this flattery, my lord. It is your station."

"Then I will detest my station and offend my stationaries. Flattery is a poison. It creepeth as the cold reptiles of the night and lodges a physic in the soul. He that loves to be flattered is worthy of the flatterer."

"And so shall you make worthy, my lord."

"Lay not that flattering unction to your soul, Sir William."

"But if you hate flatterers, my lord - "

"Then I am most flattered."

Among those books Edward bought from William Seres, stationer, were a gilt Geneva Bible, a Chaucer, a Plutarch, two Italian books, Tully and Plato. He was building a permanent library and not immune to the Italian Renaissance which was the temptress away from Puritan values.

"Remember your garments are a boon to the economy, Lord Edward."

"And what are my words? Is speech a drain on the treasury?"

"It can be costly. Yes, speech bears a heavy burden."

"If words offend then I shall fend with words! Let me wear silken tongues and velvet verbs and a codpiece filled with grammar!"

These expenses were inflated to soak Edward the ward and enrich Sir William until Edward became Sir William's daughter's husband. Sir William made his fortune off the court of wards - one of the most lucrative positions in the country. As Sir William's estates went up, Edward's went down. Edmund Spencer, ever a friend to the young earl, alluded in verse to Sir William and the Duke of Alencon selling Edward's lands to finance a war, while Edward endured genteel poverty with only four servants.

But the Earl of Oxford was becoming educated more than any man of his time, versed in the classics and renowned for it more than his curious Catholic cousins. He veritably chomped at the bit of knowledge and chewed off more than he could swallow. Learning was all good fun. "A favorite of the muses since youth," chimed his tutors and flatterers, and he enjoyed the best in scholarship: Laurence Nowell, map-maker and geographer; John Hart, master of penmanship and author; Sir Thomas Smith, linguist; and even that celebrated Welshman, Dr. John Dee, the royal astrologer, whose specialty was espionage for Sir William, which he sent in coded messages that he signed by the curious signature, "007". When not otherwise engaged, Dr. Dee chose what time the queen would go forth, what was propitious in the stars, whose fortunes were rising, influences inclining, moods ascendant, etc.

Smith would write eventually that for all his temperament and passion, Edward had lived some years among the many books in his house, and was a perfect scholar, to be honored and respected, despite his trend to arrogance.

It is a tendency induced by dullards, made to mollify an impatient spleen. The heart is crammed with it, and pride. I have seen beggars mounted who run their horses to death while empty vessels make the greatest sounds. I thank God for my humility. It serveth as straw upon a poor man's floor. Who calls me arrogant, they do not know my plight, for is it proud to seek justice from disgrace? Is it folly to demand fair treatment when all who know me drain me, cheat me, rob me, milk me at the teats of fortune as though I were a cow? Use me and call this their right and me their friend, or if I note what they steal, then call me an ingrate, and arrogant, that I can not thank them enough for their theft? Who is arrogant here, the earth that's plowed or the spade that turns it? I am not arrogant, O, a thousand times no, but abused. I am not falsely proud but set upon by maggots. What is arrogance but a perfumed defense?

It was the age of thought and the time of doubt, when "such dull and heavy-witted worldlings as were never capable of the wit of a comedy. . . found that wit there that

76

they never found in themselves. . . You should see all those grand censors. . . flock to them for the main grace of their gravities."

In truth, Elizabeth's age was yesterday and today and perhaps it was tomorrow too, and forever. Or never.

X

In Elizabeth's reign, the job and devotion of every citizen was to defend the young Protestant nation against Spain and the Catholic League. *Fight, fight, fight! We heard it on every side. Catholics, Protestants, Puritans, prigs from the city, poachers from the country, rustics, rebels, rowdies, churls of every sort, Homo trium literarum, and all at constant conflict. The economy was in such flux that hordes of beggars roamed the country, slept in barns where not invited and entered homes at open gates. Her majesty could not be safe without her bedchamber, Privy chamber, Presence chamber, and guard room. When she rode forth it was accompanied by two thousand horsemen armed with spears, bows and guns. Yet she could walk among the people spontaneously, smiling and thanking each one for his love and support and prayers, and linger, she looking at them in radiance, they gazing at her like schoolboys, asked their names and bashful to confess their letters, until someone stirred to recall the danger, and she was gone in a clatter of hooves.*

Building her country and church, she even assumed certain Catholic mythologies, becoming an object of veneration comparable to the Holy Mother, by declaring herself the Virgin Queen. It was Lord Edward's declaration, taken up by his poet friend Edmund Spenser who would write about their "Faerie Queene" - Gloriana, Diana, Venus the Goddess, Mother of England.   A disparate citizenry needed uniting.

"I declare you the Virgin Queen!" announced Edward in her hearing chamber where he appeared unexpectedly.

Her majesty came from her bedchamber in disarray and screamed at him: "How dare you burst in on my privacy!"

"I proclaim you the Virgin Queen! All England and the world will venerate you - mother of our nationhood!"

She turned on her heel and left him declaiming to the walls. "I am not dressed for this!"

Her courtiers and maids in waiting whispered between themselves, she would also be the queen of dalliance.

"Who calls our mother that?" Edward challenged.

They shrank in silence. "Assume a virtue if you have it not."

None dared utter such thoughts as who they thought the royal strumpet.

Leicester with hair twisted stumbled from her majesty's chamber and marched barefoot in nightshirt to his own quarters, which the queen had purposely ordered to be assigned him at the far end of the palace.

When she once had nicknamed him her "Robin Goodnight", on another stage he became her "Robin Nightwork", where Edward made a fool of him, writing plays for the court and private theaters.   Once, in performance, she dropped a glove. Edward picked it up, and kept his rhymed meter, even adding a couplet as he returned it, and continued the performance, while she, offended, said nothing to avoid the scandal her anger might induce, but sat, transfixed, and watched the play unfold through which her Edward made her court a plaything where his truth was told - that she and Leicester had a child out of wedlock, Arthur

Dudley, who was given to be raised by a country squire, under pretext of being born to a Maid of Honor.

Such things as what the queen did were not admitted to the populace, but Edward held them up for scrutiny in his private plays. "I write for the privileged eye, the educated ear, the knowing few, your majesty. We few, we happy few, we band of brothers, by your leave."

"Well then, perform for me, and no one else, Edward, if we would be privileged."

"All things are ready if our minds be so."

"And let no one else be advised," she said.

Nor could Edward contain himself and keep his own counsel, thinking of them, the queen, the court and all he knew there, but had to let out what he took in, for he was driven by a passion. "All the world's a stage! As trees host birds, as leaves host worms, and rocks give passage to the ants. I am a courtier on it; this - my hive, my forge, my foundry, a mill of courtiers I must grind to flour." He could not keep it silent.

"Remember Leicester", I was so often told by Lord Sussex. Remember Leicester's father, I am reminded. He was the Duke of Northumberland, Lord Protector of his majesty, Edward VI. He was executed in 1553 for conspiring to enthrone Lady Jane Grey, the wife of his son, Guilford Dudley. The Dudleys had a crowning hunger. They were ambitious to sit on a throne. They did indeed lust openly, and crave and conspire so, it sickened me. But I was made powerless. All that remained was to "Remember Leicester". I was restrained by his actions from action and it rankled.

In these times, trust vanished quickly, treachery grew, and censorship was on every tongue. Edward was admonished for his impulsiveness, his plays of personal persuasion, his plays on words and his plays of political assassination, for whatever he would show became the subject of scandal. The more he dressed it up in words the more words were offensive to the offended who were offending. For that he gave not a fig.

I must have liberty withal, as large a charter as the wind, to blow on whom I please, for so fools have. And they that are most galled with my folly, they most must laugh. . . Invest me in my motley, give me leave to speak my mind, and I will through and through cleanse the foul body of the infected world, if they will patiently receive my medicine.

What kind of fool was this who looked at men in women's dress and laughed at their femininity?

The Prince's jester, a very dull fool. Only his gift is in devising impossible slanders. None but libertines delight in him; and the commendation is not in his wit, but in his villainy; for he both pleases men and angers them, and then they laugh at him and beat him.

The problem for the Earl of Oxford was excess. Born to all the dreams of mind and matter realized, received from the court, from the hand of the queen herself, from two universities at an early age, graduated both Cambridge and Oxford, at ages fourteen and sixteen, and the law at Gray's Inn before the age of twenty-one, he had contempt for wealth and impatience with privilege, most especially his own, and lies were not to his liking. He had no time for deceit. "I shall be a common man, an ordinary, simplary, fundamentalary fellow - the most extraordinary of my class. I shall dare to be the equal of my inferiors - zah!" Edward cried from the rooftops and shouted down the chimneys of Theobalds, where there were more than twenty-seven chimney pots smoking, and ladies jumped from their chairs and cats from their baskets and games with balls of wool as his voice came thundering from the hearths of fire, coals, and ashes lifted out of the grates.

81

Sir William found his gardeners trying to engineer a method by which they might coax the young lord down, wondering aloud how, "m'lordship came to climb the roof"?

"By common law, Sir William, and a common touch. Now even you can praise my common aspiration, for it has brought me here!"

At twenty-two he declared himself to literature, and in his own hand signed his own name, publishing the famous book by Castiglione, 'The Courtier', becoming thereby the first peer of England ever to put his thoughts to print while still living and take personal credit in its preface:

"Although nature herself has made nothing perfect in every detail, yet the manners of men exceed in dignity that with which nature has endowed them; and he who surpasses others has here surpassed himself, and has even outdone nature which by no one has ever been surpassed. Nay more, however elaborate the ceremonial, whatever the magnificence of the Court, the splendor of the Courtiers, and the multitude of spectators, he has been able to lay down principles for the guidance of the very Monarch himself. Again, Castiglione has vividly depicted more and even greater things than these.

"For who has spoken of Princes with greater gravity? Who has discoursed of illustrious women with more ample dignity? No one has written of military affairs more eloquently, more aptly about horse-racing, and more clearly and admirably about encounters under arms on the field of battle. I will say nothing of the fitness and the excellence with which he has depicted the beauty of chivalry in the noblest persons. Nor will I refer to his delineations in the case of those persons who can not be Courtiers, when he alludes to some notable defect, or to some ridiculous character, or to some deformity of appearance.

"Whatever is heard in the mouths of men in casual talk and in society, whether apt and candid, or villainous and shameful, that he has set down in so natural a manner that it seems to be acted before our very eyes." The English translator "has resuscitated that dormant quality of fluent discourse. He has recalled those ornaments and lights which he had laid aside, for use in connection with subjects most worthy of them.

"For this reason he deserves all the more honor, because that to great subjects - and they are indeed great - he has applied the greatest lights and ornaments. For who is clearer in his use of words? Or richer in the dignity of his sentences? Or who can conform to the variety of circumstances with greater art?

"If weighty matters are under consideration, he unfolds his theme in a solemn and majestic rhythm. If the subject is familiar and facetious, he makes use of words that are witty and amusing. When therefore he writes with precise and well-chosen words, with skillfully constructed and crystal-clear sentences, and with every art of dignified rhetoric, it can not be but that some noble quality should be felt to proceed from his work.

"To me indeed it seems, when I read this courtly Latin, that I am listening to Crassus, Antonius, and Hortensius, discoursing on this very theme. And, great as all these qualities are, our translator has wisely added one single surpassing title of distinction to recommend his work. For indeed what more effective action could he have taken to make his work fruitful of good results than to dedicate his 'Courtier' to our most illustrious and noble Queen, in whom all courtly qualities are personified, together with those diviner and truly celestial virtues? For there is no pen so skillful or powerful, no kind of speech so clear, that is not left behind by her own surpassing virtue."

The preface remained as popular as the book. When professor Gabriel Harvey of Cambridge discussed Lord Edward's literary greatness six years later, it was to "let that courtly epistle, more polished even than the writings of Castiglione himself, witness how greatly" the young earl excelled in letters.

Harvey knew the earl of whom he wrote. They were students together, raised at Saffron Walden in the tutelage of Sir Thomas Smith, disciplined by "Foul Fowle", only Harvey became a scholar while Edward chose the course of action to make his mark in the slumbering world of indifferent minds.

Educators of the times, like Queen Elizabeth's tutor Roger Ascham, believed books were more valuable than personal experience, that 'The Courtier' could be absorbed even by the middle class, and one might learn better from books in a year than from experience in twenty.

With Edward's preface a new note sounded through English writing: a passionate patron who, backed by the queen, took language for his cause and literature for his monument.

XI

As the youth of Edward deVere was passed in a home of the highest standards kept by the queen's most trusted, if pedantic and blustering minister, Sir William, the Cecils were in that new class of people whose fortunes depended on the favor and good will of others, their betters. They were the first to prosper as bureaucrats and had much to gain as Lord Edward's foster parents. Their gain was all profit.

"But Lord Edward, may I remind you about the servants. One of your estate does not speak to them, but orders others to speak for you to them, thus: 'Master John, can you please ask the maid to bring my boots?' And Master John will oblige you, because he is your servant, and your boots will be brought, and a servant to help you step into them. I must caution you also, Lord Edward, not to pass your time in listening to the staff. They only complain, and you are above complaint. And do not consider them your friends, Lord Edward. When they ask you for money, or speak in base and filthy words, that is beneath you. I am your purse and they should not forget that. I am your purse."

"But am I not your support, Sir William, while you remain my purse? Am I not the pocket where your purse is kept? That there would be no purse with you, lacking my support of the purse?"

"Of course, my lord. The purse must have support, and you are that. But what is there to support if not the purse?"

"And so the fish needs water, but does not drink, Sir William. Remember, I am your water. And you are in my pocket."

To the Cecil's own children, fine disciplines of denial and abstention were applied, and often what was worn by little Robert, the hunch back, was sure to be from great Edward's household laundry.

"Haven't I seen that handkerchief before, Robert?" Edward asked.

"I don't know," came the answer, sniffling.

"Haven't I smelled of that handkerchief, Robert?"

A big sneeze replied.

"I wonder if my shoes are traveling in Europe, and my coat isn't somewhere on the high seas?" Edward laughed, and all the other children laughed too. But little Robert, the hunch back, wiped his nose in the corner.

As the poet often says, oblivion can be inevitable and the name of a man lies buried with his bones.

Clue! Men's names that live beyond them are inventions. And though Edward would build his monument he would never have his tomb. "Not everything that history offers us has actually happened. And what has actually happened has not happened the way it is presented, and what we know to have happened is only a very small part of what actually happened," says Goethe.

Imagine, then, a public figure who yearns for a private life, the peace of peace, the modesty of obscurity. And imagine in the shadows behind him a hunch back whose only glory is in watching the fires of another shine, as he studies his father's precepts and learns to bide his time, to wait his turn, to apply his lessons to the deviousness of obsequiousness, the discipline of hypocrisy. While Edward read 'The Courtier', Robert Cecil studied 'The Prince' which gave the world Machiavelli.

Sometimes I see myself surrounded, in a jungle of intrigue, by other's ambitions surmounted, by their desperation craven, bitten by snakes and pricked by spiders, engorged by worms and poisoned by vipers, all passing slyly in a fawning human form, each face made flaccid by familiar courtesies, the truth of their minds benumbed by the frozen muscles of their stone-masked expressions. Thus are they inclined to bow, "and how are you, m'lord? Is all well? Your digestion easy? Did you your varlets swallow? Your palate pleased?" Sometimes I'm tempted to cry out, "No! Bake me a human pie! I crave the cannibal's meal and you I want on the principle platter!" But I whistle and walk away, and assume a care-free manner, for what is ambition to me? I possess the universe in a poem.

To Edward, balancing privacy with notoriety, which came from poetry about his velvet life unveiled, made choosing obscurity easy, and hardly required debate in his mind. There was a special fate for one who stood famous. Truth to tell, it was to end anonymous.

For I do not know what manner of man I am as I become a man. To be to the manner born predestines me to great heights, and what must a man from great heights reach? A great fall, and yet I do not chose to fall. Rather, then, descend? Or are there heights not yet attained to be reached by digging down and burrowing deep beneath the surface? I shall take my lessons where I find them and where I look shall be everywhere!

Though he wanted to be a soldier and fight for glory, or a philosopher and fight for truth, when he recalled his experience on the Northern border, he would rage at the memory of his cousin's execution, remembering a duke who'd been a reluctant conspirator, who'd tried to be a good subject but allowed himself to be used by the traitors beneath him. And no one listened. Or if they heard, they indulged,

87

and called him grieving. Poor Edward, grief-stricken over the Duke of Norfolk's death! Poor Edward, to be pitied! And he found such treatment pitiable and dared it to treat him worse!

How could I grieve for a man said to be in heaven? Would that not make me grieve for what's divine? Better the fool. And if he is rather in hell, why grieve at all?

But Edward's return from the Scottish rebellion is remembered for bringing home the song 'Greensleeves'. The court of the queen took it up and Edward became more celebrated for his musical tastes than military ability, to the queen's delight and her maids in waiting, who devoted their waiting on Edward.

As the lute accompanied singers, and strolling musicians in consort with the handore, cittern, bass viol and flute performed the lilting melody of 'Greensleeves', Edward met the musicians. At court, Antonio Bassano's family provided them, with cornet, fife, trumpet, sackbut, viol, violin, harp and boys' voices, while the queen herself participated on virginal, which like a piano had gold and silver strings that were plucked by quills.

There were five sons of Antonio Bassano, and two of their wives, all Edward's age, who shared their music with him. One, Baptista, was Antonio's youngest brother, who was married and had a baby daughter, Emilia, who was already participating in their performances. She was born in January, 1569, in Shoreditch, where her father bought several buildings and land. There also her uncles, Eduardo and Andrea, bought property in Norton Folgate, creating a community of artists, and Edward was invited to their homes for feasting, and he accepted. This was a society that courtiers and those of the nobility did not accept, but Edward went to visit them eagerly.

The queen would have him with her, to pique her when she was down, to challenge her when she was up, to tempt her when she was bored, and to delight all her ladies in waiting. Soldiers and men showed Edward only their envy, their rivalry, their disdain, while at court he was teased and desired.

But with the Bassanos he was treated equally, for his skill and appreciation in music, where many a holiday afternoon unfolded around the large, pear-shaped lute with its long neck, awakening their neighborhood as one of the brothers plucked his cittern with an ivory pick and the deep-pitched pandora wailed through the walls.

Little Emilia asked Edward what he would do if they were at court now, and everyone laughed as one of the adults suggested that no doubt some maids in waiting would be urging Edward: "Come, under the sheets to kittle!"

No one heard of his grief or that he was melancholic. He was praised for skill at the dulcimer and virginal and called more knowing than musicians who made it their business to know.

He asked Antonio if perhaps the boy singers would not be qualified as actors. He might start a troupe of them performing plays.

Pear cider, mead and sack were served to all, and ale, which was made monthly and bought from the parish church of St. Botolph's, Bishopsgate. Emilia's mother, Margaret, scolded her child for trying to drink from her uncle's tankard, much to the laughter of all the men present, and even the boys who envied the little girl for her beguiling ways.

Edward published a song book and 'The Earl of Oxford's March', still played four centuries later to the delight of the ladies, the contempt of the gentlemen. 'Greensleeves' remained popular at court for the rest of

Elizabeth's reign, and forever. But when it was played, Edward turned his head to the outdoors and looked up at the heavens from the moated walls of Theobalds, his home that was no home but a prison to youth and discipline where he was raised uncomforted by parent or sibling or distant relation. It was Sir William and Lady Mildred's home. He was their ward and no more, their meal ticket and no better.

"I will live in my own place," he vowed, and thought of the happy - and many - Bassanos living so close in so many places.

"What is it with my lord today?" he was asked by Sir William.

"Nothing. As the sun breeds maggots. Only thoughts."

"Do you know me, my lord?"

"Yes, you're Pondous the fish monger, for didn't you pass the law that we eat fish on Wednesday as well as Friday? And weren't you paid well for it by the sellers of fish who saw in you twice their catch?"

"Not I, my lord," Sir William assured the young lord.

"Then I would you were so honest a man."

"Honest, my lord?"

"Ay, sir. To be honest, as this world goes, is to be one man picked out of ten thousand, like a fish from the sea."

"That's very true, my lord. But in truth, you are melancholic."

"Melancholic? Then I smell a rat, and where does the rat live, but feasting off the dung heap, so what is that odor that makes us melancholy? It is the swamp of human waste I smell. Who knows? I have a sense of the scent. Don't you? But what do you know of truth? Can you eat it? You were born on the Diet of Worms, Sir William - Corambus."

90

"But you do have moods, my lord. You are out of humor."

"I am out of breath," Edward answered.

Later Edward would tell himself, *I must not express only fire. Is her majesty not amused? What does she ask me?* "If I were in truth the Virgin Queen, then should I not have a miracle birth? Give me a child of your brain who can recite Ovid, converse of Aristotle in his native Greek, ignite fires and calm seas - all by miracle. Give me an Englishman to beguile me, born and raised who knows nothing of the world and yet speaks of the universe with tongues of sugar and gold. Make me a child by divine knowledge, whose entire store of wisdom exists in a thimble. Let him hold the world on his finger, and yet be humble, of common English cloth, a stable boy, a barn-sweep, to make my kingdom complete." *I received from her majesty such tasks as would make a seamstress numb. Yet I have woven a fabric greater than my Lord Burghley's two hundred tapestries.*

For a song he leased a country estate to the great composer William Byrd, and the deal was reported by Shake-speare in 'All's Well that Ends Well', even referring to a most familiar personage: "I know a man that had this trick of melancholy, sold a goodly manor for a song." The song Byrd arranged for the manor was 'The Earl of Oxford's March'.

But many events at the court of Elizabeth were reported as newsy gossip in the plays of the age with Shakespeare's references. Still she was offended by them, but resisted her offense and dismissed them, being beneath her, or above her, or beyond her, and not to be taken seriously, for they were only the witticisms of a courtier.

"I tire of clawbacks and lickspittles," said her majesty.

91

"Then off with slavish weeds, servile thoughts and milkish toadies! Supple knees are a proud man's fees," Edward replied, and bowed, and mocked his bow with sweeping gestures. "I am Sir Oracle, Ever an O, and when I Ope my lips, let no dog bark!"

XII

Edward came of age with a sense of the dangers of privilege, and met a new form of challenge. As he was raised with Sir William's daughter, Anne Cecil, seven years his junior, when they played and held deep discussion in privacy at Cecil House, Sir William had the youngsters spied upon by a servant, showing no sign of trust in Edward's liberal ideas and ways.

"Shall I lie in your lap, Anne?"

"No, my lord."

"I mean, my head upon your lap?"

"Ay, my lord."

"Do you think I meant country matters?"

"I think nothing, my lord."

"That's a fair thought to lie between maid's legs."

"What is, my lord?"

"Nothing."

"You are merry, my lord."

Though it was not to be said, the young lord was regarded as a corrupting influence, with a bad tendency to lewd people and depraved ways in the rowdy houses of the city. That he would socialize on holidays with common musicians! It was scandal. Such thoughts were brayed in the street as: "A spaniel, a woman and a walnut tree, the more they are beaten, the better they be!" And it was wished that someone be found who could thrash Edward, but there were none equal to his station.

"And how is my daughter?" asked Sir William of Anne.

"My lord, as I was sewing in my closet, Lord Edward, with his doublet all unbraced, no hat upon his head, his stockings fouled, ungartered, and pulled down to his ankle, pale as his shirt, his knees knocking each other, and with a look so piteous in purport as if he had been sent from hell to speak of horrors - he comes before me."

"Mad for you?"

"Not for me."

"Mad for your love then?"

"My lord, I do not know."

"What said he?"

"Why, he took me by the wrist, and then he - and then I - and then we - and he - and I - and he again - and we - and me - and my - I do not know, but truly I do fear it."

"There is something fishy in Lord Edward, Anne. Beware of him, and keep your distance."

From behind a curtain Edward heard their words, and his thought of something fishy was of Sir William in him, everywhere around him and about him, like a giant tent, all beard and piety. He burst from the closet and cried "Havoc!" to the fright of the women, the fleeing and screams of house cats and the apoplectic dismay of the speechless Sir William, who was deprived of all pretense by this erupting visage of fury.

Edward brandished a sword he used to fence with, the curtain he tore from its rings he used to feint with, and all sorts of shouting and verbal nonsense. The general chorus was for calm, Sir William the most appeasing and Edward the most offended, until calm was attained, in no small degree due to the appeals of Anne who could affect miracles with her eyes and change the course of great thought with a blink. "O God!" moaned Edward. "How I do need a woman."

"A woman?" inquired Sir William.

"A woman, yes, no other!" Edward answered.

"I am shocked," gasped Sir William, before whom Edward whispered the nickname Pondous.

"And so am I. But would you rather I gave you a taradiddle?"

"Why, what diddle?" asked Sir William.

"Why, nothing, no, not if it were untrue," said Edward, and enjoyed his game.

Then, "Do you see yonder cloud that's almost in shape of a camel?"

"By the mass, and 'tis like a camel, indeed," said Sir William.

"Methinks it is like a weasel."

"It is backed like a weasel," said Sir William.

"Or like a whale?"

"Very like a whale," said Sir William, still serious.

And Edward had the laugh to himself. "Between man and woman are four stages of action. They are attraction, passion, contraction, and satisfaction. We have gone through none of these, Sir William. Your daughter Anne and I have barely played at Shoe the Mare. Perhaps you worry that the fairies who steal babies will come at your daughter, Sir William. Might I suggest you place a Bible in the birthing bed to protect against bad fairies, and secure your daughter, though she be born well if not well born already, Corambus."

When Edward discovered he and Anne were spied upon by an undercook hidden in a closet, the next time he was alone with her to talk of private matters, he drew his sword in rage at this invasion and stabbed the curtain and shouted as if at a shadow. Or was it a rainbow? Or was it a crow? Anne screamed.

"How now?" cried Edward. "A rat? Dead for a ducat, dead!" he declared.

The undercook, Thomas Bricknell, died on the floor before them and no one gave him another thought.

Said Edward, "I'll lug the guts into the neighbor room."

"The servant plunged upon his sword and veritably killed himself before my lord, and used the sword of my lord to do it, to take his own life. It was a monstrous thing." Sir William testified in writing that the act was *se defendo*, self defense on the Earl of Oxford's part, rather than admit to his own complicity in putting a spy upon the young man who lived in his house and went so far as to speak with his daughter.

"*Se defendo!*" cried Edward. "Rather *se offendendo*; it can not be else. For he offended me before I defended myself, and by offense I took defense!"

" It is *se defendo*, Lord Edward. *Se defendo* it shall be, so long as you are ward in my house and I am Master of Wards." He sighed as old men sigh when young men wear their nerves, and muttered. "O weary me, to raise such headaches who would lose their heads."

"Now I'm offended, that you deny I was offended! That's an offense indefensible!" cried Edward. "A little land well-tilled, a little wife well-willed!" But his offenses were ignored.

When Cecil swore that the servant had run upon his ward's sword, and the court believed him, the matter was closed and forgotten by all but Cecil. He retained its memory until one day he could use the matter for his own purpose and benefit against this upstart Edward. He carefully filed it away in his records, an archive of slander and treason by which he kept his tally of everybody, and waited. The fox oneday would catch this trying, this confusing, this mocking, arrogant, unsuppressable, errant earl of a boar. All he needed was patience, and the record of Edward's blasphemies, well-documented each and every one. Sir William Cecil would have his day against such foolish nobility. A deVere might fly high, but a Cecil would have him by the bye.

I feel the very gods themselves have taken away my ceremony. They've clipped my wings, my sail, my spear, and I am left with nothing shaking at the night. To the fox I said, 'Let me admonish you, my lord: Do not barter your love for food for it will inflate you beyond support. Even your sturdy ass will waver and honk hee-haw at such a burden as you propose out of love. Better a starving glutton than a nourished ascetic.' But the whale found no humor in me, when I called his donkey an ass and then called for his ass.

"Now I will remind you, my lord, of how I have saved you in the duel."

"Why yes, Sir William, and not even drawing your sword."

"Because I have no sword, my lord. And I think unkindly on your sword."

"And it thinks not at all of you, Sir William. It is a dumb sword. It neither reasons nor speaks. And yet all fear it."

"Certainly you jest, my lord."

"I would not jest with you, Sir William. Rather, take my spear with which my father and I killed the boar behind the ear when first you came to us at Hedingham. You are my warden. I am your ward. Though now I'm twenty-one, I'll have my own place and keep to myself. This is not a jesting matter from one who jests at scars. A man should not be left to himself. Who never felt a wound? It is ill news to be a jest to oneself."

The queen decided to tame Edward's spirits. "My Turk" she called him, and insisted he display to her courtiers his skill at dancing. He declined to make such a fool of himself at court with foppery before the French ambassador, who was in audience on a special mission, to win the hand of her majesty for the French heir to the throne, the Duke of Anjou.

When her majesty sent for Edward a second time and commanded him to dance before her, he sent word back that he was out and would not dance for Frenchmen.

"They bore me who would romp with her majesty, merrily swinging high off the floor! What does the Puritan say? Shaking, unclean handling, kissing, bragging and groping make it a very kind of lechery enjoyed by women chiefly for its kissing. What does she want of me, the gaillard?"

The attendant who bore the message lowered his head without an answer for his lordship.

"Five steps of the gaillard, then a caper, a cabriole, a leap! Perhaps she wants the coranto, the Spanish canary for these Frenchmen. Is that what they request, our jig?"

"I have no reply, m'lord," said the servant.

"Then there's the lavolta. She'd admire that, I'm sure, waltzing with leaps. Send her morris dancers, sir! For commoners. And I'll have none of that! Tell her majesty I perform the slow pavan alone in my chamber for my sorrows."

Courtliness beggars commentary. What drudgery: Rise, dress, dance, eat, chat, smile, lie, laugh, all to please frippery and Imperia. I'd rather ride a horse at hunt.

What Lord Oxford demonstrated to all was the freedom with which he could decline before all eyes to satisfy the queen's wishes with impunity. He was her acknowledged favorite against which there could be found no wrong in him. So long as he amused her, and entertained her, and professed undying love and fidelity to her, he could pique her and resist her.

She begged me to write her poetry. I gave her some in her own voice. She said she might have written it herself. I said she had, for all the heart and mind found in it:

"Then spake fair Venus' son, that brave, victorious boy,
"Saying, 'You dainty dame, for that you be so coy,
"I will so pluck your plumes, as you shall say no more,
"Go, go, go, seek some other where, importune me no
    more.'"

She laughed and had me dance the gaillard with her. Every morning she would dance though where she found the will I had no clue, since all she ate were sweets.

"My good lady, would you grant me a folly?"

"Why, Ned?"

"I wish a license to be your fool."

"But of course. To all my court I wish it known, Lord Edward will be my fool. You are now my allowed fool, Ned."

"Thank you, Madonna."

"For there is no slander in an allowed fool, though he do nothing but rail."

"And jeer, scoff, mock, twit, jape, flout, and sneer, Madonna."

"Madonna? You call me Madonna?"

"I call you Olivia. I call you Rosalind. I call you The Rose Without Thorns. The point is, I call no other."

"Enough foolery, Ned. I weary of solemn idolatry."

99

"Then boo, hiss, hoot, rave, bark or yelp, Madonna, to put vituperation in a syllable, to vilify honorably."

She adopted a policy to dally with this French duke, later the Duke of Alencon, unattractive as the French were considered. One had a pock-marked face and was short. The other was an idiot. Her flirtatious marriage negotiations with these continental nobles had the singular effect of forestalling their forming or signing an alliance with the King of Spain against her, a possibility so formidable that, had it happened, our tiny island nation would have been wiped out in the fury of their combined forces invading. But she was a daughter afraid of no member of the opposite sex, or nation bent on her destruction. She was the daughter of the king who broke the Catholic Church, with God's help. When her majesty showed an interest in marrying the French noblesse, much of the court and country were enraged by her dalliance. They did not appreciate her gift at selling empty promises and forestalling actual wars, and when her suitor sailed she seemed to have a broken heart and wrote a sonnet to it:

"I am and not; I freeze and yet am burn'd;
"Since from myself, my other self I turn'd."

Once heard, applauded and appeased from grief, she sat among her many cushions and declared her broken heart was healed, so pass the candy.

Edward brought the issue to the fore, riding a footcloth nag through the Strand towards Westminster. A footcloth nag is a horse covered down to the hooves by a nobleman's colors and crest in a blanket for all to identify.

I dressed in a French ruff, a French cloak, French hose, and in my hand held a great fan of feathers like a

100

woman, against the side of my face, mocking what a woman under French influence might seem. It was a riot to the people who were aware and a scandal to the court who heard it soon enough. 'What, do you mock me to the sundry?' railed her majesty. 'I imitate you, Madonna. There is no greater flattery.' She breathed serpents and hissed fire, but withdrew to her private chamber for prayers, and pouting. The people of England would not hear of another Frenchman on our throne. She did not care to hear what our people would not hear, but she was made to hear it.

Thanks to a gentleman of rank dressed up like a woman in marital servitude *on display to the file.*

There was no rebuking him. Edward's public display was a private disgrace, but not to be remarked, least it grow worse, for the public hung on him, and doted on his slightest act just as her majesty did. No John Stubbes punishment was given to Edward. He was the satire of a satirist, incarnate. *I am a pasquinader, a jongleur, the very epitome of a poor poet!* He was their sun king at court, their grace in his disgrace, their Phoebus, in other's shame, their glory. Half the known world esteemed him; the other half was dumb.

Her majesty eventually abandoned the idea of becoming French by marriage herself. When next the public enjoyed a good laugh with the earl, he was on parade with the queen's entourage to Plymouth.

Such popularity with the uncultivated was not lost on the queen who could appreciate the persuasion of crowds and their influence upon her policy. For poets truly were the unacknowledged legislators of the world.

"You enjoy the mirth of the populace, Edward. Is that because you would outshine me?"

"No, your majesty. I am but this star of England. You are the sun in the universe. Beside you, all have shadows and at best are the pale reflection of your warmth."

"Then you mean me no ill?"

"I mean you well, ma'am. And if well be ill then I mean you nothing and if nothing be ill then I am at a loss to mean you anything, for to me you are everything."

"I will consider your meaning, if you mean anything, Edward," the queen said.

However, she had not tamed her Turk.

XIII

The queen decided her shining young earl should be married. Sir William hinted that the bride was best to be his daughter. Marriage between a commoner and a noble? That would bring the noble down, and the commoner up. That would, after all, make Anne Cecil the Countess of Oxford, and their children descendants of the oldest and greatest family in England. Sir William, son of a landowner and, after all, no more than a tradesman himself in matters of law and governing policy, would become a grandfather to his own new aristocracy, the inventor of bureaucracy before the word was invented, ascending heights he never dreamed.

Where is the spirit? High on a man, as noble and high as can be, though he stand in the mud and worms ooze between his toes like every other common beast. For everyone stands on the ground however high or low they be, and when it's filth, then all are filthy. Yet only the noble of spirit stand high. Thus is it easier to wallow than soar, for more of our earthlings do it, more fitting to be common than uncommon, more common to be common, in fact.

Elizabeth objected that the Cecils were not of a sufficient class, and class was what ruled in England. Even Sir William could accept that, not the fact but the argument. The Cecils were commoners, after all. Yes, he agreed, but noted that within her majesty's power was the power to change his class.

"And how, my Leviathan? By raising you or lowering Lord Oxford?"

103

"But none can lower my lord, your majesty. He will never lower."

"And will you rise? How will you rise? Like dough? Through levity and hot air?"

"I have a daughter, your majesty. She is dutiful, faithful - in faith dutiful, in duty faithful. To me she will give everything."

"She is so sweet, Sir William. Sweet little Anne," said Elizabeth, and noted, "No challenge to her queen when ruling the heart of an earl. She will have him, she'll think, but I will have them both!" And her majesty accepted the bargain. She made Sir William a lord.

"I give you the new Lord Burghley, Sir William."

"Lord Burghley, your majesty?"

"Because you are a burly lord, Sir William. I put matter with matter and give you a title for a nibble, Sir Spirit, though I doubt I do nickname you, for those of your kind, they say, have no sense. Do you have no sense or are you all nonsense, Sir William?"

"I sense your meaning, your majesty."

"They say it is a foul air that makes no sense. I say, the odor makes for melancholy. You have no ill humor, Sir William?"

"But I will be called Lord Burghley, your majesty?"

"Yes, and no more of it. Lord Burghley for yourself. You will be a baron, the lowest form of lord. Countess of Oxford for Anne Cecil. I sense a noble stream befouled by a rivulet and yet all flows as one. Now make the arrangements."

And so Cecil attained the title of baron. Not much of a title, the lowest rank possible for the most powerful minister, but at the age of fourteen his daughter became Edward's betrothed. How long Sir William had schemed to become a lord and how little Edward had schemed to be anything. Sir William went home from the court to Lady Mildred and gave her their new kingdom. They had fish for dinner.

But Edward declined to be married in September, 1571. When the wedding day approached he was gone, to the continent, without royal leave, on the run, with spies of the secret service dispatched to bring him back. Sir William's spies, much to Sir William's consternation, for he was all feathers and froth and could make no sense of anything sensible, found Edward most cheerful and amiable.

Edward declared that if he had to marry Anne, he had no intention of a consummation with her, that his devotion was to her majesty, to their country, to their crusade, and to nobility, freedom, knighthood, the military and the ideal of her virgin rule, no less. The queen was his only love! And the queen loved hearing it. Just what she wanted, had intended - another man with a net around him, a wife whom he would tire of and a lord whom she could lead, unchallenged.

It was great fun, making slaves where free souls thrived! These courtiers of hers, they didn't even know the steps with which they misstepped into her winsome trap. Couldn't they see it? How she toyed with them! Like herself, her court would be imprisoned by destiny.

Her most telling captive was her mutton. He danced so well she made him Captain of the Guard, and when whispers grew too loud about the dance they did, she gave him four hundred pounds annually to withdraw and dance no more. Christopher Hatton, who gave himself to her majesty and built her a castle that ruined him financially, as then she declined to visit it, which he had never entered, having declared she must be first to see it. Instead she demanded repayment of his debt for it. Her mutton took sick and wept himself to death. Poor fop! My poor Cousin Fop!

Had a large proportion of gifts and endowments, but too much of the season of envy; and he was a mere vegetable of the court, that sprung up at night, and sunk again at his noon.

After Hatton's death, the castle was dismantled and its furnishings packed off, but said to this day to have been one of the greatest in all England. Only its entrance remains on a field of green, with no place for entering.

Lord Oxford was twenty one. The queen was thirty eight. She was amused. Indeed, she was flattered. One could say more.

But first she had Edward returned from abroad, and arranged for his marriage before Christmas. On December 19, 1571, it was on her orders obtained, but on his decision abstained.

Cakes of milk, eggs, sugar, spice and currants were made. Fruit, grain and tiny oaten cakes were sprinkled over the pair. Some kept their cakes to put under their pillow to bring pleasant dreams at night and others, to feed the poor. The feast of wine, bread and sweetmeats was served for three days, that all the poor of the parish could partake. Sops were made for floating in the wine and muscatel was served with plumbuns.

The bride wore a white dress with love knots in various colors and her house was festooned with wreaths and flowers. Gifts of candlesticks, fireplace sets, gold and silver basins and ewers, cups and warming pans for beds, together with room hangings were given.

Rosemary, a good omen, was dipped in the bridal cup of wine before each sip and there were roses everywhere.

"What's spoken under the rose is never told."

"You are as good as a chorus, my lord," Anne said to her new husband who was everywhere about the wedding guests and nowhere at one time.

"I could interpret between you and your love, if I could see the puppets dallying," he answered her.

"You are keen, my lord, you are keen," she sparkled.

"It would cost you a groaning to take off my edge," he said.

"Still better, and worse," said she.

"So you must take your husbands," he replied.

There were Anglicans and Puritans mixing among the guests, like sun and shadow on a fair afternoon, with gossip of the day, the Ridolfi Plot having narrowly missed success at putting the Scottish Queen Mary on their throne, with its threat of restoring the Catholics to power. It was enough to make the Anglicans and Puritans declare themselves one for all and all for one, united as Protestants, every one. Even the Catholic clergy was invited. For a dozen years now, by order of the queen, they were permitted to marry, and so the priests of Rome came to the wedding with their wives.

"If love does not grow by day, it will die by night," they discoursed. "On that subject, a good man might inflame a saint." They laughed.

"Ay, a dishonest woman can not be kept in."

"But an honest woman does not venture out."

"So marriage can be either good or ill, but a man can make it good, if he will."

The queen on the subject of marriage pronounced her thoughts for all: "In truth, I greatly fear not being loved by my husband, which would be a greater misfortune than old age, for it would be worse than death, and I can not bear to reflect upon such a possibility. So I have no husband."

To the Spanish ambassador she said: "It is not fit for a queen and a maiden to summon anyone to her. As we have said to the King of Sweden: It is well known how my sex is rushed headlong into everything and especially so in affairs of this sort."

She complained of being misjudged for refusing to marry: "The world, where a woman remains single, assumes that there must be something wrong with her, and that she has some discreditable reason for it. I have only this, as we informed the French ambassador when he urged my marriage with the King of France, who was sixteen and half my age at the time: I feel that the Queen Mother has not been fully informed of my age, which is such that I am afraid the king and she would reproach themselves, and what discontentment would be my lot, for I should be disagreeable and be neglected by him as the late mourned Queen Mary, my sister, was by the King of Spain. I should rather die than find myself despised and neglected."

Then from marriage, the discourse turned to love, often a fair neighbor to the former.

"Of all the men who declare they will die for love, how many are dead?" asked the queen.

She added: "Love is mostly talk and heat, which in the end, like a fire, is mostly dust and ashes, cold as a hearth in summer."

Proposed one courtier: "A maid should ask a suitor if he thinks she is wise or honest."

"Ay, and if the answer is not, then he is neither wise nor honest in his intentions." More laughter.

"But if she is wise and honest, then so is he!" Increased laughing.

The cause of anger in Edward was that Sir William did not convey so much as a hint of a dowry. It was the custom of the age that upon a daughter's marriage, the father gave his son-in-law control of her property, or control of his own, befitting their station. Thus Edward publicly was disgraced by this breach of custom, and their vows were demeaned by Sir William not giving anything, not even the rights to her own property, to Anne and her husband. Thus were the bridal couple joined and empty-handed.

Though custom dictated that a woman was carried over the doorsill of her bedchamber on the wedding night to prove that she did not walk to the place where she would lose her innocence forever, the newlyweds did not spend even one night together.

Though the queen witnessed the wedding in Westminster Abbey, she could do no more than return to Whitehall amidst her gallants' hollow laughter. Edward was disconsolate and did not sleep with his bride.

It was a wedding night for fools. Away from home, girls in the street can not avoid talk - too much and they are considered light, too little and they are considered dull. The fault is to go in the street at all. And thus is my description of the virtue of girls. Yet woman's virginity has so much marvelous honor in it that wild lions are tamed in its presence and reduced to purring reverence, wrote Edward in his golden book.

Even a queen could not command that!

"How do you, pretty lady?" asked the queen of Anne at court, where Edward was not to be found in the following days.

Anne sang. "He is dead and gone, lady, he is dead and gone; at his head a grass-green turf, at his heels a stone."

"What is this?" Leicester asked the queen on joining them.

Anne sang. "Tomorrow is Saint Valentine's day. And I a maid at your window to be your Valentine. Then up he rose and donned his clothes and dupped the chamber door, let in the maid, that out a maid never departed more."

"Pretty Anne!" the Earl of Leicester declared.

"Indeed, la, without an oath, I'll make an end on it. Young men will do it if they come to it. By cock they are to

109

blame. 'Before you tumbled me, you promised me to wed.' He answers: 'So would I have done by yonder sun and thou had not come to my bed.'"

"How long hath she been thus?" asked Leicester.

"I hope all will be well," Anne continued. "My brother shall know of it, and so I thank you for your good counsel. Come, my coach! Good night, ladies, good night, Sweet ladies, good night, good night."

Anne returned to her rooms which she had obtained by writing to the great Earl of Sussex to plead that he intercede with the palace schedule makers to allow her three rooms instead of the customary one room at court for sleeping, so that she could tempt her lord and husband to be there with her in the comfort he was used to, and the rooms were granted, but not his lordship's presence by the Earl of Oxford.

What do you believe, that I would make a pudding of a plumb cake? Ay! And there's the rub. To tumble and not fall, to dally and not delay! Mine is the voice of liberty, and my queen is free! So I! So I! Forever! raved Edward in his golden book, its pages written at different stages, bound by crimson strings, then unbound and rebound, as parts were saved and parts discarded as he passed through different ages.

We are come now to the darkness, not of night but the soul, for I tell you there is no weather and the ship on which you sail has no sons, yet destiny is its port. Beware, the enemies within, that mock you comfortably, and lead you blind. No man can know where he is bound yet every port is charted. Darkness envelopes all and ignorance is our state. We live in shadows and yet of substance aspire. We yearn in doubt, yet of a likelihood find truth. Truth is our only claim. It lights the night. It tempers day. It calms the seas. It lifts the winds. The truth: That's all you know and all you dare to know. How strange, how sad, misfortune's tale is this - that all's for nought where goodness is amiss.

I could not lie with Anne, my wife, for she was my sister by adoption, and my foster-father gloated on it, willed it, gave his authority to our incest to fulfill his own ambition. Thus greed upon itself was made to feed, for which he did not dower one estate to bless us, but took us to disgrace and proved what his intent was with our name - our EVER-lasting shame.

Part Three

"A Motley to the View"

XIV

The name of the game was "the Tournament". It was already passé - a sport of privilege enamored of few who recalled more chivalrous times and attempted to re-live glamorous moments out of the fading but historic past which all were proud of but only they who could afford the accouterments pursued.

Tilting on horse involved armor and javelins aimed in the lists at mounted opponents, colorful banners and knights in feudal attire, with the queen and her ladies in waiting seated at twelve noon at the windows of a long room facing Whitehall to watch and approve near Westminster. A broad staircase before the tilt yard approached the queen. In the yard were wooden stands for all who had eighteen pence to gain entry. Thousands of spectators filled them. Those milling about the tilt yard were allowed in for free. Two knights rode into the lists with a loud blast of trumpets.

King Henry VIII had revived the love for King Arthur's chivalrous heroes, and the king himself had tilted. "The beauty of chivalry rested in the noblest of persons," wrote Castiglione in 'The Courtier', which Edward kept with him always, his gospel of impeccable conduct.

To Elizabethans, the days of knights in shining armor were a part of the colorful, fading past, fast being replaced by politics and the indoor warfare of courtliness.

That was embodied more in a new class of bureaucrat like Sir William, Lord Burghley, the Great Lord Treasurer, prime minister to the queen, with whom her majesty had bonded like a Merlin's curse upon their victory over the beheaded Duke of Norfolk.

But on a day such as this, politics were all but forgotten. The tilt lists were sixty paces long and forty wide with a gate at either end and a strong bar to keep the people out. One gate opened to the east, the other westward, barred with a rail seven feet long. A constable called the challenger and the defendant to tilt, inspecting their partisans, which were long handle spears.

Before the tournament, the pledges and hostages of the challengers and defendants were brought in and confined below the royal box, remaining captive there until saved by their champion's valor.

The crowds were so great that in town, a servant from each house was ordered to stand watch through the preceding night till sunrise, to control people and keep them from looting and wantonness. The bow and arrow laws were still in effect, requiring of each citizen to own and be adept in archery, on which the national defense depended, should occasion arise. Muskets and arquebuses were only starting to appear.

The Knight of the Tree of the Sun was Lord Edward. He dressed his servants not only in Oxford colors of Reading tawny and black but wrote a flowery speech which was read to the queen by a page before his turn in the lists. The speech was in rhyme and the servant, who had memorized it, cut merry capers as he recited, to the laughter of her majesty and ladies. Chivalry once more was in flower and Edward the knight to be valiant, the queen the sun of which he was a branch of her tree. When the recital was done, the happy lad handed the queen a gift which she accepted and then signaled her permission for her knight to take arms.

The constable called out to know whom this knight defended, and lifted his visor to confirm the man inside his armor.

Edward's answer, "Her majesty, the queen!"

He ordered the clerk to read the charge and the rules. He administered the oath: "You bring no illegal weapon, engine, instrument, herb, charm, or enchantment to this challenge, but you shall each put trust in no other thing than God."

"Agreed!"

The heralds cleared the lists and warned the crowds, "No speech, word, voice, or countenance whereby either the challenger or defendant may take advantage!"

The crowds marveled and cheered at Edward's lion skin colors deepened with crimson velvet, indicating power, pride and grandeur blended with overwhelming courage. To all he was the Red Knight. Her majesty, wearing peachflower pink, gazed on him with smiles, and a scarf in one hand waved.

Burghers muttered: "There is no man of life and agility in every respect in the Court like the Earl of Oxford."

The constable called for quiet. "Are the knights ready to begin the triumph?"

"They are, my liege."

Then he pronounced in a loud voice, "Let them go, let them go, let them go."

The thunder of hooves, the rise of dust, the throaty yells, and the crashing of shattered spears brought the charge to an end. It lasted till five o'clock and continued for three days.

The Earl of Oxford prevailed against seven challengers, among them Thomas Knyvet and Thomas Cecil.

The effect was such a success that her majesty ordered him escorted by two ladies into her Presence

Chamber hung with rich tapestries and the floor strewn with rushes of hay, awarding him a diamond-covered notepad for his win, and he offered her a sonnet of thanks.

"Ay Ned, how deft you are with your agile spear!" she told him, enjoying the flowery speech adopted from former times.

"It takes much practice, my lady," he replied. "Better a willing sheath than a declining foil."

"Your wit is not in your lance, Ned, but how you shake it."

"Wits tilt, spears prick, yet no blood's lost in thought, my lady."

"Joust on, Ned."

Now the Earl of Oxford was known as a tournament champion. So it was to Warwick Castle with the queen, August 12, 1572, accompanied by all her court, for a week of festivities with every official in the region and country folk invited to see their monarch and attendants.

The maids of honor vied to bring Edward their ewers of rosewater, and wash his hands in sorrel juice. But Edward rode before the crowds and was admired as "a lusty gentleman", "a gallant horseman".

Among the humble people was the bailiff from the neighboring village of Stratford, with his eight year old son to see the mock battle at night with fireworks and two hundred theatrical soldiers on each side shooting in imaginary warfare for the queen's and country folks' amusement, which Edward had rehearsed all afternoon.

Lead that evening by Oxford and another courtier, Fulke-Greville, it raged out of hand when a fireball fell on the thatch of a farmer's house by the bridge. The cottage burned to the ground, waking the farmer and his wife. The earl and his opponent struggled to save their lives, and rewarded them with twenty-five pounds twelve shillings eight pence for their ruin. The farmer, Henry Cowy, in his nightshirt was grateful.

But the people declared that Edward's staging of a mock battle was worthy of a king.

The queen danced the evening out in the castle courtyard for all to see to their pleasure and her delight, and allowed the common country folk the chance to curtsy before her, which they did - and happily fell on their faces, the men full of mead with honey and everyone else tanked on ale with barley which they had bought at church.

These festivities required much preparation - weapons, munitions, trained men, coordination between opposing sides to carry out the semblance of war. Fire was flying everywhere. A canon ball even went astray through the wall of a house leaving a hole the size of a man's head, but no injuries.

That eight year old boy peeking between grownups' legs would ask his father, the bailiff and soon-to-be alderman, if one day he could go to London and join the makers of all this merriment and celebration. No response is recorded.

"You there, move aside!" shouted a horseman. "Don't forget your boy!"

The bailiff complied with an, "Ay sir! I'll not forget the lad."

"What's your name? I say, do you have one?"

"A name sir?"

"That's what I asked. Move aside, what's your name!"

"It's Shags-spoof, sir!"

"Shags-spoon? That's not a name, it's a utensil!"

"No, Shags-spook sir. That's my name. I'm the bailiff here abouts!"

"Well move aside, Shags-pox. There's nothing in that name to keep you!"

Stratford had a particular importance when I was young - not only because I started a touring company performing from a wagon in Stratford but, in the summer of my twenty-second year, I participated in this spectacular tournament. My grandmother, Elizabeth Trussel lived nearby, at Bilton Manor. And the Avon, sweet Avon, gently through the reeds would flow, with flowers blooming by the stream where I, a boy, lounged in a dream that all the world was mine, and all I needed was to rise and go.

I was allowed to spend my holidays and festivals with my grandmother, until I came to regard the Avon as home, its sweet pastures my native country, its blooms my blossoming.

Edward sat at dinner in Cecil House and declared he would use the great hall of Theobalds where Sir William held his own court of petitioners seeking an audience with the queen, by Sir William's leave. The guests listened and served their meats from trenchers placed before them which they stabbed with a newly introduced tool for stabbing, called a two-prong fork, and carved with their matching knives. Wine made from grapes, currants, ginger, oranges, elderberries and cowslips was served in Venetian glasses and silver cups. They drank as they listened.

"I will stage a play there, to practice the art of mummery, quackery, imposture! I'll give you Piety, on a moth's wing, Innocence on a spider's leg. I'll give you the grand quiche incognito, for a farce."

Sir William was speechless and gagging on his sardines. His eyes popped out. "You'll not! You'll not! No theater in my house. No troop of pantaloons under my roof - never!"

120

"Then I'll go to the country," said Edward. "To my grandmother's house will I go, near Stratford."

He formed a touring theater troupe and hauled cart-loads of costumes and props to the countryside, seventy miles north from London to Stratford, to stay with his grandmother and perform miracle plays, sketches or masques at country fairs before farmers, picking up actors to play the parts along the way.

And I penned little stage scenes and poems which I published as 'Anonymous' or 'Never Ever' or signed with my initials, 'E.O.', in the literary reviews of the time. Perhaps I did it for history, or simply for my own amusement, but look deep, my son, look deep, for again, you'll find a clue here, in my signature. I sought not to serve myself but her majesty, to bring no idle praise to my effort, but fire to the heart of every Englishman! And you shall find another signature, and a clue in that, Edward wrote in the golden book. *They can not silence destiny, though voices shout it down, nor pluck out the tongue of truth, though they'd stuff my mouth with cabbage and call me dim-dimwitted. I am mad as a moonbeam, you see; the stars dance at my command; my jests are for the impoverished who are fat on themselves and see nothing but their own importance. Trust me, my son, though I make of trust a strumpet. Believe what I tell you, for it is the truth here - deVere. Only a fool would call me mad who takes what I have swallowed at the tables of the hosts of the world and gives it a fillip. Therefore I'm a fool for calling myself mad. But I am your true father. This lesson is for you. This book, this secret statement, this passage of my blood to you: preserve it!*

The great night of fire and pretended warfare was perhaps exhilarating to the queen, but within the week, on Sunday, August 24, 1572, in Paris, Catherine de Medici

121

suborned her agents to murder the Admiral Coligny of France, leading to the most bloody slaughter of Protestants in history, and the Protestant cause of the 16th Century gained its martyrs, at the hands of their bloody Catholic enemies.

Enough to take amusement off the queen of England's royal agenda for a more sober look at the sedition which Jesuits in England were fomenting. This was an age when one's faith was political and on the continent the Protestants were the victims, the hunted, the prey of Catholic supremacy. In later centuries the slaves of Africa and still later the Jews of Germany would be the oppressed, but in Elizabeth's age hers was to save the Protestants. Not since the days when Henry VIII took all the monasteries from the Church of Rome and gave their lands to his nobles, had those faithful to the old religion been so on the run, scrambling to say mass in hiding, to conceal the known clerics, to save their necks. The days of being carefree surely ended in the summer of 1572 in Warwickshire.

The price in fighting conspiracies was oblivion, none more prominent than the St. Bartholomew's Day Massacre in 1572, which took 3,000 men, women and children in Paris, then 10,000 in rural France over three weeks, and 50,000 Protestant lives in the end.

Religions extol the virtues of modesty. Monks will devote whole lives to attaining humility. And authors learn early about rejection, revision, and refusal, which rights they never conquer. These are the rights of the censor. Even playwrights could be silenced, whole troupes of actors disbanded on a whim, for a bad show or a worse joke. To give offense to the crown in a word was tantamount to treason, punishable by pruning the limb, yet I with my tongue was tolerated, encouraged, emboldened. It was enough to encourage me in my extremities to growth.

As a member of the ruling commission which licensed printers their right to publish books, Edward sat with his fellow peers like Sir George Buck and Sir Julius Caesar, his neighbor Lord Lumley, the Lord Chamberlain, and others in power over the censors of the age and appointments to the Stationer's Company. It gave him an advantage when seeking his license to exist and perform. But it did not make him invulnerable.

Of all that was rank, none were so foul as players, and nothing as debased as the drama, seedbed of discourse, dissent and sedition. Hence, I embraced it with a high hand and a Hey, Ho, the Wind and the Rain.

Edward deVere was the highest ranked member of England's nobility, with staff and wardrobe at his beck, and always a secretary at hand, not the sort of man who could slip out the back door and melt into the shadows unrecognized like a nobody.

He was decidedly not a common man nor descended from the middle class, and he was reminded of it constantly.

Or could he slip away to darkness?

They say that to a man who is master of his universe, all is possible, even the impossible. And to be master of one takes imagination.

The next year the queen would leave on another royal progress, but stop short, dismiss her ministers, including the now Lord Burghley, and go to be alone at her property, the ancient deVere estate, Havering-attre-Bowre on the Thames, with a thousand acres commanding her exclusive view of the surrounding counties and ships from all seas passing up the river. But though she went alone she stayed not alone.

Lord Oxford, age twenty-three, in the very cheek of his all, was there, forgetting about his Lady Anne.

The queen and her lord would remain secluded two months on the estate to the delight of each other and the

123

report of none, but one. A doctor who found the queen's conduct odd, reported it to Lord Burghley, how she was so secretive and pensive she wanted none of her ministers near her, and seemed wan and distracted, even pale and possibly ill, though he was not allowed to examine her.

Best of all is that she sent her mutton away. Christopher Hatton was sick, as always, so she dispatched him to take the waters at a spa on the continent, and dispatched her personal doctor to accompany the frail fribble. How I laugh at his portrait hung at Kirby Hall to stare down the fools of the world with his frills in manly mockery. To all the world he was a man. To me he was a fribble. He gave the artist a fat purse, to make him seem a man, I'll warrant! What unseemly seeming. As soon as he was gone she forgot him - and remembered me. While I remembered Leicester.

Elizabeth and Edward would go to the Archbishop Parker of Canterbury soon after.

"What for?" I asked. "To goad Dudley," she answered. As if she would make Leicester jealous! "I'll make him whatever I please!" she told me. And so it was, as her majesty wished. Typical of anyone named Dudley, my lord was immersed in his own game of love, bed-hopping with a Maid of Honor or two inclined to dishonor behind her majesty's back at court. Here was the truth, that Leicester could behave in no honorable fashion but was compelled to deceive to be pleased. So while Leicester gamboled, her majesty held my arm and ambled by the light of the sun, the stars and the moon.

I was such an innocent then that I little realized how useless I was except to be used by her. But even a wise man must have his experience with ignorance.

Though I believed myself to be marvelous, impervious, dashing and a delight to the eye and ear! I was,

124

alas, mostly a delight to myself, for yes, even your father whom you know only as ancient and decrepit, and perhaps modestly wise, in his time had a father too, and was a boy once.

I dreamed such dreams as make the mountains rise, of glories past and brave triumphs enough to tantalize.

In secret would they confide their relations to the archbishop, and the queen would declare their betrothal. She had seduced the youngest heir to the oldest line of England's nobility, and stood to declare it, come-what-may!

"But I am a married man, your majesty. To the lady of your choice. You chose her for me."

"You have not consummated it, my lord."

"At least not yet, my royal highness."

"And your sovereign will speak to that. I will speak on the morrow to that. Tonight let the warm air speak. You are my lord. I am your fantasy."

"And speak well, I hope."

"Have I ever spoken ill?"

"Then speak no more."

In this Ver time of spring, at heart young, I experienced the meaning of poetry, and commenced a dedication to writing of the romantic heart which captivated our queen. I was at the court, the center of earthly power, and in it I found lust. She called me her Adonis and we indulged each other. She mastered my heart and imprisoned my feelings. But still I resisted her majesty.

"Measure my strangeness with my unripe years. Before I know myself, seek not to know me," I told her. The favorite words on her lips were "sweet boy", praising my "soft hands, sweet lips and crystal eyes, whose full perfection all the world amazes."

To which I would record her spoken passions, "within my bosom, whereon thou dost lie, my boding heart pants, beats and takes no rest, but, like an earthquake, shakes thee on my breast." Together we savored every hour of the day and night, where the day became the night and night the day. "They that love best their loves shall not enjoy."

I played the role of reluctant lover as she drew me out and drew me in. You know the hobby-horse. How can a man forget it? Never would I forget it. Never. Ever. The knowing woman and the learning boy. The flower and our queen. She was all-giving and all-taking, the secret of the sunshine, the answer of the moonlight.

"Ah, you are so young."

"And I love my Sylvia. Who is Sylvia, what is she, that all our swains commend her? Holy, fair and wise is she--"

"She is the sun!"

"How much I'd rather be traveling abroad than living dully sluggardized at home," I said. Then, bringing my love, and a pair of gloves, I promised her every gift the continent could offer.

"Wit?" she asked.

"I'll travel to Italy, and find wit."

"And wisdom?"

"I'll visit Germany, and the philosopher of the reformation, Sturmius. He should give me wisdom."

"And beauty?"

"I'll visit Paris, and bring it back to you. What light is light if Sylvia be not seen? What joy is joy if Sylvia be not by?"

"And though I enjoy this duel of wits, shall I have you always under my thumb, Ned?" she asked.

"I can't shake a finger at you because my hands are tied, your majesty. But I'll bring you the genius of flattery, and adoration," I promised. "Who is Sylvia, what is she,

that all our swains commend her? Holy, fair and wise is she - Titania our queen!"

I penned a play begun as a masque at court, the display of witty repartee between familiars to the viewers, augmented by the clown invention like a prize fight referee. All who sat with our queen were amused with the verbal antics. By my pen I would put my neck on the block or my head in a noose, bringing it with a dare to the point where her majesty's patience was tried to straining by my impudence and ungranted familiarity, although I assumed it was granted, took it as granted, by rank and station undenied. However, time and I together would learn, there is nothing less succulent than what is assumed.

Do you hear me, my son, though I am long since stilled and this voice is the wind and gone, these words are the leaves of the fallen season, and nothing remains of myself but this ink, these pages, this little bit of self? I am you now, and you are free!

She was the authority with absolute power but she was easily bored or amused. She needed my linguistic somersaults to beguile her. On my diversions she was dependent. For her support I was indentured. How we needed each other yet dueled with fancy manners and artificial play, a courtly queen and a courted courtier earl. While the play served its purpose, 'a pleasant conceit' as one who saw it then described, its pages were tossed in a trunk for years until I went on to other contrivances. Came the day when I thought to revise it, not by discarding and reworking what was, but by adding a new line and characters.

Over and over in the plays were stories told parallel that had only the hint of a connection, as though a series of guests were gathered together to chat about their separate interests, who apparently had nothing in common except

127

their proximity, and were as good taken out of context, excerpted, as an act from any variety show. Like the talking philosophers in 'The Courtier' and Sir Thomas Smith's writing. Years later, upon revision, in a spontaneous act of weaving, the author performed revisions the way young ladies reached into family rag bags for suitable swatches of cloth they could sew together to make the most beautiful array of complexity in quilts. This literary tailor marveled at the skits once performed, stitching them into five-act productions. His inventive deviltry remained in tact. The words of a gruff producer at the office can almost be heard shouting, "Track down that story about so-and-so. It was a skit last Saturday night. Build it up to a full production. Give it everything you've got."

That's how my plays grew, from their origins as little conceits, into grand comedies flowered. Yet where am I for all of that? As dust, as hay, as grass, as mud parched in the empty stream. How does it suit a man to create a kingdom, and lose his throne? To know a terrible sanity, and be called mad? To see, and yet kept blind?

It is the folly of reflection to dote on worms and call them monstrous. I went from innocence and glory to all-knowing perfidy.

Occasions did arise in the theater where fools from the country were presented, not as they see themselves nor as they really are, but as fools, the way people in silk with pomander, out for pleasure, saw them.

There was on every page an accumulation of testimony, witness to the lives of the people known, for better and worse, the elite who really were.

The pages of plays teemed with *roman a clef* characters: William Cecil, Lord Burghley as Polonius (Edward's foster father and father-in-law); Anne Cecil (his daughter) as Ophelia (Edward's first wife); Edward's

128

cousins Horace and Francis Vere as cousins Horatio and Francisco, with their comrade Marcellus Bacx; and Sir Robert Dudley, Earl of Leicester, as Claudius acquiring, by unsavory means, all the estates and property belonging to the inheritance of Edward when the good earl, his father died, leaving young Edward a ward with no control in his own affairs, and Anne Cecil again, as Helena in 'All's Well That Ends Well', as Mariana in 'Measure for Measure', as Anne Page in 'The Merry Wives of Windsor' and as Desdemona in 'Othello' (which title was punned into an "oath on L.O."); Christopher Hatton as Malvolio and Peregrine Bertie, Lord Willoughby, who was Edward's brother-in-law and the first ambassador to Denmark, as Sir Toby Belch in 'Twelfth Night', and Hatton also as Christopher Sly in 'Taming of the Shrew', although another lays that role to Christopher Marlowe, and yet another to a country rustic from Arden forest named Shackey.

Their summer in Havering-atte-Bowre did not end exhausted or in boredom, but Elizabeth granted her Edward license to travel abroad, "in due time, my Ned! After you pen me a poem of love. I'll be your Venus. You be my Adonis!"

She took from her dress four crimson ribbons and bid me, "With these your manhood I bind up. With them will I entwine you always, holding every word you give me."

"It is done, most beauteous woman!"

So I, unangered by the perfidies, address to you my state, and caution. There is no advice to give, for to presume wisdom is to confirm ignorance, and all the pontificating can not warm a heart, all the correctness devised can not embrace the lost, the rejected, the different. We are what we give, what we accept, what we embrace. Clearly I have no advice. The pool of friendship feeds many streams. But I will cry rage at the indecencies! I was a perfect courtier and

129

perfectly doomed! How arrogant was Pondus, who effected humility, filled with obsequy and babbled apologies, all plaintive supplications and fraud's modesty! Trust none with your goods, he said. And how he reviled clothing. It can be in and out of fashion, he said, but money in pocket is never passé. So I was robed, and he was enriched. Only fools and women value looks, he said. He gloated. He poached. He boiled. Then Raleigh took a turn at arrogance. One draught of wine - healthy; two draughts - pleasing; three draughts - shameful; four - madness. And he could lose his head without lifting his cup. All these pompous villains, these leaches sucked with others' fruits, these swine of stone who would devour the very rock and castle of England like the morning worms on whom they feed and crawl. Let me not presume your grace to wail against their infamy. They seized me without my leave and what you have for a father is the outraged sensibilities of Lucrece, for they did violate me, and proclaimed their innocence, abhorring violation but not its administration. They were Tarquins each, and I played the merriment to rectify their scene, but ended how you find me, rags and shadows, the empty-handed beggar at my manor's door, bereft of good, exhausted on futility, my part to rant with rage, the source of jibes and mock, extinguished. I am that I am - as air, as the brook, as nothing.

Three seasons passed and the queen returned to Whitehall before, on October 6, 1573, events occurred which gave her cause to act. From Titchfield Manor, near Southampton, rode a messenger by horse with urgent news. The Countess of Southampton was delivered of a son, and the son was not well.

Elizabeth dismissed her advisors and departed for the western counties with only her medical attendant, Dr. Julio, and ladies in waiting, Mistresses Ashley and Blanche Parry chief gentlewomen, dressed often in white but black preferred. She had six personal ladies in waiting, all of them well born and discreet with not a desire but for her grace's comfort. Her courtiers were dismissed as these ladies went alone.

Hatton hated Oxford but he was forced to keep his courtier's place, a step below the earl. While the queen called Hatton her "mutton", a sheep, "an affected fribble", Edward remained her stag of the hunt, her hart, her buck, her wild boar.

She remembered their nights together as she read Edward's poems he sent her, and her ladies in waiting combed out her hair, then wove it to a wire frame. She read her Maids of Honor those lines that appealed to her most, even when a swarm of bees at the window threatened to hive in her coiffure and they were forced to flee, as all the ladies dreamed of Edward and she alone was the only one who had known him. She did not drop what he wrote. Her arms had leant "his neck a sweet embrace. . .face grows to face."

From abroad, Hatton wrote her a note of thanks for being sent abroad, mindful of the advice received from Edward Dyer, her majesty's cousin and sometime poet, on how to appeal to the queen and out-flank the popular earl: "Remember, that you use no words of disgrace or reproach towards him to any; that he, being the less provoked, may sleep, thinking all safe, while you do awake and attend to your advantages."

Here was Hatton's effort, this courtier who was so in love with himself that when the queen gave him a gift of a bell on a chain he pranced about and asked those in his hearing if they liked its ring, to which the Earl of Oxford seemed dumb, and asked, "What ring, the chain?"

When the mutton affected not to hear the earl, Edward increased his scorn by degree. "I know thee well, a

131

serviceable villain, as duteous to the vices of thy mistress as badness would desire."

Wrote Hatton, expressing pleasure for his gift of the bell: "God witness I feign not. It is a gracious favor most dear and welcome unto me: reserve it to the sheep, he hath no tooth to bite, where the Boar's tusk may both raze and tear." So envy in jealousy's name was still but a lamb to some.

At this time, in Titchfield Manor, the 2nd Earl of Southampton and his Lady, the former Mary Browne, daughter of the Earl of Montague, about whom Edward wrote his first poem and staged play when he was eleven years old, lost their newborn son in his infancy. The news was vague and unclear and none at court could be sure of it.

But their child was replaced by another in June, 1574 - or was the same, or was not the same newborn whom they named after the father of their queen, Henry - who would become the 3rd Earl of Southampton, Henry Wriothesley (pronounced Rosely).

All was made to appear confused by the queen. Her presence asserted chaos on order. The child in time would become the queen's favorite, her darling, her pride and joy and privileged pet, when he was old enough to come to the court, to the mystery of some, but the surprise of none. Proposed at the age of nineteen to be made a Knight of the Garter, which honor was given to none but intimates of the crown, to sons and heirs, Henry proved rash in his behavior so that the intended investiture was reversed. He was regarded by the knowing with knowing. Even as her majesty was called the Rose Without Thorns, Henry Wriothesley was called The Tudor Rose - her heir and son - and Edward deVere was his rumored father, now both feared and loathed.

I have told you this, rehearsed our bond until you tired of me and it and her and all, yet can't be done with it myself, for you, my son, were my all, my crown, my scepter, my throne, my rose, and she became our thorn, which only brought you closer to me, only made me dearer to you. We had the fabric of a family, we three, only she wished more - the world, the seas, the foolishness of strangers, and so one family was lost, and a kingdom with it. Edward printed the letters large in his golden book.

"You have beguiled me, and spirited away my blood!" he told the queen.

"I have done nothing. I have saved England," she answered. "I now send forth plenteous tears to charm the world! Ah! for my husband, my dear Lord Edward! And so shall you."

The queen now promulgated a declaration in Parliament that her crown would pass upon her death to none but the natural child of her body. But until her death she would have no child so far as anyone admitted or knew, and all the world would commend her.

I am destroyed, who had something, and thought it nothing, and now have nothing, which is something. Perhaps it is time to understand, Edward declared. *To sleep, to dream - to wake, to seem. Who is my queen? Is she my mother? Or my betrothed? My wife? Or my cousin? Am I my own son's brother? Who am I, that those most dear should mock me? The heir to the crown or the king to the queen? A son? A husband? A father? A brother? Everything or nothing? All for one or one for all? Or one in one and all in all. It is a shame of a sham, but something no less. It is a disgrace of which I am innocent. And yet all innocence is lost to this disgrace. For surely I have seen that he who plays with fire burns. Who plays the fool is fooled. I am deceived by all, confused by some and yet I'm fooled by none, for the light shines clear. My place is privileged beyond the rest, and I have much to give thanks*

133

for; the gift of speech is foremost. Yet when humility tempts me, I am ravaged by questions: who am I to be humble when others, molded in the very mud and clay of modesty, stand like towers astride me, and disperse the meek. I shall confine them their pretenses. The question is, whether to take arms against this rising sea and, by opposing others, end them?

Edward had his portrait painted by a Paris artist, and a copy of this sent to the 3rd Earl of Southampton, that child who could grow up used to the familiar face of the twenty-five-year-old nobleman, the Earl of Oxford, which became a favorite picture for the young lord, who was fatherless, to talk to when he was alone where it hung at Welbeck Abbey.

And thus was I accepted into your heart as your father. I now could see myself as the father of a king to be, though not to be a king myself, the betrothed of a queen, though married most where I was married least. Whether 'tis nobler in the mind to suffer outrageous fortune, I shall not muse. You know what we have done across the boards.

The "boards" described were the stage. But to reveal to the world that her majesty was involved in this birth, or a mother of any but England's nationhood, would have been to destroy the myth of the Virgin Queen, the Mother of England who could negotiate for a marriage of state with any one of the monarchs of Europe, and have no child to prevent her union, yet was never free to marry whom in her heart most moved her.

Indeed, it was with my poet friend Edmund Spenser we created and recreated that appearance of a Virgin Queen for her glory who knew most and knew best, but said least, whereof we spoke.

It would destroy the royal power, and give an unstoppable advantage to the Catholic movement, if her child or betrothal or son were known. So this secret was

134

kept. At all costs, it was concealed. And the Virgin Queen prevailed, Mother of all England.

But I hoped and hoped and hoped where daring least to hope, that there at least was hope to hope.

> "From fairest creatures we desire increase,
> "That thereby beauty's rose might never die,
> "But as the riper should by time decease,
> "His tender heir might bear his memory;
> "But thou, contracted to thine own bright eyes,
> "Feed'st thy light's flame with self-substantial fuel,
> "Making a famine where abundance lies,
> "Thyself thy foe, to thy sweet self too cruel.
> "Thou that art now the world's fresh ornament
> "And only herald to the gaudy spring,
> "Within thine own bud buriest thy content
> "And, tender churl, mak'st waste in niggarding.
> "Pity the world, or else this glutton be,
> "To eat the world's due, by the grave and thee."

Hence would I learn less love, more love, and more hope, less hope, as I abandoned the world of me and yearned for the world for he; but he was dazzled in my light, and obscured by the shadows it cast, and would at once be poet, actor, soldier, framed in vision and freed by inspiration. He became the devil to do and to dare. Yet I could not resist the father's plight, and appeal:

> "Look in thy glass, and tell the face thou viewest
> "Now is the time that face should form another,
> "Whose fresh repair if now thou not renewest,
> "Thou dost beguile the world, unbless some mother."

I knew the truth: "Thou art thy mother's glass, and she in thee calls back the lovely April of her prime; so thou through windows of thine age shalt see, despite of wrinkles, this thy golden time." But reasoning with youth was most unreasonable. Vanity, vanity was his great profanity.

XV

Edward deVere, being granted his license to travel abroad, did just that, to Germany, France and Italy. Unfettered. Unrestrained. Unshackled. For sixteen months he remained, a very debonair young Lord Oxford, traveling the world, the report of ambassadors and gossiping courtiers. Introduced to the king and queen of France, who asked if he was married and remarked that if he was then they would make a beautiful couple.

"Married! My! a thousand times wed, and a thousand times a thousand vowed to wed no more. I've wed too much, and not yet wed at all! How am I married? Ask me another riddle."

He read Greek, wrote and spoke Latin and French, visited the court of Henry, King of Navarre, where he hinted at having an affair with Queen Margaret of Valois.

"Dost thou understand this much English?" he asked. "Canst thou love me?"

She feigned misunderstanding. "I can not tell."

"Can any of your neighbors tell? I'll ask them. Come, I know thou lovest me."

She turned aside. "I do not know dat."

"Then I will kiss your lips. You have a witchcraft in your lips. There is more eloquence in a sugar touch of them than in the tongues of the French Council and they should sooner persuade."

Edward met Pierre Ronsard, the aging poet who was living at Croixval in the forest of Gastine writing 'Sonnets for Helen'.

They shared verses. Wrote Ronsard, in Sonnet XV, Book II, of his masterpiece:

"Shall I compare your beauties to the moon?"

Edward, bursting with the vigor of a colt at pasture in the springtime to match the elder master in versely duel, offered his sonnet in reply:

"Shall I compare thee to a summer's day?"

They smiled, and Ronsard offered his appraisal of the young Lochinvar from England:

"Soon the proud Thames shall see
"A flock of white swans resting in the grass. .
"To tell the famous praise of English kings
"Unto the crowded nations of the world."

They parted in mutual admiration and fellowship, the aging classic poet who transformed French, and the tempestuous English noble whose passion flowed from his youthful eyes, heat from his nostrils, dreams from his lips.

Said Edward of himself, *Never be a bagpipe - all drone, no tune.*

Then he was on to Germany's leading Protestant academic, Johannes Sturmius, then Italy - cradle of the Renaissance and seat of all learning - Verona, Venice, Florence, Padua and finally to Mantua and the tomb of Baldasarre Castiglione, perfect author of 'The Courtier', his most beloved book. In the Chiesa di Santa Maria delle Grazie he stood before the monument to Castiglione and marveled at the artist who made it. That an author could receive such homage moved him.

138

"Would that such a monument oneday be made to England's lonely star."

Guilio Pippi Romano was the master of Mantua. He had a studio with dozens of craftsmen under him, each artist a specialist - in sculpture, architecture, ceramics, glass working, wood carving, frescos, murals, furniture, etc. Romano served the Duke of Mantua everywhere. Edward found himself gazing on his statue of Hermione, "who, had he himself eternity and could put breath into his work, would beguile Nature of her custom, so perfectly he is her ape. He so near to Hermione hath done Hermione that they say one would speak to her and stand in hope of answer."

Drama must be married to poetry and elevated to equal rank.

If Romano could build so grand a tomb to Castiglione, then perhaps another author, with craftsmen in words and plot and researching history and the classics, could build such a monument to literature. All he needed was a few good men - *and I would create a language!* It would require only the fortune of one man completely dedicated, and a studio of his own making, filled with every degree of writer living.

I shall do it! I'll do it! No one in England can do it but everyone together will!

In Padua Edward met Ottonello Discalzio who was the great professor of law at the university, then Dr. Falloppius and Dr. Fabricius who were the creators of modern medicine (identify the Fallopian tube), of whom Sir Thomas Smith had been in awe. There it was understood that the "blood of man courses through the natural gates and alleys of the body, swift as quicksilver." Something Edward made note of, to use in his writing, which would not be described in English until William Harvey wrote the book on circulation of the blood when he graduated Padua and Cambridge University more than a quarter of a century later.

In the south of Italy, at Palermo, Edward challenged all comers to a tournament of jousting, including Don Juan of Austria, the great soldier of the age. He was answered by none, and much applauded for standing alone to the honor of England.

So Edward returned to Venice, where he had gone in October, 1575 to meet a little old man named Vecellio Tiziano in his house at Biri Grande, Contrada San Cancian. He was rumored to be one hundred years old and had been visited by popes and Kings Francis the First, Charles the Fifth and Phillip the Second. He was admired for being the most romantic and lyrical painter of his time. Together they had sipped wine. Five versions of a subject called Venus and Adonis were signed by him, one remaining in his studio where Edward saw it and returned to see it again.

But on August 27, 1576, Edward was met by a greater host than the artist. In his golden book he wrote: *Titian is dead.* Then followed a plan to write a poem of homage to his queen, based on the artist's picture of the immortal lovers, each line of the poem to describe each line of Titian's masterpiece. How better to create his own than to describe another's?

Now I am Eos, and arrive in Paris at dawn. Eos was the Greek word for Dawn, which note he signed "E.O." as he sat in the ancient Roman arena of Lutece, its worn marble benches resonating with the memory of performances past, of Terence, Plautus and Seneca, as though the actors had quit the stage but minutes ago. The tiny arena was alive to him, fifteen hundred years in age. He felt new and reborn in its embrace. The white marble, the dark earth, the rising sun through the leaves overhanging the stage and people in canvas garments walking up the adjoining street with tools

140

and sticks to their daily work, puffing pipes and stroking beards. They gave no regard for this arena which was empty but for himself. Nothing had changed down through the centuries. There stood the stage. Here circling it was where the audience had worn the stone with their bottoms. Here Julius Caesar came, and Charlemagne himself had sat.

In that dawnlight, as the breath of choking smoke hung above the chilling air and the cobbles were bright with morning mist, I felt a rumbling far off, rising into the surge of a thunderous wave which swept upon me, louder and more moving, until I could hear what it was, and see and feel and know it: the applause of a momentous audience which had invisibly filled this theater, from the graves of fifteen centuries of satisfied spectators. I knew the theater then, and it called me.

Edward won renown as a sportsman, athlete, patron of writers and players, musician, author, jurist and privy counsel to the throne. Yet he was humbled to be in this masterpiece of time, this sacred grove, this cherished spot, this place that never changed, the ancient arena of Lutece by Romans built.

The "Italian Lord", an ape who aped with apish ways the style of foreign dress, as he was called following his travels, on his return home, was greeted: the very icon of an aeon.

But Italy was not admired of our Puritan, Protestant England - this seat of the Catholic Scourge, this nest of Renaissance, this cradle of art. It was regarded as deviltry and I, who adored it, infected by this damnation. To be admiring things Italian was equivalent to the plague.

So his English return included importing a gift for the queen of perfumed yellow gloves from Paris that became the fashion statement of the '70's at court. He was the most highly remunerated noble of her reign - and often its most envied, which comes with that territory salted by treachery, for even his income was denied him. Still it was whispered in the shadows at court behind masks and fingers that he, Edward, Earl of Oxford, was the queen's favorite, her chosen, her preferred, to whom no wrong could be done, who could do no wrong.

I have a kingdom, and yet I have no child. What have I who have everything the world could want? I have nothing that wants me, mused Edward. *O, to be! To have! To hold! This is a tale much told.*

He dealt with it lightly and seemed to give not a whit for money, except as it supported his lavish literary projects and life-style at court. So his inheritance of vast estates, forests, keeps, castles, open lands, farm animals, horses and permanent staff was only good to him so long as he could sell them and invest in publishing and the theater, those fancies of the queen, those dalliances of liberal thought. He sold fifty-six estates in four years to men of that new class of landowners - commoners. Sir William's holdings increased as Lord Edward's shrank.

The Bassanos made frumenty which was new wheat boiled and dried with milk and eggs, colored with saffron, served with honey and sugar at their holiday table to greet their noble foreign traveller and fellow musician, family friend. Also served was brawn, the dark meat of a boar fed on oats and peas for a year, then pressed. There were tankards of ale all around and Baptista's child, little Emilia, sang and danced like a forest sprite.

"Did you visit our Venice?" they asked. "And our village of Bassano?" They had family in Italy who dealt in merchant ships.

Burbage built the first indoor theater in London, reminding Edward of the Great Hall at Hedingham Castle, across the Thames at Blackfriar's stairs, during his absence

142

abroad. In their neighborhood, the Bassanos could point out two more theaters, The Cross Keys Inn and The Bull Inn on Bishop's Gate Street, not a stone's throw from where they lived. Other places of entertainment were appearing: The Clink, which was "the chief resort of stews on the bankside of Southwark". It was a row of houses under the Bishop of Winchester, painted white with signs on the front: The Boar's Head, The Crane, The Cardinal's Hat, The Swan, The Bell, The Castle, The Gun and The Thatched House by the waterside. Some were tippling houses, others tabling dens, all given to the merriment of Londoners.

Few were the pieces they had to stage, and poor were their merits if they did have them. James Burbage was building a company but support for players depended on those with necessary finances.

Sir William muttered at this squander on theater which threatened to drain Edward's purse and impoverish his daughter, the unconsummated Countess of Oxford. "Upon my honor - the best actors in the world, either for tragedy, comedy, history, pastoral, pastoral-comical, historical-pastoral, tragical-historical, tragical-comical-historical-pastoral; scene individable, or poem unlimited. Seneca can not be too heavy, nor Plautus too light for his generosity. O, my daughter! My ducats!"

"Edward, you have a way that touches both your sovereign and her foot maid equally. I believe it is the common touch. Are you aware how far you reach?" the queen reprimanded him.

"I have reached that often, Madonna. Are you aware of its cost?"

"Beware you don't become the common earl, from which you could become the common man." So spoke the queen and gave no thought to his expense. "You won't become so common as to use me commonly, Ned?"

"I have an uncommon regard for all that outshines what is common, but if it is held by others and they are common, then I have something with them in common, your majesty. Remember, your peerless penniless peer you urged to create a miracle child for our Virgin Queen. A kind of savior for her grace, a child who can work miracles, I believe."

"Exactly, Ned. That is our will."

"And so our will, Madonna, as you like it; for what would we but what you will!"

Never one to lose in games of words or conversation or any other competition, Lord Edward swept the floor with his feathered cap and dusted his sovereign's feet in a bow. "A bird must fly, this much I know. When launched on high it must swoop low."

The queen chose not to best her earl in talk. "Mark me, Ned, what I say here will never go from here. What you say here will stay right here. These thoughts of ours are ours - the privacy of our privilege. For those who would speak to the world have nothing to say to anyone, and those who would speak to me have nothing more to say to the world." She smiled as their eyes met. "Would you lie to me, Ned, ever?"

"But from thine eyes my knowledge I derive, and constant stars, in them I read such art as Truth and Beauty shall together thrive."

"Then you'll never lie to me, for Truth can't lie to Beauty."

"As I am ever - never. Or else of thee this I prognosticate: thy end is Truth's and Beauty's doom and date."

"You speak so fancifully as though you were the world's posterity."

144

So Edward wrote as good old soldier George Gascoigne became the author of a poetry book, 'A Hundredth Sundry Flowers', which contained a lengthy piece, 'Dan Bartholomew of Bathe' that caused a momentary gasp in the royal court and sovereign throat.

At least old Gascoigne, hearing of the queen's outrage and threatened wrath, stepped up to authorship with what courage a soldier, accustomed to weapons of steel, could muster in a world of quills and ink, to save his friend who'd been a lad when he first knew him home in Essex. As Edward declared, "I will speak daggers to her, but use none," for which old Gascoigne took the wrap.

What Edward wrote was to her majesty his good-bye, accompanied by his Last Will and Testament.

"Farewell dear love whom I have loved and shall,
"Both in this world, and in the world to come. . .
"Farewell my life, farewell for love, my death,
"For thee I lived, for thee now must I die,
"Farewell from Bathe, whereas I feel my breath
"Forsake my breast in great perplexitie,
"Alas how welcome were this death of mine,
"If I had died between those arms of thine."

Lord Edward had been signing his name in a manner indicating himself as Prince Consort, King Edward VII of England - an act of treason if not true - yet the queen chose not to object, though she saw it on his letters and knew. She could remove Edward's head if she chose, but she chose to leave it attached, more William Tell than telling.

"Write me poetry, Ned, and be my king of words," she appealed.

Sir William Cecil, having become Lord Burghley, huffed as courtiers puffed - which did not make it a fact but did not disgrace Edward either under this monarchy, before the legalization of a principle known as Free Speech. He proceeded to burn every letter Edward sent with that treasonous self-proclamation of his son-in-law as King Edward VII.

"Indeed, my kingly signature might be called the beginning of free speech, don't you think, n'uncle?" Edward grinned as Sir William groaned.

And so to those in the know was he King Edward, and to those who knew not, was he not known, though his verses were.

The offending line in 'Dan Bartholomew' that caused the royal dry throat and threatened wrath was the narrator's complaint that he was wooed and won by a superior female force to whom he was "by faith and troth assured". That meant he was by all accounts married to a queen. Except that he had no bride. Just a monarch. And she was not about to settle for the distasteful role of anyone's wife.

"So if we're talking about an earl behind this poem, then we're talking about the queen of England here - with a little problem of love 'em and leave 'em, the dallying fickle heart, which also controls the executioner's ax, and the taxing purse strings of everyone at court, are we not, Sir William?"

"The queen wants no such gossip involving her royal person. She is by law quite free and not a word or line or any thought in print should enslave her."

"Then my phrases can set her free!"

"You are mad, Lord Edward. I am mad to sustain your madness."

If another source for the words that related to her majesty was credited as the author, who was known to be on intimate terms with her highness, and whose word would not be doubted if given as true, then a number of royal heads might be uncomfortable on their necks. But with good, brave and faithful old Gascoigne drafted into the author's chair, the compromising words in 'Dan Bartholomew' could be dismissed as fiddle-faddle, poppycock, mere poetry, the forlorn musings and ramblings of an aging heart - love songs of a soldier betrayed and forgotten, for a start.

"And so her majesty shall reward this Gascoigne for his poetical fiddle faddle and your lordship shall acknowledge him the poet of the hour, Lord Edward, or she shall have your head and that's the end of it," said Sir William. "I have tried to save you from yourself, and save you I will, if only for my daughter, and myself."

I called good George, kind George, dear George, a saint and learned from him that all's not signed that's writ; what's in a name by any other is the same, for deeds and thoughts court more than fame. What glory's in a name can also come to shame. Cultivate the idea. To sign it, any shade will do.

So old Gascoigne filled the role and, for this scandal, paid the toll, claiming the anonymous authorship. He said, "perhaps we'd best not assume an earl the author." At least good soldier Gascoigne could be counted upon to step into the breach and claim himself to be the scribbler of the disgrace that threatened to unleash the scandal, which humble role of stand-in punster the queen at once anointed by granting him an audience at her feet, and much pomp before her court, to put the scandal of her bed to bed and restore her renown for being discreet.

So my pen survived, but not my claim. To be an author of the common sort was granted. To be an author of her majesty's court was not. Most absolutely not. To mock where courtiers fussed, to jest at those pretending to their status, makes fools of those who fool with us. There is no sting more vicious than the stinger stung. I thought I was,

147

and then I wasn't. I wondered if and woke to if-n't. What became of those woodland fairies that so beguiled our summertime? They left us in the autumn.

"Why Edward, how sad you seem for one so loved by your queen," Elizabeth chided.

"Loved and yet denied," he replied.
"And when the descant sings, in treble tunes above,
"Then let the burden say below, I lived and died for love.
"Thus when the dirge is done, let every man depart,
"And learn by me what harm it is to have a faithful heart.
"And let them write these words upon my careful chest,
"Lo here he lies, that was as true in love as is the best.
"Let sorrow at the last my supravisor be,
"And steadfastness my surest stead, I give him for his fee.
"And you which read my words although they be in rhyme,
"Yet reason may persuade you so, thus lovers dote
      sometime."

Lord Burghley waylaid Lord Oxford at Windsor Castle on the way to court.

"A word with our lordship?"

Edward nodded and they went aside.

"About this matter you bring to the queen, my lord."

"I'll tell the world where I have lived, and slept, and who with whom embraces, and secrets kept!"

"No one penetrates the inner sanctum of the queen and lives to tell about it. No one, my lordship. Remember Lord Leicester."

"Then, to save my life, my honor, I must sacrifice my name?"

"Yes, my lord."

"And if I leave no trace, then no one will trace what I leave?"

"Never, ever, lordship."

"Because her majesty's all secrets, whispering, a veritable cacophony of wiles, whining in the wind of silence, and ill-meant."

"She alone stays unreported. The world reports to her, but none reports about her, my lord."

"And so I have no choice. Tell all nothing."

"Just so, my lord."

"And yet not just, just so, I see. Did you know, some say I love my cat the most curled and purring on the bed? I do of course prefer it moist cupped to my stroking hand instead."

"Quite so, my lordship. Quite."

"Quite so is it? Quite, quite!"

When Edward complained to the "great Burghley" of his miserable treatment and the abuse and advantage taken of his good name, his former guardian hung low and addressed him always as Lord Edward. But what he said had the dull thud of the heartless:

"Let fact make argument, my lord."

"A pox on this!" the earl replied. "I am an Ariel, if you take all the letters jumbled up: I, earl!"

"My lordship is feeling better today. I see it in you."

"And I will let it out. And keep it in."

"Wish you long life, my lord," Burghley bowed, and hurried to speak with the queen. "This is most capital. Lord Edward's out of his mind. The very ecstasy of love whose violent property fordoes itself and leads the will to desperate undertakings as oft as any passion under heaven. 'I, earl - Ariel!' Indeed! Lord Edward, mad! Most capital! The queen must dine on this!"

And when he was in her majesty's presence he almost foamed with excitement. "Madam, to expostulate what majesty should be, what duty is, what day is day, night night, and time is time, were nothing but to waste night, day,

149

and time. Therefore, since brevity is the soul of wit, and tediousness the limbs and outward flourishes, I will be brief. Your noble Lord Edward is mad. Mad call I it, for, to define true madness, what is't but to be nothing else but mad? But let that go."

Said the queen, who was snacking on a jumbold (that sugared dough that would some day be known as a cookie): "More matter, with less art, Sir Spirit."

Replied the dottering Sir William: "Madam, I swear I use no art at all. That he is mad, 'tis true: 'tis true 'tis pity, and pity 'tis 'tis true - a foolish figure, but farewell it, for I will use no art. Mad let us grant him then, and now remains that we find out the cause of this effect - or rather say, the cause of this defect, for this effect defective comes by cause. Thus it remains, and the remainder thus. Perpend." Here he sputtered such a splatter with his cleft lip. It blew out, like a tent flap open on each side. He pondered every word, and was called Pondous by those who laughed behind his back. Edward had noted how he tried the word "perpend" - in a spray of delight, speech puffingly puttered more like bubbles in puddles. The spraying speaker spewed on: "I have a daughter (have while she is mine), who in her duty and obedience, mark, hath given me this." Sir William produced a letter which he waved. "Now gather, and surmise. 'To the celestial, and my soul's idol, the most beautified Anne,' - that's an ill phrase, a vile phrase; 'beautified' is a vile phrase."

And so the queen endured the ramblings of her minister, and had lunch, of three more jumbolds and a sip of wine.

"Does not 'beautified' mean saintly and does not saintly mean virginal and is she therefore not fully married though she be wed?" asked the queen, and took another jumbold.

In time such sweets would blacken her teeth, to which her courtiers, to imitate, so proud, so eager, so hungry to imitate, would blacken theirs as ebony, Cyprus black as e'er was crow. But it never made hers white again, Edward wrote in his golden book.

XVI

The time had come, the queen decided, to consummate Lord Edward's marriage. His marriage to Anne Cecil, the Countess of Oxford, that is. Whether the queen and he were betrothed before or after she'd arranged for his marriage to Anne was of no concern. Anne was still faithful to her father, whom she obeyed more than she obeyed her husband (in a time when a married woman was obedient only to the man she married). Sir William would be informed. Anne would obey. The marriage would be consummated. Whether the queen and earl were betrothed or not, the time had come for her majesty to bail herself, a monarch imperious in love, out of yet another game of love. Holding all the cards, her majesty ordered her courtiers to play.

Anne, the Countess of Oxford since she was fourteen, was seventeen now and ready to serve. Only Edward had been abroad for a while.

So the queen declared the earl returned and spoke in whispers with the countess. All things understood between women, the countess did as the queen required to serve the good of the nation and in due course the countess, alone, was delivered of child. The newborn baby was promptly named Elizabeth and baptized as the first offspring of the Oxford union.

All the court was overjoyed and celebrated this birth.

"But where was Lord Oxford during all of this?"

"Taking the delights of the continent in ignorance of his bliss!"

When word was carried to the paternal earl abroad, he said that it was not his child. The only lady he'd been to bed with at court nine months previous was not his wife. Whom he had slept with went without saying, and so it was not said.

A hint that did not please the monarch.

But the good Sir William, Lord Burghley, a first-time grandfather, did what ministers do best for their masters. He made it look like nothing, produced some much-needed and most valued letters from his daughter that clarified the muddy situation and proved the honor of the mother and child, and saved his family, and his family name, and family honor, while not so much as hinting at facts or having even a close brush with truth to unclarify the situation.

The story of the famous bed trick was devised right out of classic Italian literature. Lady Oxford, who had read Boccaccio once, was acknowledged with incredible skill to have danced the artifice of leaping in bed with her husband, who was not there at the time, and under the illusion that he was going to bed with another, which is what he said he had done. Whether the candles were lit or the moon was out so that all could see what was not to be witnessed, is not reported by any, while the good little Lady Oxford was there with child to prove by her virtue intact that she was a mother who was not to be denied. *Et voila! La fete accomplis!*

It was a story much talked about for a hundred years after the fact, to the laughter and amazement of all who heard it, so much so that the name of the Earl of Oxford became synonymous with an absentee over-the-sea romp in the sheets which men were desirous of matching themselves, although Edward did not take this ridicule lying down. He was most offended by the prank played on him by some and by all, being made "a motley to the view".

It was an offense that called for no revenge.

And the queen was pleased, herself having doubtless served his wine on that evening about which there was no question, and for which she was to provide the answer.

"Why Edward, whatever made you believe that I, your queen, was in that darkened room alone with you? Certainly you don't suggest that your monarch needs usurp the conjugal rights of a lord and his lady? Dear Edward, think of me rather as the reigning sovereign of hearts and fairies, who did magically beguile you into love with your wife and the begetting of your first child, which your countess has so unmistakably named Elizabeth in my honor. Voila!"

Again, as always in Edward's life, the female prevailed. As in the game of chess, the king is powerless.

Mazes, ploys, tricks, all were artifice and wiles employed to conceal the shining sun and disguise the waxing moon - of a whim: a coup; of a craft: a stroke, and all was a somersault - for the diversion of the idle, the mirth of the trite.

Only hearing of this abroad, the Earl of Oxford was irate, where his singular recourse was correspondence. Sir William had already grown used to what could be done with that. After all, they were words, just words. "To thine own self be true and it must follow as the night the day, thou canst not then be false, my lord."

Edward's letters to Lord Burghley were burned. Replacing them, Anne's letters to her husband were filed by her father in Hatfield House for modesty and history so that all eternity could say, "There was a wife! A Mother! And virtue was her name." Sir William's notes accompanied the letters in the files neatly kept, to clarify what might be

154

obscure for eternity, that all should be clear to the honor of the heirs of the House of Cecil. And those letters remained unread for almost four centuries, they were of so little interest, and such long wind.

Scholars are not to be blamed for their lack of interest in reading Elizabethan documents, when there were no questions about the outcome. As the centuries passed, nothing changed. The dead stayed dead. Their words went unread.

History had long since determined that Queen Elizabeth was a virgin, Lord Burghley was a saint, both were devoted ministers of the public good, and England went on to glory, though each was bedeviled by a vain and pompous snit who was a ne'er-do-well cad of the first order, whom they overcame despite his ceaseless wit.

Besides, the documents were written in impossible script, S's looking like F's, V's like U's, W's like double V's, and all spelled every which way but the same, according to each individual's desire, for there was neither a dictionary nor a speller in existence, despite the best efforts of Sir Thomas Smith. So the documents remained unread because scholars had little suspicion that the truth was different than the record, which all of these documents supported, that the queen was a virgin, that the keeper of the records was a saint, and so on.

When scholars finally began to wade through the documents, incredible discrepancies emerged and only depressed the established community that laid its authority on orthodoxy. How does one change the vested beliefs of prior generations of venerated ignorance? Only the handwriting never changed, and the spelling didn't improve. It led scholars to conclude that Sir William perhaps failed to read the handwriting on the documents himself.

Sir William's son Robert, meanwhile, the hunch back student of 'The Prince' by Machiavelli, was doing his apprenticeship in his father's office, and all was going well on that front, of becoming an heir to the power of the father to move and soothe the throne behind which they sat curled up on short stools, eating figs and fish.

Edward's cause to make truth known was only so much wordage.

"What have you done today, my son?"

"Gone through the files, father."

"And what have you found?"

"Only words on papers, father."

"And what have you done, my son?"

"Cleared out the mess, left nothing around, father."

"Nothing, son?"

"Not a trace."

"Of Lord Edward?"

"Effaced."

"Such humiliation, my son. His is a temper bred in inconstancy, a nature rooted in frivolity, that puts the decent to shame."

"He inherited his properties, father. Lord Edward can be separated from that."

All they did save from Edward's writing on this betrayal was the dedication he wrote his countess, a series of puns on his family name, a kind of cold mockery, of pain held in by a high-handed chivalry: "Words of truth are fitting to a Vere, (which means Truth), lies are foreign to the truth, and only true things stand fast. . . Therefore, since thou, a Vere, are wife and mother of a Vere daughter, and. . . with good hope look forward to being mother to an heir of the Veres, may thy mind always glow with love of the truth and may thy motto be Ever Lover of the Truth . . . thou, then, a Vere, mayest be called the true glory of thy husband."

Thus in her shame was she praised and in her name was she raised. And by him whom she demeaned.

Edward also dropped a note from Padua to his father-in-law asking for more money and ordering the sale of estates, something he did often as the only effect upon his fortunes he could have - to liquidate them. He collected in cash from one Pasquino Spinola in Venice. He noted that he was not inclined, upon returning to London, to see his wife or father-in-law who "have been the fable of the world" - gossip he did not care to associate with his own good name.

Then Edward took up poetry again, as he turned to the quill dipped in gall, an inky substance from the bladder of an ox, from which only darkness flowed, and he poured forth his own:

Fram'd in the front of forlorn hope past all recovery
I stayless stand, to abide the shock of shame and infamy.
My life, through ling'ring long, is lodg'd in love of
    loathsome ways;
My death delay'd to keep from life and harm of hapless days.
My sprites, my heart, my wit and force, in deep distress are
    drown'd;
The only loss of my good name is of these griefs the ground.

And since my mind, my wit, my head, my voice and tongue
    are weak,
To utter, move, devise, conceive, sound forth, declare and
    speak,
Such piercing plaints as answer might, or wound my woeful
    case,
Help crave I must, and crave I will, with tears upon my face,
Of all that may in heaven or hell, in earth or air be found,
To wail with me this loss of mine, as of these griefs the
    ground.

Help Gods, help saints, help sprites and powers that in the
     heaven do dwell,
Help yet that aye are wont to wail, ye howling hounds of
     hell,
Help man, help beasts, help birds and worms, that on the
     earth do toil;
Help fish, help fowl, that flocks and feeds upon the salt sea
     soil,
Help echo that in air doth flee, shrill voices to resound,
To wail this loss of my good name, as of these griefs the
     ground.

     He published this plaint against the loss of his good
name in a book called 'The Paradyse of Dainty Devises' and
he signed it as himself, 'E.O.'
     To court the muse in pursuit of fame was to bring
upon my dying class a stain of unforgiving shame.
     "Thou shalt not to the world be known, Ned, for what
you think or feel, but only for your stature, station, office,
heredity and title, everything you own. All else you must
conceal, all wit, all thought, all charm are free for worthless
wits to steal. Beware you do not wed yourself to the shadow
of your dreams and become a pale ghost of your greatness.
He who weds his shadow makes only half a shape. To live a
public life, you're dead," his queen bluntly said.
     So Edward wrote his Will, leaving land, estates and
title, all, to his cousins Francisco and Horatio deVere. Of all
friends, Horatio would prove closest - the friend who found
the incredible credible, to whom one day he would declare
his death.. "Things standing thus unknown do live behind
me." That bitter day, with his faithful secretary, Anthony
Munday, and his son nearby at play, would be a harvest he
could not come to yet.

While there is nothing to be vengeful about, there is much to be grateful for, and I have learned that. Who loved once, loved too much, and who loved often, loved not enough. For I have learned to give and to receive, and of these two I know it is more blessing to receive, and the rest is blessed. I accept it in the spirit of grace. But I have not finished my life nor my story, which is only begun!

So came the defining adventure.

XVII

Returning from Paris to England, his ship was beset by Dutch pirates who boarded it in the channel, stripped him to his shirt and threatened worse, when he was recognized by a Scotsman and escaped with his life. "A pirate of very warlike appointment gave us chase. They dealt with me like thieves of mercy," when they captured him and did not take his life, because "they knew what they did," as one day would he say, reported in a play he wrote about himself.

Coming after sixteen months of absence to meet him at Gravesend were his family, Lord Burghley and daughter, the Countess of Oxford, and Lady Mary Vere, Edward's sister, but it was a welcome he did not accept, and he refused to meet his baby daughter, Elizabeth.

When Sir William tried to reason with him, Edward snapped: "Have you a daughter? Let her not walk i' th' sun. Conception is a blessing, but as your daughter may conceive, friend look to 't!"

On Anne he turned: "Be thou as chaste as ice, as pure as snow, thou shalt not escape calumny!"

Accompanied by a soldier who served as his bodyguard, Rowland Yorke, Edward marched into seclusion without spending so much as an hour with his family. It was anger, shame and suspicion planted by his Catholic cousin in Paris, Henry Howard, a "subtle serpent", that made him scorn the love and greeting of his loved ones.

Of all the Howards, how I loved Henry, how I admired Henry, how I fawned on his every verb and vergule, the very fount of learning, who could quote a line after twenty years and the soul of its thought after a lifetime. What a cousin had I! He was polished more deftly than onyx, more persuasive than the phoenix, and I had to listen when I heard him for his every thought was a lie, his every smile a bite. No serpent served calumny better than Henry with fawning ways.

In Paris, on the last leg of his European journey which had yet another visit planned to Germany, Edward's Catholic cousin Henry and friends Charles Arundel and Francis Southwell, played upon his trust. They lied to him. Henry was educated to a fare-thee-well and became known as one of the greatest flatterers ever, pretending courtesy and working mischief darkly. Edward's wife, they said, was unfaithful. Her child was his disgrace.

Such words were a vile humiliation and Edward never was so alone or cut off from his family as when he was at the mercy of his cousin's company. He felt so distraught, he was drawn to consider even becoming a Catholic, a temptation that did not feel unreasonable to a young man inconsolable in Paris, comforted by Catholic cousins and Catholic France.

But I vowed revenge, more sweet than bitters, more deadly than aspic. They saw a poet in me. I saw a soldier whose telling cut would set free liberty, a strike at chains more luminous than the sun, for as a poet the soldier gained cover. As avenger the soldier gained verse and there's a deadly poem!

"We hate to bring this news from England, Edward. Your Countess is much gossiped of; her child not begot by you; and yet the mystery is rumored who?"

"And who is that?"

161

"None will admit what's true."

"And I take stock in that?"

"You can believe or chose to disbelieve."

"That's choice? The rumor is the wound. The truth is long since sacrificed."

He had no idea what he should believe, that his wife was faithful, not faithful, honorable, dishonored, the buzz of gossips or the butt of fools, for having a baby with him, without him. He wanted no such torment.

When pestered again by Sir William to explain his refusal to meet with his family and rejection of all that was Cecil's, he replied, "I will not blaze or publish until it please me. And last of all, I mean not to weary my life any more with such troubles and molestations as I have endured, nor will I, to please your lordship only, discontent myself."

When Sir William dissembled to misunderstand, Edward went on: "This might have been done through private conference before, and had not needed to have been the fable of the world."

Sir William turned his attention to a frog in his throat, with which he wrestled mightily. Edward completed the thrust with a word about Anne: "Her reputation is disvalued in levity."

When the queen heard of this she upbraided her earl. "Less passion and more poise, Edward. You're wild as the wind and lacking in restraint. It is ill to be passion's slave." Then she dictated a letter to the Bishop Ely to illustrate her authority. "Proud Prelate! I understand you are backward in complying with your agreement, but I would have you know, that I who made you what you are can unmake you; and if you do not forthwith fulfill your engagement, by God I will immediately unfrock you. Elizabeth."

The courtier earl recouped his poise: "Better to caress your cheek, your majesty, and rustle your skirts

162

unrestrained - for as the wind I can serve you, and as the wind I assure you: only as a man can I admire you."

"You have too much, and risk of having nothing, Edward," she said.

"I'm an ordinary simple kind of everyday type man - a pleasing, pleasant people fellow, friendly to the core," he answered. "But I do not burn when I am lit. Like stone, I cast my heat and those too near will scorch!"

"I marvel at you, speaking to your sovereign like this. Edward, do you know with whom you speak?"

"My conscience is my audience; the rest are privileged spies! And spies like flies upon the wall are only good when slapped!"

Sir William, who was an audience hidden to this private audience of the queen and Edward, when he came out after the earl was gone, said, "Your grace hath screened and stood between much heat and him." To Edward he would say, when next he chanced, "You have the voice of the queen herself for your succession. You are most immediate to our throne."

But Edward did not reply.

Sir William gazed at him, then uttered a sob: "My daughter! O my ducats!"

Rowland Yorke was a bad thug whose introduction of the rapier into English fighting was followed by many treacheries before his enemies had him poisoned. By then, Oxford had long since dismissed the lout for setting himself against Lady Oxford, keeping her from her husband by the sort of malice that came to be known as Iago in 'Othello'. Yorke was all words, no better than Parolles, the braggart captain and follower of Bertram in 'All's Well that Ends Well'. But to Oxford he was a protection against enemies, little suspecting who his enemies were, and that his protection was becoming his worst enemy.

163

This Rowland Yorke was a London cadger, a loose and dissolute lout, one desperate for advantage who had none on his own but was all front and no back, once famous among common hacksters and swaggerers. He could out-brag the beasts of the barn, and first introduced to sword fighting a low-down dirty move called foining, which was the thrust of a rapier into the dueler's girdle, a viper's move that brought instant end. It reduced the exercise of gentlemen fencing to a deadly thrust. Long swords and bucklers, striking with the edge and not the point, became the lost art of the old-fashioned, as murder swift came in. Yorke first entered Oxford's house as a friend of old George Gascoigne, Yorke's comrade-in-arms, from whom he obtained the position of receiver five years before.

"I mean not to weary my life anymore," said Edward. If there was a disgrace to admit, all might have been handled more discretely, but he would expose himself to no one who could bring his name into shame, and so he kept base company rather than his family.

The old class of ancient Oxfordian nobles was being "disvalued in levity" by his association with the mercantile traits of his in-laws, the Burghleys, and he imagined they were his enemies because they were not good at being his friends. This chilled him and he rejected them, little dreaming that where they were clumsy, his Catholic cousin Henry Howard and the Howard clan were absolutely venomous.

Edward was always doomed by the trust he placed in persons who had the courage to address him straight on, for he denied none their portion of humanity, and hardly suspected the evil which those less charitable could instigate. In all cases, he invested trust, and "loved not wisely but too well," giving an ear to those who could speak, and many more who could not. How wrong his belief in strangers

164

would lead him - and how much worse, his belief in his own relations!

So the marriage to his little Anne, the playmate of his childhood, the bride of his twenty-first birthday, at the queen's direction, his and only his, became a marriage estranged, and he chose to send her to live with her parents at Theobalds, the moated grange, and gave her also their London apartment in the Savoy, and trusted she would fare better with her parents than her husband, to raise the child he refused to acknowledge or to believe was his own, her family scorned, their hopes denied, descending into the blackness of despair, and the company of strangers by himself. He even changed his name.

Such treason as this bears witness, I can not acknowledge myself, or what I am, or from whence I came, as all is bad when judgment is bad, and I am no more myself than myself, and unworthy of that, what I've been, and whom I've been with. Once damned, all damned! But I will be avenged! Edward cried. Yet only the silent page of his open book would hear him, and that was not to respond.

At home when Sir William was asked at dinner by his son, Robert, who would be king when Elizabeth was no longer, his father did not reply. "Might I be king?" asked Robert.

"You shall be king," his father answered without looking in his eye.

XVIII

The queen went on a progress to Audley's End where court was held for all the scholars of Cambridge. Greeted by deans and ducks and aldermen, with horn and trumpet and drum and quack to march her from pond to lawn to courtyard, until all were crowded inside a cold building which stones they proceeded to warm with their many stony breaths puffing vibrantly at each other, under the louvered rafters begrimed with smoke from the ages, they made merry.

Here were they addressed by the leading Latinist of his time, the inestimable Professorial Doctor of that Dying-but-not-quite-Dead Language, Gabriel Harvey, who had the ears of everyone, from the Earl of Oxford to Her Majesty herself, not to forget such other fry as the queen's half-brother Sir John Parrot and the queen's cousin and sometime poet, Edward Dyer, plus many more who were friends of each other and all, of course, friends of the Earl of Oxford.

A partial guest list is in order. To name but a few impediments to Edward's smooth sailing along the gilded path from glory to infamy in addition to Sir William, Lord Burghley, Chancellor of the Exchequer, Lord Treasurer of England, was Cecil's son, he of the hunch back, the curved spine, who would be Sir Robert, Lord Salisbury, Secretary of State and future Lord Treasurer, in the last five years of his queen's reign more powerful than any in setting her agenda, and transferring her crown to James I, over whom he would preside for nine years before falling a victim to stomach cancer; known as a scourge of the streets and the tyrant behind the monarchy to fear, if not a king, then a maker of one.

Others would come along in due course, from the educated but unprivileged classes, eager for a leg up no matter the tune they had to dance to, like Christopher Hatton, the "affected fribble", and Philip Sidney, "a spoiled pup", who would earn knighthoods for humiliations. Also were Edward's cousins, the Catholic Howards, and Sir Francis Walsingham, head of the secret service. Each was more adept at duplicity and cunning than Edward deVere, who was able to recognize greed in others but not to grab for himself. Each knew the part he was privileged to play in this piece of pleasing pageantry. And where he had a talent, natural and open, they had a desire, dark and driving, to overcome what nature endowed in him, which they gained only by deceiving.

As Robert Cecil stood in the shadows and observed of the pageantry around him, while his own clique of sycophants rubbed the hump of his hunch, and asked what he would do to outshine his foster brother to whom the honors of this day were given, he replied: "Why, I can smile, and murder while I smile, and cry 'content!' to that which grieves my heart, and wet my cheeks with artificial tears, and frame my face to all occasions. . . I'll play the orator as well as Nestor, deceive more slyly than Ulysses would and, like a Sinon, take another Troy. I can add colors to the chameleon."

Finally, of course, there was Edward's newest hire, the secretary and would-be writer who would remain at his side with pen in hand for life, erecting the scaffolding of plots, Anthony Munday himself.

"Munday, O Munday! If I had a Tuesday and Wednesday and a Thursday man, all the way to Friday, we

167

would make such castles with words, and whole Sundays of sermons!"

They had begun to produce bits of theatrical interludes which were noticed and remarked by the intellectuals and university scholars, who in passing recorded their thoughts most off-handedly, on this budding young earl.

Now Gabriel Harvey stood to speak and drew wind, and broke the air with a din. First he addressed the queen, then he addressed the guests, then he addressed the guests of the guests, and finally he turned to his proudest achievement, the student who had won all the prizes, who had amazed where the world was short on the amazing, and he spoke of and to and for the Earl of Oxford, whose "eyes flash fire ". He told the queen herself, when he urged the youthful Lord Edward to lay down the silly pen and take up the manly sword in this Elizabethan Age of coming war with all the world, to defend the new Protestant faith against the powerful Catholic League of mighty Europe, thoughts that certainly played well with his sovereign and to all young men within hearing.

It was such a great speech that Lord Burghley took a copy to file in his records at Hatfield House for posterity and to please his heirs and grandchildren who would be able to point to it and recognize their father. Well, almost. To say the least, Sir William was mighty pleased, and he was doubly pleased because her majesty was pleased, and triply pleased because his son-in-law was pleased, and what could be more pleasing than pleasing everyone? Well, please!

He even winked at his son-in-law when they left the gathering after the ceremonies at Audley's End. He asked him, since his Latin had become a little rusty in this new age of Elizabeth when the courts, both Houses of Parliament, in fact everyone was speaking and writing and communicating with everybody, from her majesty herself to the lowest

168

hautboy, in English only, and the magnificent tongue of Rome was becoming lathered.

"What did he call you, my lord?"

It was Philip Sidney who interrupted; cheeky little, perky little, puffy little, pushy little Sidney. He who was nephew of the dark-eyed gypsy and significant other of her majesty, Robert Dudley, Earl of Leicester. Philip Sidney enjoyed all the perks and prominence afforded him by his uncle's position, including the illusion that he merited such advantage, something he doubtless learned from Dudley, of whom it was said, "he rules by vanity alone!". Sidney would become glorified in history as a great and undying national hero for his service to his queen in the Low Countries where he would meet his death at the age of thirty seven. So he would receive the largest and longest funeral ever accorded an Englishman who died on the field. But here at Audley's End he would seize the opportunity to interrupt Lord Burghley, Chancellor of the Exchequer, the Great Lord Treasurer of England and Master of the Domestic Security Forces, prime minister to Her Majesty the Queen. His interruption would be to give his translation of the words that Professor Gabriel Harvey said about Lord Edward in Latin.

Sir William made quick meat of Sidney, asking "What did he call him?"

"Vultus Tela Vibrat," said Philip Sidney.

"What's that?" asked Sir William, cupping his hand to his ear to make out what the little pomposity of a man in high shoes was saying over the din of the crowd outdoors.

But in his next words he spoke the translation from Latin of the description the professor had given the much-maligned, often ridiculed, but never-ever ignored Edward deVere:

169

"He said, Vultus Tela Vibrat, Lord Burghley. Vultus means Will, you see, or Visage, or Desire, you see. Tela is translated as a Spear, that nasty thing Lord Edward shakes in the lists when he tilts. That's Vibrat."

"When he what?"

"Tilts, Lord Burghley! Shakes when he Tilts!"

"Yes of course, when he tilts! Left or right I suppose, makes no difference in Latin does it? Tilts any way he wants I suppose."

"Joust so, Lord Burghley. Vibrat means Shakes."

"Yes of course, a bit shakey, I see. I see. Thank you then. His Will Shakes Spears, then. Most impressive. Most."

And that is all we heard of that day in July, 1578.

In September, 1579, Sidney came on one of the four tennis courts at Whitehall Palace where Oxford played with the queen. Said Sidney, "If I could play, you'd have a better game."

Said Oxford, "If you had balls to play with, Sidney. But all you make of yourself is a racket from the sidelines."

Said Sidney, "But I am the heir to Leicester and all he has will be mine."

Said Oxford, "And all he has now *was* mine, is still mine, and will be mine forever. That's forever never, Sidney. If you have me, you have nothing. You're an heir to air. Remember, Sidney, who you are - a puppy."

"And puppies come from dogs while men breed the likes of me." Said Sidney, "Then you're a bore of a boar, Edward, and I'm offended by you."

Said Oxford, "Watch yourself, watch me, watch everything, Sidney. You are no more than a puff, consumed by a fire - which is but fluff without desire."

Said Sidney, "And you are who?"

Said Oxford:

"Were I a king, I might command content.
"Were I obscure, unknown would be my cares.
"And were I dead, no thoughts would me torment.
"Nor words, nor wrongs, nor loves, nor hates, nor fears.
"A doubtful choice of these three which to crave:
"A kingdom, or a cottage, or a grave."
          Said Sidney:
"Wert thou a king, yet not command content,
"Sith empire none thy mind could yet suffice,
"Wert thou obscure, still cares would thee torment,
"But wert thou dead all care and sorrow dies.
"An easy choice of these three which to crave,
"No kingdom, nor a cottage, but a grave."
          Said Oxford:
"Was ever king that joy'd an earthly throne,
"And could command no more content than that alone?"
          Said Sidney: nothing.
          And Oxford laughed. "Truly, then, I am Lord Oxford born, deVere, and that's the truth, but gentle shepherd poet William I've become, by what I am and what I've done. It's that which makes me and marks my place in this history of our age, accomplished by desire which I have and driven by the fire which I am. Remember me, poor pup, my little poca pooka, I will shake spears!"
          "You are a William now, Edward?"
          "Will-i-am!"
          This became known as the great tennis court quarrel, and it polarized the royal court, where all that knew of anything knew this, and talked of nothing else, and were drawn from every subject to what became of it - the rivalry of their lives.
          Sidney's French friend, the ambassador Hubert Languet, noted that impulsiveness lost the day for Sidney

while restraint let Oxford laugh it off, a poor place for Sidney to be pushed.

The queen weighed in to admonish her younger courtier that in all things earls were greater than mere gentlemen, who owed their respect to the greater, or common people might learn to disrespect them all, which would not be good for any.

Sidney attempted a rebuttal by noting that she was a divine queen who ruled by god, yet consented to the laws of man and her father, so he too was bound by fairness more than worthiness, and justice greater than injury. But she had enough of this talk. The matter was settled.

The Earl of Oxford was told to continue their play without further discussion. He gathered up some leather tennis balls stuffed with hair which had been a gift of the French king. Sidney was sent from the court to stay with his sister, Mary Sidney, at Wilton Manor in the country, a fine place to cool his temper and improve his poetry, which he did, writing his younger brother Robin to whom he blabbed and promised to jarl with their father about money, earning Languet's praise of Oxford for having made Sidney grow up, which none before him had done. "Discord offends God, but ruins human credit."

At Wilton, Sidney listened to his sister Mary, Countess of Pembroke, whose husband was very old and whose sons were very interested in the world of literature, as she gave him fond advice, and spoke of her dear friend Edward, who had always shared with her his love of poetry, for she was a patron of poets and supporter of the arts. She advised her brother to spend more energy on his rhymes than in personal quarrels with so old, and dear, and true a childhood companion and beloved friend as Edward. "You shall ever be in the same orisons," she told him. "Let love, not rage, become you, and justice judge what's true."

172

"But he aggravates me: mocks me, mimics me, makes me mad, my Mary."

"And he teaches you respect. He is your reigning peer."

"But always wins."

"Yet he loves you as a child or a brother, Philip. Trust him. Be a friend."

"I'll not be anything if he be everything. He makes light of me."

"Then take his humor lightly."

Sidney and Oxford already had vied for honors, rivals since youth in a variety of competitions - the hand of Anne Cecil in marriage first. Sidney lost that too. When they were engaged, the queen approved Anne marrying Oxford instead, so Sidney turned to other interests, translating poetry which he then purveyed on his own, making himself a literary light, or a literate candle at least, to lead a romantic movement designed to outflap Edward with stories of chivalry updated and made relevant in the emerging culture of popular novels to be read, while Oxford became the leader of those whose love was words, who wanted to create the very soul of the English language itself, *to cleanse and purify the word, give meaning to the line and clarity to the phrase!*

Where Sidney's movement failed, Oxford's movement succeeded, the first great renaissance in the birth of a new literature, with the publication under Edward's aegis of the first novels ever written in English: 'Euphues: the Anatomy of Wit', followed by 'Euphues and His England'. These two novels made the word euphemism a cornerstone in speech forever after, which of course represents the original great assault on censorship in English. Oxford was the dedicatee and model for its hero, Euphues, a monument on which he would for always stand.

173

The author of the novels was Edward's second secretary and go-fer to the actors and theaters he sponsored and provided with plays, John Lyly, sometimes ridiculed as his "fiddlestick". Other writers who worked for him would call Lyly Oxford's "fiddlestick" in jest, but the earl kept all of them working and read their efforts tirelessly. Sidney was advised to find another outlet for his energies.

Munday, the craftsman in charge of plotting, began to assemble their scripts as production developed and the public appetite increased their audience.

"We've begun a studio of craftsmen, Munday. Romano's workshop. We'll launch in words the conquest of the world together! Word by word this edifice we'll build till all with thoughts to speak or deeds to know will tell of it, thanks to the language we have made. This stage is ours, this infinite diadem of hope, this trencher served to heaven. The scoffed and foul pageant of those who call themselves too pure to see shall transform every man in England. What we think the world shall know, and afterwards proud Englishmen can take the beat to march their armies across this termless earth."

Even songs were needed to include in plays for the public theater, which was growing by the day in popularity.

"Beauty sat bathing by a spring
"Where fairest shades did hide her;
"The winds blew calm, the birds did sing,
"The cool streams ran beside her.

"My wanton thoughts enticed mine eye
"To see what was forbidden:
"But better memory said, fie!
"So vain desire was chidden."

174

"Come live with me and be my love,
"And we will all the pleasures prove,
"That hills and valleys, dales and fields,
"And all the craggy mountains yields.

"There we will sit upon the rocks,
"And see the shepherds feed their flocks,
"By shallow rivers to whose falls
"Melodious birds sing madrigals.

"And I will make thee beds of roses
"With a thousand fragrant posies,
"A cap of flowers, and a kirtle
"Embroidered all with leaves of myrtle.

"A gown made of the finest wool
"Which from our pretty lambs we pull;
"Fair lined slippers for the cold,
"With buckles of the purest gold;

"A belt of straw and ivy buds,
"With coral clasps and amber studs;
"And if these pleasures may thee move,
"Come live with me and be my love.

"The shepherds' swains shall dance and sing
"For thy delight each May Day morning:
"If these delights thy mind may move,
"Then live with me and be my love."

The queen attended only two college commencements in her entire reign - the one at Audley End for Edward, and the one for Henry Wriothesley, 3rd Earl of Southampton, who was known as her own and Edward's son.

Thus did these three, these singular three, comprise and become known as a family.

XIX

Inspired by an industry I could not suppress, and an appetite for solitude in which to engage my thoughts, I was awake at night and active, while during the day I was abroad and tireless, for my heart had found its purpose and my hand became its executor. Romano's great Mantuan studio uplifted me. Those who observed it remarked that I was nervous. Never was I more calm, for the power of a force so complete and natural took hold and I was helpless to resist its tide, Edward declared in his golden book.

Before turning thirty he began to employ some of the most successful writers of his time, giving them patronage to practice their writing craft, which he did for the next twenty years, even to his own financial peril, at one point providing housing where the budding young playwrights of the age could live in a colony in London at the Savoy and have a chance at theatrical production.

The theater was becoming England's popular meeting place, the afternoon recreation of the unemployed and the well-provisioned, where men without professions met women who sought and practiced professions, and gentlemen professed nothing, as a good afternoon was had by all, complete with oranges, apples, tomatoes and other fruits and vegetables provided for meals in the pits, and thrown at the musicians and actors when rotten.

It was becoming the steamy platform of public discourse, the rallying place for causes, the learning place for history and the arena of general laughter and camaraderie, a popular mixing and melting pot. It was The place to go, on any given afternoon, if the people wished to meet the people, and sometimes glimpse the privileged, too. The theaters were built across the Thames in Southwark, a district not developed for its high class, where all the streets were steaming with the dung of horses and pigs, cows, sheep and other farm animals mixing with the crowds, and drunkards slept in doorways and trollops rolled under shrubs. It was an open market where a buyer could purchase almost anything for close to nothing from just about anyone passing to Holiwell Lane from Shoreditch.

For Edward and his writer companions, their nights of smoky discourse were spent in the Boar's Head Tavern, a pub so named after the earls of Oxford family crest which was the Blue Boar. They sated the nights on sack and malt in taverns thick with smoke. Seven thousand shops in London sold tobacco. Smoking had become a cause for disinheritance. Here the young earl was known to the revelers as "Willie" and where a last name was required he was given one, by a companion of the pen and the cup, Tom Nashe. It was "Monox". Edmund Spenser loved his slumming so much with the caterwailers of cheap verse that he wrote a dialogue in rhyme about it, called 'Willobie His Avisa', which he published anonymously while he prepared 'The Shepherd's Calendar'. A cap like an oyster was pulled down over Edward's brow. Courtiers began to mention him as a madcap.

All copies of 'Willobie' were bought up and burned. The text was much discussed. To publish as Anonymous was to challenge Authority, and reveal the weakness of Authority, for Anonymous could not be arrested, nor could the Anonymous hand be cut off, nor the Anonymous silence be assured. Anonymous could rule while Authority's hand was immobilized.

178

One night, after too much sack and boasting revelry at the Boar's Head, with Captain Morrys Denys the Frenchman and others who worked for Lord Edward, they laid in a ditch and waylaid servants of Sir William, Lord Burghley, on the Gad's Hill road between Gravesend and Rochester. It was Wednesday, May 20, 1573.

They used calivers charged with bullets and carried out their attack with war cries and raging demeanor, divided in two groups, relieving Burghley's servants of their sacks of gold, which were said to be bound for the treasury, by way of the house of Burghley, of course, from the sale of what lands belonging to which Ward of the Master, God only knew! Lord Burghley's rule was described as Cecilium Regnum. He was the king behind the queen.

Among Oxford's men was one Cuthbert Cutter, someone called Dericke and another known as Black Will who were the first to attack.

"Case ye, case ye! On with your vizards! There's money of the king's coming down the hill; 'tis going to the king's exchequer."

"You lie, ye rogue! 'Tis going to the king's tavern."

"There's enough to make us all."

"To be hanged."

"Sirs, you four shall front them in the narrow lane; Ned and I will walk lower. If they scape from your encounter, then they light on us."

"How many be there of them?"

"Some eight or ten."

"Zounds, will they not rob us?"

"What, a coward, Sir John Paunch?"

"I have peppered two of them, two rogues in buckram suits!" cried one of the brigands.

"Ned, where are our disguises?"

179

"Here, hard by. Stand close."

"Now, my masters, happy man be his dole, say I. Every man to his business."

At this point the money bearers appeared, chatting to each other.

"Come, neighbor. The boy shall lead our horses down the hill; we'll walk afoot awhile and ease our legs."

The first three thieves stepped out of the shadows. "Stand!"

"Jesus bless us!" the receivers gasped.

"Strike! down with them! cut the villains' throats! Ah, whoreson caterpillars! bacon-fed knaves! they hate us youth. Down with them! fleece them!"

The travellers despaired. "O, we are undone, both we and ours forever!"

"Hang ye, gorbellied knaves, are ye undone? No, ye fat chuffs; I would your store were here! On, bacons, on! What, ye knaves! young men must live. You are grandjurors, are ye? We'll jure ye, faith!"

The robbery proceeded, the money lifted, the travellers tied up. Then along came Edward and friends from their place of hiding.

"The thieves have bound the true men. Now could thou and I rob the thieves and go merrily to London, it would be argument for a week, laughter for a month, and a good jest forever."

"Stand close! I hear them coming."

They stepped back as the thieves returned.

"Come, my masters, let us share, and then to horse before day. An the prince and you be not two arrant cowards, there's no equity stirring. There's no more valor in that fellow than a wild duck."

At this point they commence divvying up when Edward and his friends turn on the thieves and come to

180

blows. In the scramble, the looters vanish, the booty left in the road.

Amidst their laughter at this easy success, Edward declared: "Got with much ease. Now merrily to horse. The thieves are all scattered, and possessed with fear so strongly that they dare not meet each other: each takes his fellow for an officer."

"Anyway, good Ned. The fat one sweats to death and lards the lean earth as he walks along. Were't not for laughing, I should pity him."

They agreed. "How the fat rogue roared!"

What folly we made, in our besotted state, fat on wine and soup, sloppy in mud and dung, falling all over ourselves and boon companions like cats at play and pigs in the rain, each shooting the other's gun and flopping in puddles as we fumbled to load our shot, old John Apple's hand in my pocket while I scrounged a finger in his eye. We were feckless, but rowdy and pleased with ourselves. We returned the loot when sobriety had its way with us.

Lord Edward knew whom to hire and to sponsor. Bestsellers were created, like 'Zelauto' by Anthony Munday. He wrote it after becoming Oxford's secretary. It became a source for 'Othello'.

When John Lyly joined them as jack-of-all-trades, those first novels ever published in English were credited to him. Lyly became Edward's second secretary and representative to the Blackfriars Theater when he wrote all his other plays and poems for them. He admitted that an anonymous nobleman had "reared" his efforts for a year, wherein the earl was the model for Euphues himself, according to Munday. When Lyly left his employment with Edward, he never wrote or printed another word till the end of his life, though he lived another fifteen years. But Edward

181

became famous in literary production under the name Anonymous.

"Say, Willie Monox, how do we know which plays are yours?" he was asked by the ruffians who rubbed elbows with him at the tavern, and thought themselves smart to be so close to stage wits. "Mine are the gossip of the day and I wish to be known as anonymous," Edward replied, and turned his back on the crowd.

"Then let's have a drink to anonymous - and here's letting anonymous pay!" Thus did Anonymous learn the speech of billingsgate to bindleswagger.

What came to be known as the English literary renaissance, the golden age of Elizabethan poetry, was begun at this time by these few. Financed and inspired by the "wayward earl", often providing Edward their names to be his front when he wrote for publication, they formed the working core of his literary company: George Gascoigne (starting in 1562), Thomas Churchyard (in 1570), Thomas Bedingfield (in 1572), John Lyly and Anthony Munday (in 1579), Thomas Lodge and Thomas Watson (in 1582), Robert Greene (in 1584), Angel Day (in 1586), Christopher Marlowe (in 1587), Thomas Kyd (in 1589), Thomas Nashe, Thomas Underdoune and the musician John Farmer (in 1591), Ben Jonson (in 1598, before he decided to attack the earl in writing, which lead to his expulsion from the Lord Chamberlain's Men), George Chapman (who lived so in envy he was unable to work with the earl), and Thomas Dekker (in 1599). Their nights of revelry at the Boar's Head were recorded in 'First Part of Henry IV' (II, 2).

What a boiler room they were for making of words and plays. More than you could shake a spear at: 'The

Famous Victories of King Henry V' (1574), "The History of Error' (1576), 'The History of the Solitary Knight, Timon of Athens' (1576), 'The History of Titus and Gisippus, or Titus Andronicus' (1577), 'A Pastoral History of a Greek Maid, with Pericles, Prince of Tyre' (1578), 'An History of the Cruelties of a Stepmother, or Cymbeline' (1578), 'Promos and Cassandra, or Measure for Measure' (1578), 'Sapho & Phaos', 'Pierce Penelesse', 'Selimus', 'Colin Clouts'. 'Locrine', 'Menacchmi', 'Parismus', 'Thomas of Woodstock', 'Shore's Wife', 'Murderous Michael, or, Arden of Fevcrsham' (1579), 'A Moral of the Marriage of Mind and Measure, or The Taming of the Shrew' (1579),'A Maske of Amazons & a Maske of Knights' (1579), 'The History of the Rape of the Second Helen, or, All's Well That Ends Well' (1579), 'A History of the Duke of Milan and the Marquis of Mantua, or Two Gentlemen of Verona' (1579), 'The History of Portio and Demorantes, the Merchant of Venice' (1580),'The Four Sons of Fabius' (1580), 'A Pleasant Conceit at the Rising of a Mean Gentleman in the English Court, or, Twelfth Night' (1580), 'The Story of Henry VI' (1580), 'Palamon & Arcite', 'Two Noble Kinsmen', 'The Weakest Go to the Wall' (1581, which was included later in 'Romeo and Juliet'), 'The Wisdom of Dr. Dodypoll', 'History of Caesar & Pompey' (1582), 'Ariodante & Genevora, or, Much Ado About Nothing' (1582), 'A Pastoral of Phillyda & Choryn, or A Midsummer Night's Dream' (1584), 'The History of Agamemnon & Ulysses, or Troilus & Cressida' (1584), 'An Antick play and Comodye, or the Merry Wives of Windsor' (1585), 'Endymion' (1585 by John Lyly), 'The Winter's Night's Tale' (1586),'The Spanish Tragedy', 'The Man in the Moon' (1591) 'Mother Bambie' (1594), some known by their authors like Thomas Nashe: 'Terrors of the Night' (1594), 'Isle of Dogs' (1598), both censored for Nashe being too sharp of wit, 'The Woman in

183

the Moon' (1597), 'Love's Metamorphosis' (1601), and 'Campaspe', then 'Cardenio', 'Duke Humphrey', "Iphis & Ianth', 'King Stephen', 'Edmond Ironsides', 'Edward III', and 'The History of George Scanderbarge' (1601) - all works from the "school of Shake-speare" which had precious few holidays.

As this team wore out, along came young authors who would owe their careers to the theatrical earl, and say so - Ben Jonson and George Chapman foremost, who in their turn would be followed by John Webster, Francis Beaumont and John Fletcher to the stage. The theater of the golden age was run as an industry, just as Edward on his travels was inspired by the Master Artist of Mantua, Guilio Romano, who made history.

Their task was multifold, to take real persons and change their names, to use true events and change their locale, to quote real words and change their speakers, so that those who knew would know and those who didn't wouldn't. To whom the truth was familiar, it would be recognized and as for the rest, they were none the wiser.

Censorship has been around since the beginning of language changing the shape of truth. When the mother said, "Don't say that to your sister," or the father said, "Keep quiet," that was censorship. When the Lord said, "Don't eat the apple," it was The Word and The Word was the problem. If He had said, "Don't put the forbidden fruit in your mouth," instead of the apple, it would have been easier for simple humans because you could delete The Word and answer Him in all honesty, "I didn't eat the forbidden fruit. I ate the apple. That's not forbidden." Then the Lord would have His lawyers sit down with your lawyers and define what the meaning is. Someone would eat those words. That's censorship. But not all humans are simple.

In the golden book was written: *To those of us less simply inclined, driven by what pesky thorn of contrary connivance inexplicable to the simple and defiant of the complexities, every language has its problems with the curtain of silence. Sometimes it's a forbidden word. Other times it's a forbidden writer. The human animal is the only animal whose expression is so important. Wild animals never have trouble with censors. If you don't speak then you're good to eat.*

The nit-picker is sure to cut either the word or the writer himself off. How do writers handle that? They're a bubbly breed determined to survive and test the limits for which they're the first to meet the quibbler. Many live for nothing more than to censor the censor. This is what I told our studio of writers.

The critic outnumbers the writer and mostly prevails in such struggles. So the writer who knows the story by now of why he's here and what he's meant to do about it, changes his name every time he uses a questionable word or more, especially if it's a word or a name the carper wants. Because to a writer censorship is a form of editing and editing is a form of lying and lying is the death of truthfulness.

What keeps the pettifogger up nights reading everything in sight as he searches for the unknown, elusive, pesky writer, keeps the writer up nights never stopping with those words and names and awful truths.

Every era has its thorn. Since Caxton introduced the printing press to England in 1477, and the Tudor reign began eight years later, English words poured out, and many are censored. Occasionally so many words are forbidden that the cutter has taken the extreme step of cutting off the writer himself. Some lost their hands, like those in other cultures, for not renouncing their spoken words.

185

But ours is an English story, set in the verdant valleys and crackling corners of a sanguine and peace-loving people for whom freedom of speech has never admittedly been a problem. Indeed, to be English has always been a veritable declaration of speech - and all of it always somebody's truth. We who appear to be the thorn have no excuse; we are so born.

To which many remedies are tried. Like using hard words, or big words, or strange, new-fangled, convoluted, caniptious words. Everyone makes his own arrangement with the truth - what words to accept, which ideas to tolerate. All one must recognize is who complains - the monarch, the prelate, the publisher, the editor, the agent, the guardian, the godfather, or one's spouse - and take the appropriate preemptive posture to avoid punishment, or be the mouse.

The common scold is that being who, face grave, fingers gray, sitting like a pillar of propriety, all stone and dead and bloodless, his grip about the voice of others who would speak, denies all reason. Yet who would shout and scream, must go to silence silenced by the fear of him who masks himself as brave and sits in groups and circles dumb, with others robed in wisdom. The basher's gathered round the table all who nod in silence to agree and cut and slice in thunder, lightning or in rain - and make those who love truth pay for their love with silence. I speak of the censor, of course. He does not speak of conscience or play fair with words of justice who controls the truth. He does not speak at all. He cuts, this tracher does.

As for me, mine is a story about truth - which never dies - though many would kill it or silence me. Mine is a tale about the death of truth, and its life. It is one of the great stories of censorship. So we censor ourselves, but not so much as to silence truth.

186

So came the cast of real characters from real life in real plays: Welshman Henry Evans as Welshman Hugh Evans (stage manager at the Blackfriars and director of the troop known as Oxford's Paul's Boys) ((doing the same job in real life as in the end of the play, 'Merry Wives', directing the youngsters to, "remember your parts. . .Follow me into the pit.")); and again, the most powerful Robert Dudley, Earl of Leicester, who was the queen's favorite and exercised that privilege unscrupulously, as the unscrupulous Justice Robert Shallow, with Sir Philip Sidney, his nephew, as Slender (because his pockets were slender) in 'The Merry Wives of Windsor', as Boyet in 'Love's Labor's Lost' and Sir Andrew Aguecheek in 'Twelfth Night'; Michael Lok the London moneylender as Shylock; Mary, Queen of Scots, as Lady Macbeth; the real Duke Orsino as an audience mirror to the theatrical Duke Orsino on stage before him in 'Twelfth Night'; Anne Vavasour as Beatrice in 'Much Ado About Nothing'; Henry Wriothesley, 3rd Earl of Southampton, as Orlando, Florizel and Ferdinand; Queen Elizabeth herself as Titania in 'Midsummer Night's Dream', Olivia in 'Twelfth Night', Rosalind in 'As You Like It', and with her cousin Mary, Queen of Scots, blended into one portrait as Portia in 'The Merchant of Venice'; these "sister queens" in a suitable irony united, cousins by blood, showing that authors like Nature can make, out of several, one. This author took his queen at her word and hurled it back at her when she was driven to wailing - "My cousin, executed? You have shed my blood!"

These subjects of satire were the sometime enemies, intimates and adversaries of Edward and his minions.

The troubled relations of Edward and Anne with her father looming in the shadows always, using his power as Edward's wardship keeper, appeared repeatedly, as Hamlet and Ophelia with Polonius, as Bertram and Helena with

187

LeFeu, as Hero and Claudio with Leonatus, and as Othello and Desdemona with Brabantio. Indeed, none told the story of Edward better than it was told in these plays. Then appeared the Bassanos in play after play, Antonio and little Emilia. Edward enjoyed, of course, the principal parts, as Oberon, Othello, Octavio, Romeo, Bertram, Hamlet, Prospero, and Lear (another way to spell an earl).

But they were always Edward's familiars, peers of the privileged world of the court, in which Shakespeare's plays were set, or his common, personal friends. Their list grows long. Edward could look back some way, over the entire reign of his queen, to name the characters from his life portrayed on stage. The plays were the briefs and abstract chronicles of their courtly times, the gossip of the day, the chit and chat of the hour.

The frequent appearance of Philip Sidney under different names grew from their lifelong, affectionate relationship and heated rivalry. They both schooled together, before courting Anne Cecil whom Edward married. And their words over who had first use of a tennis court involved the queen herself who had to make the peace by informing Sidney that, right or wrong, he was of a lesser rank than Edward and therefore was obliged to defer to his senior and superior, which made their rivalry legendary.

Poor Sidney, a please-man, a mumble-news, a teller of speckle and tidings. He wrote his 'Lady of May' in our queen's honor, and dashed it out like a Christmas comedy to make my lady laugh. I have seen him give her majesty a cambric shirt and sleeves with black trim at New Years, where all the courtiers offered jewels. He was so out of pocket and holy, his fingers could reach Cathay before they squeezed an angel.

In their world, all relationships were based on their station, so when Edward called Sidney a pup, he was right -

a conclusion that did not assuage Sidney. They were the sort of men who loved being enemies, in whom rivalry was born, and the cause of revelry. Here duels were fought with pens, not swords, and the pup became a favorite foil to the hound of words, who would dog the stage as anonymous, the shepherd of plays, the hart, the stag, the boar of the boards for years.

Consider with Oxford that five hundred year-long history of family, title, property. Now feudal England was passing. None took its place more than the likes of Sidney, who, as the Earl of Leicester's nephew, represented the new breed - all hat and no horse, all talk and no turkey. Sidney was a parvenu, somebody we would like to call nouveau riche except that he had no wealth. He could be bought for a song whereas Oxford could not imagine the price of a tune.

Edward had the problem of social discomfort. Everyone was born beneath him. He might not feel reconciled to the fact but it glared from his appearance as visible as his Roman nose. He was the stuff that ladies dreamed of when he entered a room, lit by all eyes toward him, the envy of everyone else, dressed in velvet, silk and sable, to a fare-thee-well, and powerless to change this state with anyone, almost, even with unknown commoners, almost.

"Is that a silken garment, my lord?"

"Silk indeed, spun by the worms, and woven for lords."

As regards Burghley, his portrait as Corambus in the original 'Hamlet' which Thomas Nashe described as written by 1589, having been started a decade before, poked fun at the pomposity of Burghley's nature, but Burghley could act against the play. "Princes have eyes and ears and long arms," he once wrote. The play was bought up and burned and no copies of it remained. But the author survived that round of the censor's sickle. After Burghley's death in 1598, the voices on ice against Oxford began to melt. Another five years and the new 'Hamlet' was published. This time Burghley's character was revised, his name changed to Polonius, the venom no less potent.

You see how we do it, like animals on the hunt: hide here, move there, pop up, duck out, weave and dodge, the very guerrillas of an idea, the apes of reason, never content to sit and wait, always on the move to make our ideas triumph and seal our opponents' fate.

(There is more to a masterpiece than its mere making.) ((There is also its permission, for everyone must lower his eyes a bit when the majesty of immortality passes, though some tend to sit up and mutter, "Hey! Wait a minute! What's 'a matter? Who give you permission to burst in like that?"))

So the great that men do lives after them because it certainly has no place before them. I was the very picture of inconsequence, the shrill and pampered portrait of contumelious contempt, by which I best concealed my wit and hid my venomed tongue. In short, I seemed what I was not, a spoiled snot.

Burghley was bothered by Oxford from the day he first met him when the earl was a boy, and yet he was fascinated too, and the more he tried to control him, which he had a right by law to do and an obligation as well, the more he failed and knew he failed, and was fascinated by the advent of a fact he could not accept, that it was his duty not to fail, and would forever be his shame if he did. Even as Burghley was drawn closer and knew he had failed, the Earl of Oxford became an absolute, utter mystery to him. It seemed that the earl felt himself to be in charge. At knowing that Burghley did not fail.

I was an enemy of the state, a paradigm to conformity, the very anathema of original man, for all was freedom to me - life, breath, limbs, movement, tout. I answered to none but God, who spoke directly to me, certainly not to Pondous. What God said was set free.

Only a nobleman enjoying the freedom of access to these privileged courtiers on a daily, living basis, could know enough to characterize, and feel enough to tweak and satirize them in the intimacy of their court where most of these plays saw their first, and last, and sometimes only performances, free of the risk that he would be silenced by having his tongue cut out, as one commoner of the period had rendered when he raised his voice against the higher authority. Oxford enjoyed the license of the queen to write and to mock almost with impunity.

She had the vanity of unending desire, the drug of appeaseless ambition flooding her veins; for as much as she would be right, she could do no wrong and the wrong she did was her right, justified by all who coveted her. Yet for all that, no natural intelligence existed more acutely; she could dice a worm at a mile, parse a poser on a pike; she was the nearest thing to honey as a bee, but watch the fang, wrote Edward.

It is not difficult to imagine what power inured to the queen like an ace up her sleeve when she chose to send a message to others within her hearing, yet did not wish it to seem from her, by using her great device, deception - deVere - her courtier's wit, much as "anonymous sources" would one day provide political columnists with thunder, arming politicians, who whispered into their ears, with a necessary clout.

Such power does truth achieve, becoming a biblical universality, when it appears unsigned: The thesis of the hidden censor is becoming a synthesis. The more I fire from

191

the ramparts, the greater the chance to hit our mark. The creator who lived the words and wrote the deeds is evidenced in every line, the more he absents himself from personal design. The plays of our age are memoirs addressed like memos to the conscience of our monarch. And I, tippy-toed, like a bee in honeysuckle, am most in force when appearing least in armour. Pose like a peacock, pass like an eagle. Truly, deceit is the only weapon capable of direct attack. I play the part of a rose but accomplish the deeds of a thorn. Most feminine, I am most masculine, when torn.

"And believe this, that when he is gone and his comedies out of sale, you will scramble for them and set up a new English Inquisition. Take this for a warning, and at the peril of your pleasure's loss, and judgment's. . ."

As Ben Jonson would say (in the surviving words of England's poet laureate after his time), "it was necessary he should be stopped. His wit was in his own power; would the rule of it had been so too."

Edward's reputation as one of the best comic playwrights of his time was established nationwide. His fame as a poet was widely known, but not his work, because he was unpublished under his own name.

Popular scriveners and commentators wrote letters deploring the nobleman's preference not to be known for what he penned. Even Edmund Spenser, author of 'The Faerie Queene', in his poem, 'Tears of the Muses', introduced a character based on the earl, whom he called "Willy", and bemoaned the state of things that such a talent would so totally withdraw himself as to seem dead of late.

But Edward did give to others, including Spenser, whose first published work he engineered and prefaced with a poem in praise.

Scores were settled with people long dead as only writers can alter the course of history by creating a fiction spin. *Then, what are flights of fancy for, if not to equalize the unequal and justify the unjustified.* (That's why the press quotes "unnamed sources" rather than "true confessions"). *For there are more heads that roll in the stillness of the night than voices raised to protest at noon, and the cut of the censor still bleeds. Do not look to Olympus for the Olympians.* (They are pressed in quiet boroughs, kept under domes by plan).

Here in our land in our age all is truth and true. Damned be death for the risk of telling. To succeed, I had to be unknown, and unknowing in the deed, if I was to do it knowingly. Some go knowing into their grave unknown. That is my will. For myself, all is will.

Tom Nashe, in his 1593, enjoyable 'Epistle Dedicatorie' to 'Strange News', a satire and rapturous ode to drink at the Boar's Head, and its most familiar 'Gentle Master William', of sanguine complexion and spirit most jovial, also known as St. Fame, and Master Apis Lapis, which is yet another proxy squeezed from Lord Oxford's name, mentions "such a famous pillar of the Press, now in the fourteenth or fifteenth year of the reign of his Rhetoric (since 1578), giving money to have his illiterate Pamphlet of letters printed (whereas others have money given them to suffer themselves to come to Print)." Edward also was proposed as the Alderman presumptive at yet another drinking hole near his house at London Stone, The Steelyard, by which much revelry and liberty was taken lightly. These writers of satire were a band of comics laughingly engaged, and he most jolly in slumming amongst them, who presented himself as a dead man still living, a ghost of a writer who preferred to maintain his state: "I am but subrogation, a phantom of the shade, your vision of astral light, just vapor and pure wraith."

Think for a moment, if you will, of God who gives all freely. Each man possesses what he can of God's, and God keeps him. For this there is no pay, and yet it goes more greatly than the course of commerce. What richer beauty is there than the sunrise, but who could purchase it and steal away the night? We are so poor in everything, and accomplish nothing, without God's hand to guide us. To take His work and claim His place for ours is blasphemy. Therefore I am anonymous. And what I do is His, what's done, His will, and let that be our own. Then all is God's, as we. My pen is not employed to earn my bread and favor. I was born with ample. Nor do I speak to flatter, though others do. Mine is to tell the news and truth on which I have no claim. I pay for this. I dream too, to amuse. But what I write is of the state of things. All I am is politics. Who built the pyramids? Who wrote the Bible? Who made our nation ours? The ghosts of history, that's who. I can not usurp God's anonymity. The only mystery here should be His name and face. It's fine for fools to banquet on strumpets and glaze. Some pens move men. I am what I am. But shades make men, for all the world to amaze, while some in seasons fade.

They were Thomas Nashe, Thomas Kyd, Robert Greene and Edward. This jolly four took over a boarding house belonging to one Julia Penn who was not paid once for being put out and eaten out of house and home. Thomas Churchyard took the rooms in Edward's name while Edward housed his three daughters and all manner of writers there, until she was forced to write to Lord Oxford to plea for her pay, ending up for her trouble as a character in a play, Mistress Quickly. She would rather have had the money. As for the debt to Mistress Penn, describing Thomas

194

Churchyard's miscreancy to her betters, she said: "I am a poor widow of East Cheap. He hath eaten me out of house and home; he hath put all my substance in that fat belly of his. But I will have some of it out again, or I will ride thee o' nights like the mare."

In her letter she wrote: "The grief and sorrow I have taken for your unkind dealing with me. . make me believe you bereft all honor and virtue to be in your speech and dealing. . You know, my Lord, you had anything in my house whatsoever you or your men would demand, if it were in my house. If it had been a thousand times more I would have been glad to pleasure your Lordship withal. . But, my Lord, if it please your Lordship to show me your favor in this I shall be much bound to your honor, and you shall command me and my house, or anything that is in it, whensoever it shall please you."

She was paid 25 pounds for the first quarter's rental of rooms in her house on St. Peter's Hill, and for coals, billets, faggots, beer, wine and any other thing spent by Edward, although napery and linen were not in any bargain made, though he promised to consider that too.

My beloved son, make well your plans before you act, or otherwise they'll fail you, for no man can succeed by blind reliance on his heart; the heart is not the instrument of action, not even the main actuary; it is the soul of temperament. Your plans must flow from deliberation and rely on craft, if you would exceed your enemy, for this is your enemy's mode. Conceal your thoughts until they take a body of their own, then act! For that is what your enemy does. Use what I did, relying on my unshaped wit, as the grievous lesson of a tormented spirit; I could not help myself, nor you, nor anyone. My world was encumbered in the luxury of vice and all I could do was lament it - witless, powerless, the feast of a thousand stars, the fortune of none.

195

I have followed rules, though mindful ever of the rule that rules forever - we have no sense of the final rule. I have been cautious to give no offense, yet eager to delight, bending my words to argument but not abandoning humor. I have yet remained not too cautious, willing to offend in the course of truth, and confident in its outcome. I have trusted implicitly in life, delighting less in delight, though delighted by it, confident of the divine which through every turn will shine. I have done this in both Latin and English, not content with one if the other is imperfect. And thus I caution you, if you incautious be, Edward said to the golden book, whose pages were his final friend.

"For slander lives upon succession,
"Forever hous'd where it once gets possession."

"What plague is greater than the grief of mind?
"The grief of mind that eats in every vein;
"In every vein that leaves such clots behind;
"Such clots behind as breed such bitter pain;
"So bitter pain that none shall ever find,
"What plague is greater than the grief of mind."

This is pain and it is painful. What is beautiful is unbearable.

XX

And then Lord Edward ran off with a royal Maid of Honor, a beauty of her majesty's court whom all the men desired, a vivacious redhead named Anne Vavasour, who had dark eyes and numerous brothers in close attendance and eager defense, related to the Howard clan, initiating an affair that became public gossip.

The poetry it inspired caused shock, for what England had never seen before was an earl, a nobleman, a peer of the realm in line for the throne, putting his pen to paper and signing his thoughts addressed to the common man, or woman, common to every heart, as if the high and the low might find a meeting in the middle through words:

Three times with her soft hand, full hard on her left side she
    knocks,
And sigh'd so sore as might have mov'd some pity in the
    rocks;
From sighs and shedding amber tears into sweet song she
    brake,
When thus the echo answered her to every word she spake:
Oh heavens! Who was the first that bred in me this fever?
    Vere.
Who was the first that gave the wound whose fear I wear
    for ever? Vere.
What tyrant, Cupid, to my harm usurps thy golden quiver?
    Vere.
What wight first caught this heart and can from bondage it
    deliver? Vere.
May I his favor match with love, if he my love will try? Ay.

May I requite his birth with faith? Then faithful will I die?
   Ay.
   It was called 'Anne Vavasour's Echo', published and signed, as an act of defying more than custom, by the author's initials, 'E.O.'.
   It defied our prince's right to choose whom we would love, or that she be our only love. Because she rules our fate does not allow she rule our heart. My 'Echo' told our sovereign that in all things of the soul, we're equal. Who knows the warmth of love wears Nature's sweetest crown, than which there is no more renown nor earthly kingdom can compare, though reigning monarch cause despair.
   For Edward, it was not simply love he described, but the game of love, the joy of love, the comedy, history and tragedy of love, all in words full of fun and games, with anagrams worked into the lines like crossword puzzles, and other exercises of the mind to amuse and direct those passionate lovers of language, those elite of the world who loved words, for everything he wrote was beginning to take on two or three or multiple meanings, until he had to laugh when he cried, and weep when he could howl no more, the pain had become so funny, the fun so painful.
   For I did love my prince, more than the elements, the seas themselves, but there are tides, and all that is pure love is not pure in itself. I also hated what it bound me to. Unbridled vanity, for one.
   It was growing obvious that words were the great human leveler, and all those who understood them were on an even plain.
   Then Edward wrote, and published under his own name, the sum of his experience with Ms. Vavasour, called 'Woman's Changeableness':
   "If women could be fair and yet not fond..
   "These gentle birds that fly from man to man..

198

"And then we say when we their fancy try,
"To play with fools, O what a fool was I."

It also applied to another monarch of his heart.

Some thought the young earl and this maid were so talkative, they might have conversed each other to madness had they been able to confine their feelings to words, even if only for a week. In the absence of their queen she became his queen.

"O dear save me, Edward."

"Save you, fair queen?"

"And you, monarch! Ay, man is enemy to virginity, how may we barricado it against him?"

"Keep him out."

"But he assails, and our virginity, though valiant, in the defense yet is weak. Unfold to us some warlike resistance." She blinked her eyes which were open wide.

"There is none. Men setting down before you will undermine you and blow you up."

"Bless our poor virginity from underminers and blowers'up! Is there no military policy how virgins might blow up men?" She blinked her eyes more widely.

"It is not politic in the commonwealth of nature to preserve virginity. Loss of virginity is rational increase and there was never virgin got till virginity was first lost. That you were made of is metal to make virgins. Virginity by being once lost may be ten times found, by being ever kept it is ever lost. To speak on the part of virginity is to accuse your mothers, which is most infallible disobedience. He that hangs himself is a virgin; virginity murders itself and should be buried. Virginity is peevish, proud, idle, made of self-love, which is the most inhibited sin in the canon. Keep it not; you cannot choose but lose by 't. Out with 't! Within

199

ten year it will make itself ten, which is a goodly increase, and the principal itself not much the worse. Away with 't!"

"How might one do, sir, to lose it to her own liking?" She blinked her eyes no more, but held them wide.

"Let me see. To like him that ne'er it likes. 'Tis a commodity will lose the gloss with lying; the longer kept, the less worth. Off with 't while 'tis vendible. Virginity, like an old courtier, wears her cap out of fashion richly suited, but unsuitable, just like the brooch and the toothpick. Your virginity, your old virginity, is like one of our French withered pears; it looks ill; it eats dryly, a withered pear, it was formerly better. Will you anything with it?"

"Not my virginity, sir."

She was magic, the flash of her eye a lightning bolt, her whispering skirt a surge of fire duping my veins, and I could not see her without such pitiless joy, such mewling agony of my limbs as was sickening even for me to behold. She laughed; I was drugged; she sighed; I was weak; she chattered in that most gaily mindless trill of a voice as ever was assumed by a bird; I flew - and all this was consummated in disgrace! What I would not have done for a kiss - give up my heredity no less, were she to yield. I gave up more over time due to this flight of wooing angels. My passion is measured by the growth of my regret, for truly, I came to be more intimate with sorrow than I knew of ecstasy. Could I do otherwise? Ask Icarus. He is my Pegasus. And Diana was my sun with whom we made our new son.

But the voluptuous Vavasour and eager deVere did more, and conversed less, until she became pregnant and also bore him a son, whom she named Edward Vere.

It caused a bitter rift in the family with Oxford's cousins, the Catholic Howards, who were related to Anne. It lead to denunciations and frays in the street, brawling and

200

sword fighting which ended in the death of Robert Brenings, a manservant of Lord Oxford.

Her majesty knew only one heart, her own; gave liberty to love by license, and snatched privilege with a vengeance from the lap of custom when she felt presumed upon. There was no closet that did not lead by some corridor to her majesty's chamber, so hiding love was impossible; enjoying love was unthinkable; the court was a sack of screaming cats, all there for their lick of cream, wrote Edward.

In March, 1581, Thomas Knyvet, one of the Howard's and a new appointee of the queen's, as a gentleman to the Privy Chamber, provoked a duel with Edward. He too had a passion for Anne Vavasour.

Who can say who urged him on? Was it she in her loathed majesty, to give me warning, or was it she in her disgrace, to level grave humility? This much I know: Beware before you would offend a woman.

They met on a bank of the Thames of an evening thick with mist where the silence was cut by curses as the assailants sprang from the trees and had at each other, a light rain soaking their velvet, steel clanging steel, mud drenching their capes and mottling their blood.

An apprentice butcher named Gerard Ashby, returning on an errand for his master, learned from the boatmen on the Thames near Blackfriars of the fray about to take place in the marsh.

"O great event!" he cried and ran to an armory nearby, and fixed himself up with a pike. "A fight! A fight!"

On Edward's side were only two men, Gastrell and Harvey.

Knyvet's men warned Gastrell, "We don't want to fight you here." But the man heard nothing, hurled himself in their midst and was wounded. Then Harvey lunged with bare sword and in his efforts to save Gastrell, was cut. Knyvet's men left shouting victory.

The butcher boy never had a use for his pike and was told to remember his work. Edward's men vowed another day.

It came in July. Gastrell challenged one Long Tom, who had left service with the Earl of Oxford to serve the Knyvets. Gastrell made quick fare of him and they left his body on the bankside.

Edward and Thomas Knyvet came to blows, sword on sword, thrust and parry, circling, calculating, sweating, snarling, and telling their men to keep back, stand clear of it. Both were wounded.

"The streets of London were filled with the clamorous quarrels of these new Montagues and Capulets," wrote an excited author. Truth to tell, the queen was against all fighting. By her order, death in a duel was punishable as murder. She was told the earl had sixteen men in the deVere family livery of Reading tawny and Oxford blue ruling the streets with riot. Most of these were river men, as it developed, who overheard the fray from their boats and laid into the melee with gusto and no regard for either side. In fact, he had no one at his side. A maid for his wife, a nanny for his daughter, neither of whom served him personally, then a lad whom Sir William described as "a kind of tumbling boy, and the fourth is a son of a brother of Sir John Cutts" were his only retainers.

Knyvet's and Oxford's men stalked each other and fell to assault whenever their shadows crossed in the moonlight, with shouting and dueling, exited as little boys, with a "Hey, Ho!" and heedless of the consequences until their blood was drawn and their looks turned grave.

The day of reckoning approached and if the scandal with his two Anne's was much, it would vanish in the wake of worse.

"What is Knyvet?" Edward challenged. "More than Prince of Cats, I can tell you. O, Tom cat himself, he's the courageous captain of compliments. He fights as you sing pricksong - keeps time, distance, and proportion; he rests his minim rests, one, two, and the third in your bosom! the very butcher of a silk button, a duelist, a duelist! a gentleman of the very first house, of the first and second cause. A Howard cousin no less! Ah, the immortal passado! the punto reverso! 'By Jesu, a very good blade! a very tall man! a very good whore! That we should be afflicted with these strange flies, these fashion-mongers, these pardon-me's, who stand so much on the new form that they can not sit at ease on the old bench? Knyvet, you ratcatcher, will you walk, Tom?" All the men with Edward snarled.

"What wouldst thou have with me?"

"Good King of Cats, nothing but one of your nine lives. Come, sir, your passado!"

Then the sword's prick came inside the upper thigh.

Edward was so wounded that he could not walk for a week, hobble for a month, or limp for a year; his leg took on a permanent hitch. "A plague on both your houses! A dog, a rat, a mouse, a cat, to scratch a man to death! a braggart, a rogue, a villain, that fights by the book of arithmetic! They have made worm's meat of me. My reputation stained with Knyvet's slander. Knyvet, that an hour hath been my cousin, for are we not both Howard's cousins? O, I am fortune's fool!" Edward cursed as his retainers carried him in a litter unceremoniously off under the trees, and forgot his buckler which was left lying in a puddle. "O, the indignity of 't!"

The queen was not pleased by Edward's loves and liaisons, or his public duels in the London streets, or his permanent injury to his leg, for he would never dance again, but limp forever more, even as he displayed his skill recently improved by Rocco Bonetti, master of fence at his school downstairs at the Blackfriars theater; he would duel nevermore.

Said Edward: "I'll stand as a man to defend myself, or I'll not show at all, for a man I am, as I breathe."

As for Anne Vavasour, her majesty gave orders: "See you the fornicatress be removed: let her have needful but not lavish means."

So ended her career as a Royal Maid of Honor.

Edward and Anne were separated and thrown in The Tower to cool, she for a month or more from March to May and he for a night that ended in June. The accusations at court were scabrous. Their two houses, Oxford's and Howard's, Protestant and Catholic, were divided forever, bringing denunciation and prison which did not end those opposing factions. There was no end of bitterness. Men of the Oxford colors dueled cousins of the Howards and Knyvets defending Anne Vavasour for years.

But I had my revenge. The Howards never again would speak my name without knowing who met their match. What crippled me was devastation to them. They were leveled, razed, expunged, till death alone became their friend, salvation and mercy in the end.

Three years later a younger brother of Anne's, Thomas Vavasour, reaching the impulsive surge of his teenage years, wrote the earl, "if thy body had been as deformed as thy mind", accusing him of being "so much wedded to that shadow of thine" he deserved to be wakened by another duel.

Suddenly I was the scourge of Catholics, the prince of curses, the sweet prey of vain desire, in every tavern and home; our queen forbade my mention at court and children

204

laughed when I hobbled out to meet the night for air. It was a humiliation most devout. You could ring matins by it.

Clearly it was the enmity of Catholic for Protestant and the reverse which fired this flaming feud, exhausting political passions in lowly brawling, with the vain belief that a common scandal rivaled the end of the world for sheer interest.

Vavasour's "shadow" was Edward's other self, not the titled noble, Lord Great Chamberlain of England, but the satirical, scandalous, scalawag of a street slummer, Willie Monox, enamored of finding new words and phrases for every feeling known to a human being, and capturing them in a theater of the mind on a stage across the Thames at Shoreditch. The events of the times were still being shaped into plays as yet only partially written. Poor young Thomas Vavasour, of course, was dismissed with a laugh by Edward. He and his fellows at the Boar's Head had more serious business.

In this Edward deVere-Anne Vavasour affair the fires on both sides smoldered while their reputations burned. It was nothing like what was to become, through the rest of their lives, to all the world that heard of them, a tale of woe for the ardent Anne and her E.O.

205

XXI

By 1580, the Duke of Parma was slaughtering Protestants in the Netherlands. He was carried over their mutilated corpses, dipping his gloves in their blood flowing in the gutters of their villages, all to the greater glory of King Phillip II of Spain. Word traveled to Protestant England that even the Saint Bartholomew's Day Massacre would be remembered as a holiday compared to what was in store for them once the continent was swept. The fall of Maestricht included the butchery of women. Protestant babies were impaled on swords and sticks. Catholic victors and celebrants danced circles around the chopped off Protestant heads they stacked in rows like melons. Altar boys in vestments screamed with terrified laughter, playing kickball with meaty skulls.

In this climate, and the inevitable approach of Spain's invasion of England, Lord Oxford addressed his queen at court.

On December 21, 1580, he rose in the Privy Chamber before all.

"Your majesty, I give you this gift of Christmas Season - a warning. Whereas we have been a Protestant nation since your father, King Henry VIII, broke the Catholic Church in England and freed all good Englishmen of the Roman hold, and for the twenty-two years of your glorious reign have tolerated all persons of faith, and all faiths, who were faithful to the state and your majesty, I come to a terrible pass, for I bring you news of great pain and sedition.

"Over the past year a Jesuit invasion of one hundred priests trained in France by William Allen, a fanatic, has practiced the mass and plotted in secret within our country. In Rome, Pope Gregory XIII has honored the Saint Bartholomew's Day Massacre as a glory to Catholics, for which he has struck this medal to be worn by all Catholics dedicated to the fall of our faith and our nation's rule. He has this very month ordered the Cardinal Secretary of the Vatican to write two of my peers whom I counted as true to England and our House of Lords. To their query - would it be a sin in the eyes of God and Church of Rome if your majesty were dispatched, he wrote, and I read: 'Since that guilty woman of England is the cause of such injury to the Catholic faith and loss of so many millions of souls, there is no doubt that whosoever sends her out of the world with the pious intention of doing God service, not only does not sin, but gains merit.' Now, your most glorious majesty, I must confess, there is something rotten in this state of England."

The queen replied in solemnity: "It has been my policy to love all who are English and to tolerate whatever faith they had, so long as their faith is to England, but now you say Catholics believe in treason more than they believe in England?"

"I do, your majesty."

"And they would kill me?"

"Yes, your majesty."

"But I am England, all English, mere English. Who would kill me?"

"Those whom you know and trust, those whom you love and share this very day with."

"Whom do you know here who would kill me?" She looked around her at the frozen faces. She rose from her throne and walked among them, gazing into the eyes of every courtier. She eyed Leicester, Cecil, Hatton, Walsingham, the Howards - they who had told Edward that his wife was untrue, and then set their Anne Vavasour upon him.

"Kill you? I know who they are who would kill your majesty. They lied then and would lie now if they denied it. Those with whom I have lived; those whom I believed when they told me my wife was unfaithful: my own once beloved cousins, your majesty!"

"The Howards! Lord Henry Howard!"

"Whose father was the first poet of England whom I honored, who taught me the new form of sonnet from Petrarch - together with Charles Arundel and Frances Southwell, to my sorrow."

"They plot to kill me?"

"To kill England, your majesty."

"My most noble Lord Edward, you and I are as one person. I have known you - your father's faith brought me here. You are peerless among us - our king in your domain. You urge me to lose my faith in those I loved and enjoyed most, to preserve our state. You would have me execute my cousins, Catholics, for practicing their faith, because it is not our faith. You would have me abandon tolerance."

"I would have you save England, and God save those who damn your majesty."

Edward bowed. The court was hushed. The French ambassador, de Castelnau Mauvissiere, stepped backwards. The Spanish ambassador, Barnardino de Mendoza, looked to the left and right.

Lord Henry Howard, age forty-five, was ordered to be seized by the vice chamberlain, Sir Christopher Hatton (with bell ringing), and taken to The Tower. Charles Arundel and Frances Southwell were ordered to be seized by the head of the secret service, Sir Francis Walsingham, and conveyed to The Tower. This was done and the lives of Arundel and

208

Southwell were never restored to favor. When tried, they were found guilty. Condemned to die, they fled to the continent. Sentenced forever, they lived in disgrace until they expired as traitors, surviving in shame, existing on pity. Lord Henry Howard was kept away until Lord Burghley died. Then Robert Cecil brought him back to court with a pension, instructed to spread malice about Oxford in what became known as the Theater Wars.

He survived as a rogue, a foul-mouthed and calumnious knave; a poor, decayed, ingenious, foolish, rascally, cuckoldy, arrogant, beggarly, lousy, flap-ear'd, beetle-headed, worsted-stocking, lily-livered, eater of broken meats, three-suited, hundred-pound, whoreson of a knave; so puny, petty and peevish a knave I shall call him Tiny knave; regret I to admit he was Great in knavery; biting his lip - malice; licking his lip - folly; a most curl-lipped and seething, slimy, reptilian serpent rogue in peacock's feathers; excessive in laughing and smiling - excessive in malice and cunning; an eye of a snake, a tongue of a snake, a hiss of a snake, a squirming, damnable, yeaforsooth, slipper and subtle seething snake in the grass, in the feathers, in the quilts, in the silks, that finder of occasions; hence, in three letters: rat.

Edward deVere was, for his own protection that night against the possibility of revenge by persons unknown, taken to The Tower and held in safety, though he took no food and gave no tip on his departure next morning.

In privacy, the queen remarked to Edward, "You have placed us on the road to war and Spain will be unyielding against us."

"But England will prevail," Edward replied. "And you will live - forever."

"When Spain was my brother-in-law he urged me to marry whom he chose, and he urged often, and several. I resisted him then and I resist him now. None but one shall be the monarch of our house."

Edward bowed, and that night wrote, *I threw down my challenge and became the Iris to every hue - never more praised than when cursed, nor more cursed than when praised - by Catholics abused, by Protestants blessed, the tear in every eye, the choke in every throat. I stood at center stage and knew, my place was in the shadow. I might light the fire. I do not burn.*

Elsewhere in the audience, Sir William Cecil barely contained his glee. "In all these years not I, not Walsingham, not all the Houses of Commons or Lords could move her majesty as he's moved her in a word - one sharp, one true, one pointed, deadly word - Howard!" Sir William all but danced, but did not dance, for dancing was not Puritan. (But he was filled with a cupidinous music.)

"I dare not admit it to him. I dare not anything! He has the tongue of kings - and the ear of our queen! I dare not admit that either. O! How I'd give my ducats for his gift. One small and tiny gift. He moves her by a thought where crowds waste volumes in futility! What cost! Yet none dare tell him. Such a bird in hand! I dare not admit that either. Let me count these dares and dare-nots. (But keep them to myself, or do I dare?) How much he dares and I dare nothing.

"He stands for family name and honor and I urged it. I did that, in my cunning. My not daring made him strong. O, what treasures! Now I dare not say it. Protestant England will extol him, for her majesty moves by him. At last! What she could not see, this lord of high fancies shows her. Yet I dare not praise it. He who makes all does not make us perfect, but makes us blind to our imperfections. And there's a certain perfection. What do I dare? What she could not decide, he's made her choose and all that was but doubt before now bends to the yoke of bloody certainty.

"O most daring! I'm ready to declare a holiday while we prepare for a war! Fish for dinner for certain! And I dare not admit, I dare not anything!"

Sir William's son, Robert Cecil, made another reply from the shadowy reaches of his darkened soul in a corridor outside the courtiers' hearing, to his personal aides.

"None will extol him. Oxford's name will die as much as those he named to die. Not Protestant England, nor faithful Catholics, nor tolerance itself can survive, because deVere has forced her majesty to kill. Death will be the only cry. His name will lead the curse for all who pay the price. He's allied with betrayal and betrayed who only toyed with treachery in the name of faith. Death will be the end of him and his."

"And you will conquer him, true, Robert," panted his adherents.

"But I will tell him nothing of his acts. I'll wear the smile that clouds beguile, and applaud his face with nodding looks, for he has never needed me and I have none of him. Death comes, and knocks, and we who hear not, die not. We by stealth will live. DeVere dies. The trouble with deVere is: too keen to benefit from doing what he does unseen, he must shout history to the rooftops while I whisper it below. In the end it's I, the cats in the street and the shadows will prevail."

"Most certainly," they gloated, "deVere dies."

September 23, 1580: On the queen's royal visit to Plymouth, to honor and welcome home Captain Francis Drake aboard his ship The Golden Hind, Edward was received as the fool of the crowd, another "motley to the view."

Drake pirated so much gold from Spanish galleons, the King of Spain protested and Elizabeth replied that she'd take care to curb her famous buccaneer, thus placating the king and once again forestalling war, but when she saw the one hundred fifty thousand pounds in gold ($37,500,000) Drake plundered, visions of England triumphant ensued. She had Drake kneel on the quarter deck before her to be knighted at once.

"The King of Spain wants your head," she said, laying the sword against his neck, then she stepped back and motioned Seigneur de Marchaumont to do the knighting. This man was the agent of France urging again for the queen's alliance in marriage to his duke. He was compromised. Wanting the queen's yes, he could not say no though France was the ally of Spain. He grasped the sword, thus bringing France to the aid of England in its conflict with Spain.

"Now we have the purse to fight who'll dare demean our right?"

The queen smiled wickedly, but gloriously. Then her garter fell to the quarter deck and the French ambassador scooped it up, declaring it bounty for his duke, but she was unfazed and raised her skirt higher on her thigh than ever was shown by woman to man in public before that time, and in her most charming, endearing voice, with fingers extended, she chimed: "Return it, dear sir. I have nothing else to hold my silk stocking up but your courtesy." To which appeal the Frenchman inclined. Then our own, our magnificent, our Ulysses rose to his feet as Sir Francis Drake, the hero of the age, the harbinger of the newest mistress of the seas, on whom the sun will never set.

And on that day the Spanish knew that war with this upstart Protestant England was inevitable. The Spanish ambassador in attendance turned away in contempt.

212

The Earl of Oxford was memorialized for his actions that day by a rhyme, a published poem commemorating the beginning of England's rise and response to the death-dealing Catholic League.

Edward carried a white staff, symbol of the sovereignty of the state, as was his duty to the queen. Only in his hands on that day of celebration, when the nation and every man, woman and good English child in the street could taste the hope of revenge against their enemies, the baton became something more.

To the joy and laughter of the crowd he twirled and played with it like a toy, and let it fall, but not touch the ground, so that everyone knew how great was their monarch, that her Lord Great Chamberlain could let her staff fall, and recover it without loss. He held it aloft in triumph. It was a moment the public would long identify with Edward - how he let fall the staff and it was not lost.

A few years later it would come to cheer the public again, as a reminder of his courageous foolery, and England's glory, in a personage named Falstaff.

And so went the popular rhyme: "Then came the Lord Chamberlain with his white staff and all the people began to laugh."

Edward dictated a play to his secretary, Anthony Munday, in further contemplation of England's triumph, that all the world could know how great their achievements were: 'Sir Thomas More'.

Such acts as these we'll garner wholesale, till all the kings of England glow in glory, and monarch's fists shape fortune's twists in revelry waving our cause to destiny. The stage! The play! The history of our ancestry is pageant enough for noble souls in heraldry.

And he sat by taper light and dipped his quill with satisfaction, most content with all: "This royal throne of

213

kings, this scept'red isle, this earth of majesty, this seat of Mars, this other Eden, demi-paradise, this fortress built by Nature for herself against infection and the hand of war, this happy breed of men, this little world, this precious stone set in the silver sea. . . this blessed plot, this earth, this realm, this England. . . this teeming womb of royal kings!"

In December of 1581 he returned to Lady Anne, Countess of Oxford, in joy, in relief, and at peace as a family man.

Now let the fires burn. Let freedom ring. Let every heart that raised a cry for truth proclaim the day for victory in the word. That sweet, that clear, that simple voice for such that innocence well knew and could not say, let them that would be true and free and fair on wings of joy declare: we're not afraid or bound by any stricture, hampered, censored or obstructed, but eagerly awaited, that everyone might celebrate and sing: I am at liberty to speak, to write, to think, to be, to give, to state, to share; I am a man born free and all I have is here! declared Edward's golden book.

XXII

When Edward's brother-in-law, Peregrine Bertie, Lord Willoughby returned with his sister, Mary, Lady Willoughby, from their journey as the queen's first ambassador to the King of Denmark at Elsinore, where they bestowed on the king the Order of the Garter, it was all Bertie could do to contain himself with singing the praises of the Danish court. "Rosenkranz and Guildenstern were there! And all the other royal families!"

Edward marveled. "Why is it not Sir Toby Belch, my brother, come to tipple?"

To which his brother-in-law replied, "To the gates of Tartar, thou most excellent devil of wit!"

To which Edward's sister, Mary remarked, with a sharp eye cast on her brother and his state of dress, "My lady will hang thee for thy absence."

To which Edward added, "Let her hang me. He that is well hanged in this world - "

To which his sister said, " - And that may you be bold to say in your foolery."

For which Edward ended, "Well, God give them wisdom that have it, and those that are fools, let them use their talents."

But a household of happiness was shadowed by the death of Edward and Anne's newborn first son. She wrote poetry in mourning for small comfort. He revised his play on Troilus and Cressida, took his acting troupe on the road to the scene of his first triumph in the art of practicing stagecraft, where his grandmother lived near Stratford. His manager, Lily, prepared for their triumphant return to London by leasing a stage on the Thames' south bank. With work, it was made ready for the crowds, Blackfriars Theater. In the country he'd visited his grandmother's house, Bilton Manor, and gathered actors from the roadside and country markets near Stratford to assist him.

"Speak the speech, I pray you, as I pronounce it to you, trippingly on the tongue," he rehearsed them. "Nor do not saw the air too much with your hand, thus, but use all gently; for in the very torrent, tempest, and - as I may say - whirlwind of passion, you must acquire and beget a temperance that may give it smoothness." They looked at Lord Edward, sweating in the sunshine, and grinned sheepishly. "Be not too tame neither, but let your own discretion be your tutor: suit the action to the word, the word to the action; with this special observance, that you o'erstep not the modesty of nature. . ."

"What you say?"

"Are you deaf, man?"

"My name's Shax-fool, my lord, and I'm a ready wit."

"Well speak then."

"Just take me and shake-well, my lord. I'm no fool."

"Then speak this speech as I pronounce it."

"And Shake-a-leg, my lord?"

"Or Shake-a-mutton, man."

"I'll Shake-a-potato, my lordship. And you can Shake-a-moon at it, I'll bet."

"I see you're quite a Shax-gent, Shakey."

"I'm Shags-poor, my lord, but I'm ready to burn on a Shax-pyre if you'll put me on as a Shax-beard, I'll warrant. Or you can take my son."

"Are you the son - or the moon, my lad? How old are you?"

"Twenty."

"What would your father say to that?"

"Why, catch him and find out."

"Does he have a name?"

"Same as mine, I'll warrant."

"He's a Shax-pere then."

"He's a Shax-paw, I'll say."

Lord Oxford returned from County Warwickshire with players of all types for roles of choice parts, though he chose carefully whom he brought: only those who could speak. Those whom he left behind in the road, even when they helped to dislodge his wagons which became stuck in the mud, were those of a particular breed. They wiped their noses on their sleeves.

"I'll be coming to London, bye and bye, then, my lord! You'll be wanting a groom to tend your horses."

"And we'll be in London to greet you, Master Shake-a-leg, looking forward to your arrival."

"That's me, my lord, on two feet going before me, until I find a mount."

"So be it, Master Shake-a-pair."

"I'll shake on that."

"There's a man who's shakey."

With the coming of spring in London, at Vere House, Lady Anne was blessed. On his thirty-fourth birthday, April 12, 1584, Edward could sing. He had a second daughter, Bridget.

"Cupid and my Campaspe played

"At cards for kisses, Cupid paid;

"He stakes his quiver, bow, and arrows,

"His mother's doves, and team of sparrows;

"Loses them too; then, down he throws

217

"The coral of his lip, the rose
"Growing on's cheek (but none knows how);
"With these, the crystal of his brow,
"And then the dimple of his chin:
"All these did my Campaspe win.
"At last, he set her both his eyes;
"She won, and Cupid blind did rise.
        "O Love! has she done this to thee?
        "What shall (alas!) become of me?"

"Here Lyly, take that!" said Edward to his manager and tossed the poem at him. "Fit it in a play somewhere."

By November, Edward was suited up in armor to tilt in the lists for his third championship win at the tournament given to celebrate the twenty-fifth year of her majesty's reign.

He was the Knight of the Tree of the Sun, known at court as Phoebus, the queen's sun, and by gossips as her first, if not only, son. "By the Tilt stood a stately tent of orange tawny taffeta, curiously embroidered with silver and pendants on the pinnacles, very sightly to behold. From forth this tent came the noble earl in rich gilt armour and sat down under a great high bay tree, the whole stock, branches, and leaves whereof were all gilded over, that nothing but gold could be discerned. By the tree stood twelve tilting staves, all which likewise were gilded clean over. After a solemn sound of most sweet music, he mounted on his courser, very richly caparisoned, when his page, ascending the stairs where her highness stood in the window, delivered to her by speech his oration."

        "Half horse, half man, and with less pain,
        "Doth he bring the courser, indomitable
        "To yield to the raynes of his bridle."

218

I loved the body and the mind, the harmony of muscle, sinew, movement ordered by the universe, the blood that flushed my cheek and raised my arm and animated every toe and finger of me. I was an instrument of light, my flesh made like the sabre of the dawn, my teeth, my eyes, the courser of my thought fixed on the tilt, my brain a dagger ready for the plunge, each tremble from me wildly declared: I am a man, I'm ready for the kill!

As the playwright John Fletcher reported: "He controls his foaming steed with a light rein, and armed with a long spear rides to the encounter. Fearlessly he settles himself in the saddle, gracefully bending his body this way and that. Now he circles round; now with spurred heel he rouses his charger. The gallant animal with fiery energy collects himself, and flying quicker than the wind beats the ground with his hoofs, and is again pulled up short as the reins control him."

He was one of the ablest horsemen, of soldiers born, a soldier born to be, which was his greatest ambition. But her majesty preferred he remain on native soil, safe from death in foreign battle, charged with her entertainment in the domestic saddle.

From a household which was down to no servants at home, and actors he was supporting everywhere, living at the Savoy, bedding them down in his own stables at Vere House near the theater, a little light was beginning to show under the curtain of his veiled finances. Edward could invest in Martin Frobisher's expedition by ship to search for the Northwest Passage, a deal that was touted for its profit potential by a moneylender named Lok.

This Michael Lok would be brought up on charges of scamming, an offense for which Lok was not shy. But Edward lost his considerable investment and with it another hope of fortune was dashed.

219

Then came the darkest cut of all. Edward was called with his neighbor, Lord John Lumley, at the recommendation of Lord Burghley, to sit in judgment on her majesty's cousin at the trial of Mary, Queen of Scots.

Whom our majesty calls the Daughter of Debate. Her cousin is less able to control her own vice than our majesty is to tame her own virtue. These cousins are the opposite faces of one coin. When you flip Mary, only fate knows how the crowned head will fall. She is more inclined to tuple with a goat than settle with our Prince who kicks high in a gaillard after dinner. If there is honor in discretion, then I'll wager that the Queen of Scots gives honor to discretion but has yet to gain that honor.

The grief of this task could not be imagined. He who dreamed of justice for all and life for living was faced with a matter of terrible death.

We are in Fotheringham Castle, seventy-five miles north of London. The date is October 14, 1585. We are in closed session for the trial of Mary, daughter of the sister of Henry VIII.

"Thou art here accused and arraigned of high treason, and conspiring to take away the life of our sovereign lord the queen, thy royal cousin; the pretense whereof being by circumstances partly laid open, thou, Mary, contrary to the faith and allegiance of a true subject, didst counsel and aid them, for their better safety, to fly away by night."

Edward's father-in-law, Lord Burghley presides. The Earl of Oxford sits next to a marquise and a lord on the jury, the Marquise of Winchester and Lord John Lumley. John has the largest library in England, three-thousand-five-hundred volumes, and is Edward's closest neighbor in London. Only Edward's father-in-law's library comes close with one-thousand-seven-hundred volumes, which would eventually be catalogued at auction a century later and noted

220

for its deep and particularly pervasive influence on the plays of Shake-speare. The sources for every one of the famous plays would be traced to volumes in Lord Burghley's collection, much to the satisfaction of Dr. Samuel Johnson, for whom it was full of meaning, though he could not guess at the meaning. By contrast, Sir Walter Raleigh had a library of one hundred seventy books, one of which he admitted, when questioned, to having lifted from the lord chancellor's stacks.

But the Queen of Scots conducts her own defense and is courageous and simple, with supreme ability.

"Since what I am to say must be but that which contradicts my accusation, and the testimony on my part no other but what comes from myself, it shall scarce boot me to say, 'Not guilty.' Mine integrity, being counted falsehood, shall, as I express it, be so received. But thus: if powers divine behold our human actions, as they do, I doubt not then but innocence shall make false accusation blush and tyranny tremble at patience."

Being subtle, indignant and personal in her appeal and political logic, she is so persuasive the jurors respond to her and are moved with sympathy.

"You, my lord, best know, who least will seem to do so, my past life hath been as continent, as chaste, as true, as I am now unhappy; which is more than history can pattern, though devised and played to take spectators. For behold me a fellow of the royal bed, which owe a moiety of the throne, a great king's daughter, the mother to a hopeful prince - here standing to prate and talk for life and honor 'fore who please to come and hear. For life, I prize it as I weigh grief, which I would spare. For honor, 'tis a derivative from me to mine, and only that I stand for. I appeal to your own conscience, sir."

Only the facts are against her. Two months earlier Sir Francis Walsingham of the secret service had caught her betrayers and they were hanged, then cut down while still alive, gutted and disemboweled before a flailing crowd, seething and trampling itself to see more of the deaths close up. Mary was arrested and her secret papers of Catholic conspiracy became the incriminating evidence against her.

Says Mary: "Now, for conspiracy, I know not how it tastes, though it be dished for me to try how. All I know of it is that other accused was an honest man; and why he left your court, the gods themselves, wotting no more than I, are ignorant."

Lord Burghley says: "You knew of his departure, as you know what you have underta'en to do in's absence."

"Sir, you speak a language that I understand not, my life stands in the level of your dreams, which I'll lay down."

"Your actions are my dreams," says Burghley.

"Sir, spare your threats. The bug which you would fright me with I seek. To me can life be no commodity, the crown and comfort of my life, your favor, I do give lost, for I do feel it gone, but know not how it went. I am barred, like one infectious, myself on every post proclaimed a strumpet: with immodest hatred. Now, my liege, tell me what blessings I have here alive, that I should fear to die? Therefore proceed, but yet hear this - mistake me not, no life (I prize it not a straw) but for mine honor, which I would free. If I shall be condemned upon surmises, all proofs sleeping else but what your jealousies awake, I tell you 'tis rigor and not law. My father - O that he were alive, and here beholding his daughter's trial; that he did but see the flatness of my misery - yet with eyes of pity, not revenge."

On October 25th the jury is forced to convict. They return to the court of Queen Elizabeth. She hears Lord Oxford's report. What can he say? Burghley wants the execution now.   Others are of kinder mind.   Edward describes the queen's cousin whom all the Protestant world wants beheaded, and whom the queen can only feel sympathy for, whose sentence she agonizes over, but whose sentence she knows she must sign, yet whose execution she delays. Her cousin's fate is sealed and she loathes what that is coming to mean to her who has to order the beheading. Burghley presses for it, in the name and cause of "justice", hot for justice, righteous for justice, while the Earl of Oxford feels differently, compassionately, forgivingly.

Edward describes what none but a ruler can feel, as none but a ruler can hear, and none but a ruler can understand. He brings the words of Mary, Queen of Scots, directly home to her majesty, almost verbatim as though Mary was there in the flesh pleading for her life, begging for mercy in a most dignified stance, explaining how even a monarch can do better by forgiving.

Elizabeth asks Edward, "What did Mary say?"

He replies: "The quality of mercy is not strained; it droppeth as the gentle rain from heaven upon the place beneath. It is twice blest; it blesseth him that gives and him that takes. 'Tis mightiest in the mightiest; it becomes the throned monarch better than his crown. His scepter shows the force of temporal power, the attribute to awe and majesty, wherein doth sit the dread and fear of kings; but mercy is above this scept'red sway; it is enthroned in the hearts of kings; it is an attribute of God himself, and earthly power doth then show likest God's when mercy seasons justice. Therefore, though justice be my plea, consider this: That in the course of justice none of us should see salvation. We do pray for mercy, and that same prayer doth teach us all to render the deeds of mercy. I have spoke thus much to mitigate the justice of my plea, which if thou follow, this strict court must needs give sentence 'gainst. . ."

Elizabeth was moved to tears, and stilled, until the day of execution. But she could not change the inevitable, though she was exhaustive in delay. When it came in the end, the paper ordering the beheading had to be slipped for her signature in among countless others she did not have time to read, and so signed without seeing as she moved from room to room, from her royal closet to her chapel, to its adjoining room, to her Privy Chamber, through a gallery, to her Presence Chamber, filled with all manner of men who mattered, honored by her Yeomen of the Guard deployed in rows. On hearing what she had signed, she lashed out at her ministers and berated Lord Burghley with venom.

"It was your secretary, Sir Michael Hicks, that slipped the warrant for execution under my pen when I was playing a game of primero, Lord Burghley."

"It was not evil intended, majesty."

"But evil accomplished, my whale!"

She exhausted herself in a screaming fit over her cousin's fate, at how she had been tricked, at how she was deceived by the deceitful, at how her authority was tampered with and used. Between eight hundred and twelve hundred courtiers fled for the exits and dived for the pillows to avoid her wrath, upsetting their games of tables. But she had enough for all. Then she fell exhausted into a normal routine. And napped on a cushion. And with her ladies, did her hair.

"The cushion, no, the cushion," she said. "To lay on feathers wards off death."

"Did someone sneeze?" a voice asked. Eyes turned to Edward. "Erasmus loves not sneezing."

Edward remained to console her, her only family, as the day was mourned for a death in the family. It was brought in the name of war and a nation's destiny, that would justify such a death in glory.

224

"How will the people take it?"

"Grievously."

"How will the people express it?"

Lord Burghley could answer that. "If I had the money my experience cost me, I'd be a wealthy man. (I am a wealthy man.) ((So much it has cost me.))" He cleared his throat to a proposal. Philip Sidney had been granted a license to go to the war abroad, in the Dutch Low Countries. As a person of lesser rank, his presence was not so needed at court, and in the war he suffered a wound and died. His body was brought home but was not buried. It was kept in a rank and stale conveyor, until Burghley could make his proposition.

"Your majesty, might I suggest that we mourn him, not as the little fool of a fellow he was, about whose poetry I know less than nothing but whose words I have never much counted, if indeed I can count at all on the words of our late Lord Leicester's nephew for meaning of any sort, but let us mourn him as a soldier, a warrior, a knight of armour and bravery, in deeds most graceful and battle most honored, that the people might not concern themselves with those feelings that they might otherwise have in mourning for your cousin, the late Queen Mary, with all the Catholic sentiment on which such tears would be attendant."

So moved, her majesty was bribed by feeling, and raised her eyes to declare the death of *Sir* Phillip Sidney. It was a cause for national mourning. Sidney became a knight in hero's death, his body placed in Westminster Abbey where its odor was offset by burnt offerings. The country was invited to weep for him, for his deeds, for his battles, for England's glory so bravely attained.

In the street, people said Sidney was a gentleman, a perfect courtier, example to the world of what the best of England was, modeled on Castiglione's 'Courtier'.

225

"We invented him," said Sir William.

"We invented well," said Elizabeth. "(Though Edward published the book.) What men are is less important to us than how men serve."

"Their service to the state is greater than their soul, your majesty."

"Their soul is England. That's all the soul there is, Sir William."

The longest, largest, grandest funeral in the history of the nation ensued, and would never be equaled or repeated. It served the cause of morale so well that every brave Englishman with a heart which might have rebelled in mourning for Mary, instead mourned for Sidney and raised the national spirit, while even the rain over London wept. For the Queen of Scots not a tear was shed.

"I mourn her, Ned, though England mourns a silly man. I mourn the cousin whom I loved. She more resembled me than all the prattling sycophants aligned behind me on this sceptred isle; except her papal embrace, her stubborn queenly mien, she was a sovereign true. More than cousins were we - twins - in every way but faith. I mourn my royal sister, Ned."

"Her fault was in her stubbornness; she wanted one crown crowning all," said Edward.

"We must move the people, or they will move us!" Elizabeth declared. "How do you propose we move the people, Edward? Bend them to our will and mold them to our fate, lift them to our cause and carry them to our gate?"

"The play's the thing," he smiled and bowed. "Wherein we'll catch our kingdom."

"Can you make us plays to make us proud?"

"I'll engage myself to glorify what lives in glory already. 'The Famous Victories of King Henry'."

"Only shout it to the rooftops!"

226

"The very winds in English sails will carry English tunes and every sailor on the decks shall mark time with our passage. For nothing is so sure to stir them as the tale of the red and white, the war of the roses, of Owen Tudor's and the Lancaster lines. Let me stage again the triumphs of the Henrys, that every man in every field can feel his own heart rise and take arms in this sea of troubles and bring glory home to raise."

"I'll be Richard II, know ye not that?"

"I do, and so will others, madam."

"Then I'll be all the kings!"

They fell to wild dreaming and toasted the world of their imagining, in the popular words of the time.

"Kiss me this once and then God be wi'ye, my sweetest dear! Kiss me this once and then God be wi' ye, for now the morning draweth near."

With that, her fairest bosom showing, opening her lips, rich perfumes blowing, she said, "Now kiss me and be going, my sweetest dear! Kiss me this once and then be going, for now the morning draweth near."

He was the shepherd who waked from sleeping, and spying where the day was peeping, he said, "Now take my soul in keeping, my sweetest dear! Kiss me and take my soul in keeping, since I must go, now day is near."

To which she replied: "Stay, O sweet, and do not rise! The light that shines comes from thine eyes; the day breaks not: it is my heart, because that you and I must part. Stay! or else my joys will die and perish in their infancy."

Edward laughed, then said: "My Love in her attire doth show her wit, it doth so well become her: for every season she hath dressings fit, for winter, spring and summer. No beauty she doth miss, when all her robes are on: but Beauty's self she is, when all her robes are gone."

And a good night was had by both.

"What a king am I to have you as my queen!" he laughed.

"And I will have you for myself alone if I must steal you from eternity. 'Let none enjoy you ever' will be the measure of my power. Ever mine - forever lost to every other! Our secret will be ours to own. And who you are to me for all the world will be unknown. Your anonymity will be the measure of our secret. You can speak and write all things, but I will have the last word."

"To be acknowledged, madam, is overpaid. All my reports go with the modest truth."

"You are gracious in your silence."

"Pardon me dear madam: yet to be known shortens my made intent: my boon and I make it that you know me not till time and I think meet."

And even as she had him banished she had him brought to her at Hampton Court. Willingly and proud to serve, he left all thought behind that he would ever have of immortality. That was for the gods - for him remained: uxoriousness and mutability.

When he left her, Edward stood alone in Westminster Abbey before the tomb of his erstwhile rival, his much-begrudged friend, the soldier-poet Sir Philip Sidney. "What a rogue and peasant slave am I! Is it not monstrous that this player here, but in a fiction, in a dream of passion, could force his soul so to his own conceit that from her working all his visage waned, tears in his eyes, distraction in his aspect, a broken voice, and his whole function suiting with forms to his conceit? And all for nothing."

"When in disgrace with Fortune and men's eyes,
"I all alone beweep my outcast state,
"And trouble deaf heaven with my bootless cries,
"And look upon myself and curse my fate,

228

"Wishing me like to one more rich in hope,
"Featured like him, like him with friends possessed,
"Desiring this man's art, and that man's scope,
"With what I most enjoy contented least;
"Yet in these thoughts myself almost despising,
"Haply I think on thee, and then my state,
"Like to the lark at break of day arising
"From sullen earth, sings hymns at heaven's gate;
"For thy sweet love rememb'red such wealth brings
"That then I scorn to change my state with kings."

XXIII

As Lord Oxford served Elizabeth, she saw him well-paid. He was the chief juror on two of the most tragic trials for treason in her reign - the Queen of Scots and the Earls of Essex and Southampton, their heir, the consequence of which could mean beheading, which grief was yet to come, for it would mean a mother ordering and a father judging the crime of treason on their son.

Here again is where the pleasure of reading the record of events tells more: she chose to give her first peer of the realm the means to enact their dream. She who had ever given payment to her favorites, her lords, in the form of lands and leases and licenses for import and exclusive entitlements, made this one exception, this only time in her entire reign. She granted the use of cash taken directly out of her treasury for distribution to the servants of her lord and premier earl as necessary.

This commission cost the parsimonious queen more money in cash paid to Edward than she ever paid anyone for anything in her entire reign, the equivalent a quarter of a million dollars yearly by today's rate, and she ordered it paid without question or review, for life. It was a gift she never gave another soul, though her lovers came in numbers and her servitors became legion - Leicester, Hatton, Raleigh and Essex, whose services were rewarded in land grants and trade monopolies, never in cash on the barrel head. All of them would lose favor and some of them around Oxford also would lose their heads, while the enduring earl kept his top on always, to the end, which was in sight. Edward received the money for eighteen years until his death. From that day on, he was referred to by all as "Great Oxford".

On June 26, 1586, by Privy Seal order, her majesty ordered paid one thousand pounds yearly, delivered to him quarterly, without question or review nor any accounting of how he would spend it.

"And together we shall bring into being the golden age of poetry!"

"A love song to your majesty, a love song to our love, your majesty."

"You are, Ned, as always, my master of words."

Leaning from a window, she called: "What does a man think when he thinks about nothing?"

Walking in the garden below, he replied: "A woman's promise."

She was in a coquettish mood, he in an obedient one.

"Being your slave, what should I do but tend upon the hours and times of your desire?"

"Tell me what I desire, Ned."

"I have no precious time at all to spend, nor services to do till you require."

"Nor dare I chide you, Ned. Your every word is sweet."

"Nor dare I question with my jealous thought where you may be, or your affairs suppose, but, like a sad slave, stay and think of night."

"Yet don't you worry where I am - how happy I make those?"

"Not as a king, a prince, a lord, nor even as a master would I be known to any but Our Lord, your majesty. Only as a man do I strive to attain the highest state of men - compassion, forgiveness and comfort to all souls. For what your grace granted me, I am forever grateful, and humble in that gift."

"Only as a man? But Edward, and you are my King Edward, my Ned, my faithful, my true, my dearest, to all a prince, to me my prince."

"You to your beauteous blessings add a curse, being fond on praise, which makes your praises worse."

"I am your fantasy, Ned."

"The fools of Time, which die for goodness, who have lived for crime."

And he was praised by his personal affairs secretary, Angel Day, for being "from infancy ever sacred to the muses"; by William Webbe, "most excellent" among court poets.

How has such a memory been lost? Intentionally, and by design. Replacing it is an even greater memory - their idea. It was Equality. It was Respect - for even the least citizen. A common memory. In time they would give it a name and that would be their heredity. "Let no unkind, nor fair beseechers kill; think all but one, and me in that one Will." It would be a memory wrapped in glory.

"Though all my wares be trash, the heart is true."

"Are you my poet 'Willie', now? My pastoral god of rhyme, my Pan, sweet William?"

"I am yours - E.VERE where."

And so it was reported from courtier to courtier, and from the court to Paul's Churchyard where the gossip of the day enjoyed the sunlight bandied about, and the people who were inclined to show interest were informed by the lawyers at the pillars, under the plaque to Vitalis deTesta, and all sorts of others were told while busy transacting business along Humphrey's Walk, which news was carried all the way to the sellers of print at the bookstalls in the yard. "O, learn to read what silent love hath writ."

With the approach of war with Spain, a war that was to last eighteen years under threat of overwhelming imminent invasion by Spanish hordes on English shores, her majesty turned to her cousin, Lord Oxford, her friend since childhood, and commissioned him to fight in their battle for the hearts and minds of her people, their people, the English people.

"And do I go wage war at last - as your prince, as your king, as your lover, as your husband, or as your son? Advise me who I am. You are my everything."

"You are my native poet of the realm, with a bit too much the scent of truth, none else. Methinks you frank beyond your sense. Blunt is he who dumb shall be. You might woo me more - if you loved truth less."

"Woe me more - if I loved Vere less."

"O Ned, you are ever the cause of your own heartbreak. Your lips are the enemy of your soul. What passes one, the other kills. Beguiling, incurable, damned art thou."

"And so dear mother, then, the truth."

"Ned, you are my son."

"That's why you tolerate me?"

"I have no choice in what I've borne."

"Except the choice to bear."

"Not even there."

"Who is my father then?"

"My step-father was my lover."

"From this I sprang?"

"From which Lord Burghley placed you with the earl, your father, and you became the Lord Great Chamberlain, heir to our oldest house and most ancient title."

"To my father, I am a bastard then."

"From which I thought to make you heir to me and king."

"At which you failed."

"But we have hope, together, we can make a king."

"If it suits you your desires. Otherwise, I'm damned. He's damned. We're damned. All damned. Such shame I would not wish upon the lips of heathens. In a world of God, we all are best forgotten, madam."

"You can not call me mother?"

"Is it your desire?"

"Mother - or lover."

"What's in a word? A rose, a royal rose, such as your own, by any other name would share its scent the same."

"You will become my minister of words, for patriotic propaganda without portfolio, to serve the office you know best, which only my ministers at the highest level know, to serve forever the Church of England."

"Once again I might give them a show."

"You might even let our staff fall that every brave man of England should rally to our call, Ned."

"I'll note it: 'Staff fall.' For a comic effect."

"You are the great earl, Ned. Most valued to our cause."

Lord Burghley, Oxford's judge and Puritan censor, with others present at court who were the legion of Oxford's enemies, were forced to stand silently by and agree.

"Let me not to the marriage of true minds
"Admit impediments; love is not love
"Which alters when it alteration finds
"Or bends with the remover to remove.
"O, no, it is an ever-fixed mark
"That looks on tempests and is never shaken;
"It is the star to every wand'ring bark,
"Whose worth's unknown, although his height be taken.
"Love's not Time's fool, though rosy lips and cheeks

"Within his bending sickle's compass come;
"Love alters not with his brief hours and weeks,
"But bears it out even to the edge of doom.
"If this be error, and upon me proved,
"I never writ, nor no man ever loved."

So with a flourish of her signature on this commission, by Privy Seal warrant of June 26, 1586, the golden age of English literature was launched as an English ship, light and set deep in the water, easily turned in any sea, as the writing of plays about English heroes fighting for English glory rolled out wherever a stage could be secured to the raising of the public's passions, and securing duty's patrimony. But it was paid out for a different reason, to silence the claims of an earl to a crown.

For Edward, just to be left alone was a liberation. But he had to look back and remember the past, that pageant of mist and rain, of voices raised to all manner of things, and canon fired, with alarums for kings.

In his own writing, he was concerned with the themes of his good name, enduring fame, immortality and the true outcome of celebrity, power and courtly life, the same concerns as would one day pronounce the greatest words of Elizabeth's age.

I must be allowed my tale to tell. He wrote and whispered by the tallow light.

So he sat at his table through the night and thought of past and present, his mother, his queen, his wife, his mistress, all. "She should have died hereafter; there would have been a time for such a word. Tomorrow, and tomorrow, and tomorrow creeps in this petty pace from day to day to the last syllable of recorded time, and all our yesterdays have lighted fools the way to dusty death. Out, out brief candle! Life's but a walking shadow, a poor player that struts and frets his hour upon the stage and then is heard no more. It is a tale told by an idiot, full of sound and fury, signifying nothing."

To which gravities in the dawnlight he was interrupted at his task by a servant coming in to bring him morning broth. Seeing the servant poised to speak, he snapped:

"Thou com'st to use thy tongue: thy story quickly!"

He was told the outside was inclement. Such interruptions were more foul than the weather.

He turned to his labors. "Where, alack, shall Time's best jewel from Time's chest lie hid? Or what strong hand can hold his swift foot back? Or who his spoil of beauty can forbid? O, none, unless this miracle have might, that in black ink my love may still shine bright."

At dawn I'll think of my hero Tom encouraging me in the building of our theater; thus ever Radcliffe, 3rd Earl of Sussex. I engaged a dozen successor Toms to write the plays and prepare the books so we could daily deliver performances just as he did with our armies on the Northern Border, and with our players for her majesty, when he was Lord Chamberlain. For no man more wondrously inspired the birth of our stage than this Tom, and our several Toms who took their inspiration and opportunity from him. Next to that was I uplifted to weave at least one golden thread with all the others in dramatic tapestry, but none more than great Tom. Tom begot what time alone's forgot.

And yet what good was brought? The Duke of Norfolk is not returned, nor any life, once lost, regained. Thus sadness seeks the joy of light and weeps unwept in shadows cached behind the veil of night, unclaimed.

I lowered my eyes, so much disgraced, mindful ever of my memory effaced. For in her fickle fever to be queen of love she bore me, possessed me, and defied the wrath above.

236

I was an innocent, and innocently gave, to tread the path of innocence, that met defilement. I little dreamed, 'the more exalted such a man may be, so much the more contemptible is he. A gambling prince would be incompetent to frame a policy of government, and he' - who gives offense the spirit of pretense - 'will sink in general opinion as one unfit to exercise dominion.' So falls a soldier who becomes a sinner. So fell I, this star of England, from the sky, this lewd disgrace to every land.

The shame in this is that my shame was bliss.

Part Four

"For truth is truth, though
never so old. . ."

XXIV

In the last years of his marriage to Anne, a third daughter, Susan was born. Like her sister, Bridget, who at fifteen would marry Francis, 2nd Lord Norris of Rycote and Earl of Berkshire, Susan at seventeen would enjoy one of the most glorious unions of the age, for her husband would be Philip Herbert, 1st Earl of Montgomery, destined to be with his brother named "the Most Noble and Incomparable Pair of Bretheren" who, with aid from their eldest sister, Elizabeth, the Countess of Derby, and her husband, the practicing playwright, William Stanley, England's wealthiest man, would publish that most famous of tomes, 'The Complete Comedies, Histories & Tragedies of William Shakespeare', celebrated as The First Folio.

Not to neglect in this project also would be the mother of the immortal brethren, Mary Sidney, Countess of Pembroke, sister of Philip Sidney, friend also of Lord Edward and in her own right a poet, who also sponsored Ben Jonson to be named poet laureate, then urged him to become the Folio editor, through whom the family could work until the Folio was done at her home near Stonehenge called Wilton Manor.

But Anne Cecil, the tiny Countess of Oxford who remained true to her father's precepts, and dutiful to her family, even to her husband's exclusion, would wander too near the water and die of complications from child birth at the age of thirty one, spurned and scorned in life, in death deplored, desired and adored.

Said Edward: "There's a great spirit gone! Thus did I desire it: What our contempts do often hurl from us we wish it ours again. She's good, being gone. The hand could pluck her back that shoved her on." And then: "I loved Anne Cecil. Forty thousand brothers could not, with all their quality of love, make up my sum! That you were once unkind befriends me now." He gazed with dismay in the watery grave.

And told of it much later: "We wept after her hearse and yet we mourn; her monument is almost finished, and her epitaphs in glittering golden characters express a general praise to her, and care in us at whose expense 'tis done." He paused, then added: "Thou art like the harpy which to betray, dost with thine angel's face seize with thine eagle's talons."

For he understood at last, and looked upon the truth, that Anne was held as much as he beneath her father's fist, that tyrannical grip that could admit no tyranny.

Then from the water which formed a mirror of her life he saw more than his own face. He saw their past together, his tender love in youth, his fear of marriage with her whom he loved almost as though she were a sister, a child he so often protected, his reluctance to consummate their marriage, the child declared to be his whom he was sure he had not fathered, justified by the laughable folly to become forever known with his name as the infamous bed trick, from where their first daughter Elizabeth was born, and years of solitude resolved by their forgiveness of each other's failings, and the birth of Bridget and Susan. Then he knew how Elizabeth was conceived while he was absent, how the secret was kept, how Anne had suffered in that shame, for she was fondled by her father, Sir William, Lord Burghley, founder of the House of Cecil.

When Sir William saw his personal ambition for a noble dynasty slipping away from his grasp, escaping, the

242

risk of losing heirs that bore the Oxford name, because his daughter's union was unconsummated, and his son-in-law was fled to Europe to become the "Italian Lord" enamored of the Renaissance more than family matters, *he made a choice of such darkness as would damn the light.* He took his willing and submissive child Anne alone inside his private chamber, and made her come to him. He lifted her skirt and told her, "It's all right. It's all right. Come sit here on my lap. All right now. All right." He gazed at her white skin and trembled for the House of Cecil which he knew now would merge forever with the Oxford line by the birth of an heir to the Oxford name.

"I tell you what mine authors say..
"With whom the father liking took
"And her to incest did provoke.
"Bad child, worse father! to entice his own
"To evil should be done by none."

It made her mad, who had no madness in her, and could not bear the thought of madness. She rued the day she was her father's daughter. We were together in our last delights, and first together, where her father shadowed all our nights. Now she is gone - O, Anne! I love thee in such sort as, thou being mine, mine is thy good report. Again the fools of Time, which die for goodness, who have lived for crime.

Now Edward knew, it was the Puritan father Cecil who had fathered their first child, Elizabeth, on his own hapless daughter, and he could only cry for vengeance but exact no part of it, forgiving her.

In the court of the queen are reptiles for an age, crawling with worms and sluggardized in themselves, all

243

matter of vermin hatching schemes. I loathe them who have
cost me my life. Watch those fawning vipers, my son!

Edward stood in a shadow of the Cecil family shrine
- a monument in the Chapel of St. Nicholas down a
horseshoe corridor beyond the great altar of Westminster
Abbey, where he and Anne in the presence of the queen were
wed. It was filled by Sir William's loquacious chronicle "in
glittering golden characters" of Cecilian history, seen from
his view to serve his view, reciting everything, justifying
nothing, in Sir William's endless nattering of untrue truths
engraved in stone and glazed with gilt meant to make it right,
but making it only endless. He could not erase from his
nature the remorseless compulsion to justify his perfidy to
posterity - for he had been, was, and forever would be only a
commoner grown great - on the blood of a noble he taught
others to hate.

Workers were preparing Anne's place there, "the
monument. . almost finished" beside her mother, and where
in time the rest of Sir William's intended would lie. Edward
stood again alone in Westminster Abbey, the light from high
above now frail and feeble, candles flickering, almost as
though Anne's sweet, dark eyes were looking in on him,
casting their trust upon him since earliest memory. He
overheard the workers:

"Is she to be buried in Christian burial when she
willfully seeks her own salvation?"

"She is."

"How can that be, unless she drowned herself in her
own defense?"

"Why, 'tis found so."

"It must be *se offendendo;* it can not be else."

Edward could bear to hear no more. He stumbled as
though he was a drunken man from that shadowed place, to
where he did not know.

244

"Are these ghosts I see before me, gathered in a row, or are they the pale significance of my own thought grown clear? Who arc these people I know not, yet seem to know, uttering the reflections of my crippled mind? Out, out, you shades! Out, night!"

XXV

Dawn came, and with it Edward, beside the Thames, his jerkin open at the neck, his garters awry, his hair a tousled mess, his face contorted almost like a madman's, asked a passerby who did not stop: "Who's left? Who's left?"

1588 is the birth of the age of Lyly, Munday, Nashe, Kyd, Greene and Marlowe, which becomes, within the year, the invasion of the Spanish Armada, and its massive defeat. But it begins with the death of Leicester, he of the gypsy eyes, who no longer needed to be remembered, yet was.

She mourned for him in a thousand ways. She wrapped his final letter in a ribbon tucked away beside her bed. She stood and stared at vacant windows and muttered to herself. "I have known him better than any man alive since I was eight years old." Then, "He hath known me better than any man alive since we were eight years old. We were the same. We were as one. All the rest is error." And she kneeled to pray.

Who thought of Anne? Who mentioned Anne? Who even cared for Anne? O faithful, O true, O loving Anne who bounced, yet sank, who was a cork, yet failed to float, forgotten by those who had her and used her, seized by opportunity and cast aside by chance, or lack of it. The queen made haste with you, Anne. And now she preys on others, and prays alone for herself.

With a little consolidation, 1588 becomes the age of The Bard. This was the job Oxford enjoyed most, and did hardest, coming out of mourning over the death of his wife one month before the greatest sea victory in naval history, to commission his own ship to face down the Spanish Armada, investing in a marine expedition searching out the Northwest Passage, and then withdrawing from court and all public display to devote himself to the craft he knew best, which he had followed most, to be heard from little more as a figure of popular gossip or sport or fashion or flirtation. He would no longer be known for the apparel he wore.

At the time of the definitive sea battle against the Spanish Armada, off the south coast, at Plymouth, England had only thirty-four ships and another one hundred sixty-three borrowed, privately-owned light vessels. One was the Earl of Oxford's 'Edward Bonaventure', of whom great leadership and bravery were reported as he charged.

At 2AM on July 20, 1588, the English began their long-canon assault from behind the Spanish Armada, "built high like towers and castles" which were doomed that day to destruction, as her majesty's home-grown volunteers lead by Lord Hunsdon entered on the global stage, the unchallenged dominant force in trade and policy for the next three hundred thirty years. Elizabeth was now truly the mother of her empire - forever. *As the queen bee in the hive, the spider in the web.*

It is not difficult to see Edward in all manner of outfits, hell bent on doing something remarkable even if he hadn't quite figured out what, until it was decided for him, and history beckoned her fickle finger to come hither, not as a soldier, nor statesman, nor chivalrous knight, but to write, edit, produce, publish and perish in the lists of writing for the cause.

It is a player's stage to live, a soldier's place to die, I
would recall my mentor, Tom Radcliffe, the Earl of Sussex,
teaching me so long ago. And like a soldier I had dreamed
of being. "Trust the flow of ideas, Edward. Trust life if not
the living, my son. Every man his time will come."

One need the government had at the time was for
pamphlets to counter an illegal flood of propaganda trying to
start a Puritan insurgence against the Anglican Church.

Lead by a prelate named Oliver Pigge, the
clandestine revolutionaries were grinding out incendiary
religious tracts and the government could not catch the
printers, so it ordered counter-propaganda.

In came the pens of Oxford's men, John Lyly,
Thomas Nashe and Robert Greene, issuing such epistles of
prose as 'Pappe with a Hatchett', 'A Fig for My Godson',
and 'Crack Me this Nut'. It would make for great debates
between the talking or barking heads of the day, and many
reeling, drunken heads at the Steelyard, Cellar and Boar's
Head. Back then, printing presses in the basement and
distributors in the dark were the only free exchange of ideas.

The whole affair came to an end when the future
father-in-law of Oxford's oldest daughter Elizabeth, the Earl
of Derby, arrested these dissenters. Here again, 'As You
Like It' recorded it. A character named Oliver Martext made
political points for the Oxford cause.

Lord Oxford was known then as a practicing
playwright, "the very best for comedy", as one reviewer
wrote, Frances Meres in 'Paladia Thamia' (1598), while
George Puttenham complained in 'The Arte of English
Poesie' (1589) that "I know very many gentlemen in the
Court that have written commendably, and suppressed it
again, or else suffered it to be published without their own
names to it: as if it were a discredit for a gentleman to seem

learned. . .of which number is first that noble gentleman Edward Earl of Oxford."

His refusal to publish in his own name what was regarded as the most inspired work of his time, a favorite of the muses since youth, of a perfection sublime, so versed with talents in his circle that he held sway with his own troupe of players, Oxford's Men, then Paul's Boys, and took over the Earl of Warwick's company, performing what later were known as Shake-speare's plays, was common knowledge: He was the mogul leader of rapier wits, champion of tilts. And when the Lord Chamberlain Hunsdon (who was a Howard cousin) lead the English Fleet against the Spanish Armada, and was absent during the '90's, it was the Lord Great Chamberlain, the "great speare" himself who organized that troupe of players and kept them out of jail, if he was not in the Cellar or the Boar's Head or the Steelyard carousing.

While still alive, the four who lead the others and called themselves "the four quills who could prick", would argue over cups of sack and sugar, noting that Oxford was the enemy of small beers. "What talk you to me of living within my bounds? I tell you, none but Asses live within their bounds," said Edward. "This world is transitory; it is made of nothing and it must to nothing. I pray, wherefore his gold laid under our feet in the veins of the earth, but that we should tread upon it, and so consequently tread thrift under our feet? I thank heaven on my knees that have made me an unthrift," he announced as Willy Monox, and brought out his tawny purse to empty it for the barmaid, to pour another "nipataty", and wash the night through. Let fall the staff again! they chimed. "When men know the goodness of the wine, 'tis needless for the host to have a sign," he told his pal, Edmund Spenser. So heated could these nights become that on one, Thom "Moth" Nashe was obliged to quiet down

249

their furors by declaring of friend Willie: he was only "a little fellow. . .who hath one of the best wits in England."

What a joy Oxford's creation became - the common man who replaced the nobleman in fame. "Make but my name thy love, and love that still, and then thou lovest me, for my name is Will."

Such times they had that one of them, Robert Greene, would die on September 3, 1592, of too much Rheinish wine and pickled herring, while another, Christopher Marlowe, by a stab wound in a barroom brawl on May 18, 1593, and the third, Thom Nashe, alone in undated poverty soon after, though he called himself the poet who could count himself most wealthy.

Thus four quills who could prick came to one and that one, I, with all the words at my beck, undone. Thom lived with an acid tongue and iron chin. He died with a sugared word on a grateful lip, not rude. He'd declared himself the lion of truth but as he faded, it was the lamb of love and gratitude. Christopher was defiant, in breath, in stance, in look, and no doubt went as he came, full of popery. Robert laughed and raised his glass and chortled again and cackled at that. But when it came to a turn of the line, none were more my boon. Within so short a time my three most valuable were gone, the four quills shaved to one. I faced literature alone. The sport was done. Words now came to mourn. I cared not for form. What had been comedy was dead. The blackest ink of tragedy lay ahead.

Such sin as this we'll not forgive.
For evil done God lets not live.

"My mind to me a Kingdom is, such perfect joy therein I
     find,
"That it excels all other bliss that world affords or grows by
     kind;

250

"Though much I want which most men have, yet still my
      mind forbids to crave.
"Some have too much yet still do crave, I little have and seek
      no more;
"They are but poor though much they have and I am rich
      with little store.
"They poor, I rich, they beg, I give, they lack, I leave, they
      pine, I live.

"Some weigh their pleasure by their lust, their wisdom by
      their rage or will;
"Their treasure is their only trust, and cloaked craft their
      store of skill;
"But all the pleasure that I find, is to maintain a quiet mind.
"My wealth is health and perfect ease, my conscience clear
      my chief defense;
"I neither seek by bribes to please, nor by desert to breed
      offense.
"Thus do I live, thus will I die, would all the world did so
      well as I."

XXVI

The first performance of 'Hamlet' at court was in February, 1589.

"I give you tonight my latest comedy which I call a tragedy. Its every point will prick you. Its every thrust will pierce you. But who will blood shed? None but I am dead. For this is my tragedy - the likes of which is lifelong comedy to you. May you laugh my parries and thrusts away and I'll accept your swords, your kindest 's'words' of praise for parries and claps for thrusts. Our scene is Elsinore."

The play was set at that very court where his brother-in-law, Sir Peregrine Bertie, Lord Willoughby d'Eresby, was the first English ambassador to attend, *puffy, jowly, huffy, comfy, coughing in his hankie, a vast and infinite man, and much for my sister to handle.* Now at this court of Elizabeth, to see that court again, sat Edward's sister Mary and her husband, *still every bit a force of nature; when he coughed - the world; when he growled - the universe; but when he smiled - a little bit of heaven; his wink - the stars; his grin - the sun; how fortunate my sister!*

The house grew dim, by knowledge of the hour and minute of the twilight turning to dusk, as the windows grew shadows and candles replaced the day. The stage was set, a mirror setting of the audience where sat the queen's court in full array.

Lord Burghley did not smile at Polonius, although he was named Corambus in this version. And when Ophelia drowned, not one eye in the house was dry, for all remembered Anne Cecil - father, husband, daughters, and their queen. When Gertrude laughed she frowned. When Claudius frowned, the queen glanced to where Leicester would have sat were he alive, where now his nephew Essex sat, and did not change expression. When Osiric popped up, so did Christopher Hatton (with a ringing sound). Only Marcellus Bacx, Francisco and Horatio deVere mirrored the expressions on the faces of Hamlet's people, Marcellus, Francisco and Horatio as the dying Hamlet spoke his last words to his cousin Horatio.

It was not an enjoyable evening, nor even a comedy as promised. The scenes were not funny but serious, although the players spoke quickly, running their lines together, which as a delivery was comic. Thus they were able to play the longest of works in the usual performance time, but still an offense to all who came to laugh. The queen stood up.

"What," cried Edward. "Frightened with false fire?"

"Give me some light. Away!" she declared.

"Lights, lights, lights!" bellowed Lord Burghley, very much at a loss in the dark and stroking the tapestries and his beard along the wall before his fingers could find the bell rope to pull. After this first performance, that old fox said, "He made my daughter appear mad." The queen said, "He made me seem lascivious." Robert Cecil said, "He sliced me with a point envenomed." Hatton said, "He held me up as a palpable fop." And others said, "He pointed Leicester to be a poisonous murderer." Leicester, the gypsy of the narrow eyes, the queen's allowed poisoner, of whom was said that if he came to dinner only he got up, was only remembered because the queen would not forget him. *He was there in memory, like a shadow. He was the ghost of ghosts, as all who lived at court were, shadows.* The courtiers whispered. None were satisfied with their portraits.

"Why, let the strucken deer go weep, for some must watch, while some must sleep; thus runs the world away," laughed Edward.

Burghley summed it up. "He played me for a fool." And their conclusion was, "A fool will we play him." On that the queen and court agreed. All bent their heads to the task.

"Strip him of his ascendance. Leave him naked on his barren stage stripped of sword and plate, ragged as a country fool, clothed with nothing but his shameful state, for birds to peck and pick at, only as a man."

When the play was done no hand applauded. The queen made a sign to her oldest advisor, Sir William. "I want this play destroyed. My cousin makes a mockery of us all. And of himself a fool. No performance of this again. Never ever. Every copy shall be put to the fire."

"Yes, your majesty. I would have said the same myself, but as you said it, I said not, though saying - " The act was never done.

The queen cut him short: "Enough said, Pondous."

The queen's cousins, Dyer and Parrot, observed, "Lord Edward is no longer her majesty's allowed fool."

Robert Cecil, in his corner, commented to Edward: "How did you fix the name Laertes on me?"

"Why, when you 'tease' an 'earl' you have 'Laertes'."

"But I never teased you, Edward. It rather seemed you made Laertes more like my brother Thomas."

"Perhaps you did not mean to tease, but you did envy me."

254

"And so you make us one, and fall on me - the point envenomed."

"As we as boys did play at dueling in the maze and hedgerows of Theobalds, it is ever the same."

"Forever."

Horatio cornered him. "You have endangered yourself, cousin."

"Was it so bad?"

"No. You all but brought the house down."

"That bad."

Horatio nodded in silence.

"Would not this, and a forest of feathers - if the rest of my fortunes turn Turk with me - with two Provincial roses on my razed shoes, get me a fellowship in a cry of players, sir?"

"Half a share," Edward's cousin replied. "You might have rhymed."

Edward laughed, and referred to his annual stipend which his queen had ordered the treasury unquestioningly to pay him for his words. "I'll take the ghost's word for a thousand pound. Didst perceive?"

"But your wounds were words, Edward. They can wound with swords. That's the point. End of sentence."

"Then I am dead, Horatio."

"Not so long as you're alive."

"Much longer. O - ever so much longer than that, Horatio. For a dead man living is a living dead man. That's my sentence. I'll go to court no more with plays."

"Good choice."

"I'll play them elsewhere. To the pits, the smoky breath of the multitude. After all, these are the most common commentaries of all the actions of our lives. We'll to Coventry to stage this, the darkest hour of my tale, the storm from which no hope could hope to sail."

255

One of the queen's maids in waiting, a friend of his eldest daughter Elizabeth, approached Edward in a quiet hall of this palace at Hampton Court, under the portrait of the Lord Great Chamberlain himself, where it gazed down on them, robed and dignified, his great dome and receding hairline familiar, his right hand clutching a little book. Such sad, clear eyes and sharp features. In this did immortality reside. It would move from castle to castle to manor to school to gallery and eventually to America over three hundred years, acquiring the name, 'Ashbourne Portrait of Mr. Shakespeare', before it would reach the Folger Shakespeare Library in Washington, D.C., and then be called someone else, as though identity was forever destiny, and this man's destiny was obscurity.

"Lord Oxford, may I have a word?" the maid asked Edward.

"What is your name, my lady?"

"Elizabeth, your lordship. My father is Sir Thomas Trentham of Staffordshire. I want to say I felt your play most deeply. It was - moving."

"I am fortunate you say so. Your feeling gives me new life to touch one as lovely as yourself for which I am deeply touched."

"We might be friends. I love poetry so much."

"And if poetry, why not a poet? We have gone to the heart already, I'll give you that."

"Yes, why not? If I lose mine honor I lose myself."

"If you read not my blemishes in the world's report but trust your heart to find my faults and weaknesses for you, we'll find much to say."

So it was. *Some men and ladies meet toe to toe while others by shoulder to shoulder go.*

Edward took up a life (in 1589) as simple as a monk's in a cell, like his ancestor Sir Aubrey deVere, 3rd

256

Earl of Oxford, who built churches. His acting company, Paul's Boys, which had a reputation of performing to the discerning audiences of the well-born who deplored the caterwauling pit-dwellers in the more common theaters, was disbanded suddenly, and his friends bemoaned it.

When his players presented a Puritan as an Ape there was such controversy that all the Puritans demanded redress, and the humor was gone out of it, Lord Burghley the least amused.

"Tell us, Willie, is it shut down on the queen's disfavor?"

"It is a Puritan wind that blows none well."

"Has her majesty dismissed you, Willie?"

"Certain Puritans have puffed up and breezed me out."

"Are you becalmed at court? Well then, the Boar's Head takes you in! Make this the court of kings in ragamuffin weeds!"

His friend Edmund Spenser lamented his withdrawal from the tavern life into a cell as though deceased. "Our pleasant Willy, Ah! is dead of late:" Further grieving that gentle spirit, "from whose pen large streams of honey and sweet nectar flow."

Said Edward alone in his room to his bed, his chair, his table, his lamp: *So I am banished, who have done no more than write love letters to my queen, love letters every word and dot and I, and to none other, whispered, cried and shouted to her fickle heart, her O so pernicious soul that gathers lovers as the fingers of the hand pick fresh strawberries, innocent strawberries by the dozen, one by one. And who would lie to her, who tasted her hot breath in darkness and her dripping tongue like wet plums dipped in cream beneath the moon alone at midnight.*

What all I was and all I've done, disgraced

For what I am and what I'm known, effaced.

This world, these words, are fruits I've ripened in the orchard of our passion. They are the brief and abstract chronicles of our times. They are my true and faithful testimony, witness to the lies that all about her tell, baptized in the sanctity of our love, made holy in the trust we bear each other till death itself. Now I am banished! The moon can not put out the sun nor she command my silence more completely. What an unfaithful woman. That I see her in every sprite who breathes and yet she expresses faithfulness by unmerciful betrayal! How will she next amuse herself at my poor, wretched and unresolved expense? What's after banishment?

The grave - and for amusement, her order to relieve me of my name. Great gods! cut out my tongue and call me waste upon the trash heap of eternity - a grape in the comedy of love - and do less harm than this! Thence comes it that my name receives a brand. She is corrupt with arrogance, yet I am made to rot. What flaw is this that carves my banished name and feeds my memory a wormy grave upon the wall of ever-lasting shame, from which desire finds no grace to save?

Hunger brought me to this darkened end. She damming, damned me to an obscure place before I knew desire would offend, in pride too proud, unable to efface what we, carefree, began with such renown. Love robbed me of the truth, that shrine to fame, as by the glow and glory of her crown our flaws took air, to my enduring shame. Give me the shadows of a hidden grave to fools who claim their folly makes them brave.

Elizabeth Trentham comforted him as they took horses riding through the park *and the sun danced on the waters and made the shrubs and trees applaud us with a silvery light in the breeze, as rabbits hopped beneath the*

258

brush and forest mites obeyed their pact with nature, while birds made nests and sang in the trees and all about them was for us exclusively.

"Fling away ambition; by that sin fell all the angels. The heavens are just; murder can not be hid. Time is the author of both truth and right. And time will bring this treachery to light," she said, my queen of hearts.

"Vain pomp and glory of this world, I hate it! I feel my heart now opened. O! how wretched is that poor man that hangs on princes' favors!" I told her. I was unconsoled, but well-companioned. More than the heavens themselves was I festooned in fever with her All my miseries were as yesterday's. Tomorrow beckoned ravishment.

XXVII

Because the law made Oxford a ward of the queen's private minister, and the law provided Lord Burghley generously for it, and because Edward never paid that debt incurred by law until obliged to at the age of forty, even when he married his foster-father's daughter, he was perpetually at pains to raise money for his own projects, literature and the theater, behind his father-in-law's back. Such a law as this of course was written to the warder's favor, to deplete the ward's estate at worst, to enrich the Master of the Wards at best.

All his life had passed in debt to his father-in-law, and what he'd received was begged for, and what he'd spent was on theater, literature, the queen's own glory and renaissance, but still the law provided that his Master of the Wards, Sir William, and Lord Leicester by the whim of the queen, would keep control of his wealth. Such was the punishment of the son because his father died.

My father whom I could not call my own,
Whose name was all I had of him, alone.

Fairness owed little to the Earl of Oxford when matters of his estate came up.

"No Ned, you can't complain. After all, I allow you to write. Where all England is silenced, I give you license to speak. You have riches greater than any lands, Ned. You have thoughts," said Elizabeth.

"But Cecil is a commoner bent on being king. He rules all England behind your back! He slanders me with

260

shadows like I was a ghost to myself and dips my flaws in the cold river of praise to freeze my reputation on the shores of weakness. When I resist, he calls me dissolute; when I sip he calls me drunkard. Those who disagree with him he labels slanderous. Free discussion is forbidden in the name of conspiracy, right wings flapping left, so the bird can't fly. Cecilium Regnum is the curse of silence. And the rest is silence. O, o, o, o."

One attempt of Edward's to raise cash was by selling his London home, after the death of his wife, out the back door to a descendant of the 11th Earl of Oxford, William Cornwallis, who bought Fisher's Folly, as it was called, outside London Wall in Bishop's Gate Street opposite Bedlam Gate and Bethlehem Hospital, a priory used for the sick since the thirteenth century, without knowing that its seller was not entitled to sell it.

Lord Burghley heard of Edward's sale and weighed in furiously, letting all who did business with Oxford in the future know that their business was rather with the queen's treasurer, hereafter.

"Let the world understand, Lord Edward has no right to his own money so long as Sir William lives."

What did Oxford do with his brief windfall? Same as always. He befriended friends, his writers, and musicians, the Bassanos. He was known to be more proficient in music as a pastime than many a musician who practiced it as a profession.

What happened in the house Oxford sold, Fisher's Folly which was nearby his other home, Vere House in Oxford Place, when William Cornwallis moved in, has puzzled scholars for four hundred years. Fisher's Folly had been the London residence of indigent literary talents supported by the errant earl. Together they lived and supped and penned their barbs against an ignominious and

261

indifferent world around a communal table. William Cornwallis' wife Anne found some old manuscripts of poems which Edward left when he and his literary knights decamped. She proceeded to copy them into her own book.

The year was 1590. The poems were 'Verses Made by the Earl of Oxford', and the book survived. Included in it were 'Anne Vavasour's Echo' and 'XIX from The Passionate Pilgrim'. That last was printed a decade later by William Jaggard under the name of "W. Shakespeare" and went down in history as written by Shakespeare, credited to Shakespeare and acknowledged as Shakespeare's, though scholars never explained how it came to be written by Oxford first. They simply relabeled it: "of doubtful authenticity".

Thus I say, and thus shall you note, that when a man of means makes mock of mice, how these rodents of wit grow mighty, and the man of means is made a man no more, but is forever reduced to the state of their cheese, for eternity to nibble on. Thus be not surprised: I laughed at the mighty and by them am disguised. They could not daunt me so they damned me. Thus is it, ever: for those who would speak, silence; for truth, lies, and the truth teller's declared the rat.

If homes were cash cows for the strapped earl, 1589 was a year spent milking them on the road, because he was on his own as a widower and homeless. He lived where the spirit took him and slept where the spirits left him.

Oneday he met a young woman of twenty in the road. Her eyes were olive, her figure voluptuous and Italian. She gazed on him with a recognition that brought him to a halt. "You smile, my lordship."

"Do I know you?"

"Since I was born, sir. You danced me on your knee."

"I have not danced since, I know."

262

"You look well, sir knight."

"The look is better with your glance."

"I should be flattered, sir."

Now he found himself interested, and approached the young woman, who was breathing deeply and expanding the stays in her blouse. He sighed and his eyes traveled. "Do you have a name to go with your beauty?"

"I do, and you know it."

Edward pondered her mischeviousness. "Then you're not just a fairy of spring."

"Is that how you took me?"

"Indeed, I took you more for a woman in full bloom."

"And is that how you'd take me now, my lord?"

"Taking is not so sweet as giving, dear mistress. It gives me pleasure to give what is mine by right, knowing I can earn what will only be gained by might."

She drew herself up proudly and her smile was full blossomed. "I know your might, sir. But I see we have my door in sight." She paused.

He looked up. "This is where my friend Baptista Bassano lives."

"And he's my father, no less."

Edward was appalled to recognize Emilia grown up and invited her to accompany him. It would come to this:

"When my love swears that she is made of truth,
"I do believe her, though I know she lies;
"That she might think me some untutor'd youth,
"Unlearned in the world's false subtleties.
"Thus vainly thinking that she thinks me young
"Although she knows my days are past the best,
"Simply I credit her false-speaking tongue;
"On both sides thus is simple truth supprest.
"But wherefore says she not she is unjust?

"And wherefore say not I that I am old?
"O, love's best habit is in seeming trust,
"And age in love loves not to have years told:
"Therefore I lie with her and she with me,
"And in our faults by lies we flattered be."

His father-in-law had assumed responsibility for raising his three daughters, Elizabeth, fourteen, Brigit, five, and Susan, two.

One of his unsold homes was Billesley Hall, located three and a quarter miles from Stratford-upon-Avon, which had been left to him by his grandmother, Elizabeth Trussel, in whose family it had been for four hundred years. In that house is a room that to this day is called Shakespeare's, by the guides who show the tourists where the bard once was. Here, legend and the locals state that 'As You Like It' was written, inspired by its proximity to the Forest of Arden, though the world would have us *not* know who the author and owner was who sat in that house, in that room, to write.

The Trussel family, incidentally, on another branch of its tree, was related to Will Shaxpere of Stratford. Nearby, and located on the banks of the Avon river, was yet another Oxford home, Bilton Hall, also left him by his grandmother. Here he did live, and write poetry without interruption, baptizing him most surely, authentically, geographically, a 'sweet swan of Avon'. It was a place that still stands. A mere one hundred twenty years after Oxford, it was bought by another great writer, Joseph Addison.

As for property, Oxford was to own seventy-five estates in ten counties, sell forty three and buy four in his years of fabulous wealth, sliding down the slippery slope to poverty in the name of good friendship, show business and poetry.

264

Edward had a depleted fortune before he was thirty nine. As a widower who no longer had charge in raising his three daughters, he slipped into the underworld of revelers, drunkards, bohemians between nights of riotous celebration with twits and tops at The Steelyard and The Boar's Head.

Emilia would work a spell on him, to her own dismay and his despair, which neither of them wished. She was so bright in all things reasonable and so alluring where reason could not travel. When he called her, she came. When she nodded, he bowed. Yet twenty years divided them. Though he took her where he traveled and she listened to everything he said, she absorbed him like a sponge and then declared her independence.

What she wanted was marriage. The man who would win that honor was Alphonse Lanier, a soldier, who went to Ireland in military service to the Earl of Essex. Emilia would have a daughter. The baby would die. She would move back to live with her parents in Bishops Gate in her husband's absence. Again she and Edward would meet. The baby was most on her mind.

She confessed to having passed time with one of Edward's writer friends, Thomas Kyd. They met often at the Bassanos where Jeronimo, Andrea and Isabella, her father's brothers and sister, became characters in a popular play on which Kyd was working, 'The Spanish Tragedy'.

"That play is of considerable interest to me," Edward admitted.

"And am I of interest to you?"

"More than plays."

She would yield to him, and they would forget the time and differences between them, and then her grief for her dead baby would end the moment with remembrances of Odillia.

"My love is as a fever, longing still
"For that which longer nurseth the disease;
"Feeding on that which doth preserve the ill,
"Th' uncertain sickly appetite to please.
"My reason, the physician to my love,
"Angry that his prescriptions are not kept,
"Hath left me, and I desperate now approve
"Desire is death, which physic did except.
"Past cure I am, now reason is past care,
"And frantic-mad with evermore unrest;
"My thoughts and my discourse as madmen's are,
"At random from the truth vainly express'd;
"For I have sworn thee fair and thought thee bright,
"Who art as black as hell, as dark as night."

By 1591 he had enough of sack and malt and all the
fast friends of the night. While the queen would have
nothing to do with him, the court was a foul place of intrigue
and ill-feeling, more a nest of insects deserving scorn than
praise.

His thoughts began to turn elsewhere.

"No longer mourn for me when I am dead
"Than you shall hear the surly sullen bell
"Give warning to the world that I am fled
"From this vile world, with vilest worms to dwell.
"Nay, if you read this line, remember not
"The hand that writ it, for I love you so
"That I in your sweet thoughts would be forgot
"If thinking on me then should make you woe.
"O, if, I say, you look upon this verse
"When I, perhaps, compounded am with clay,
"Do not so much as my poor name rehearse,
"But let your love even with my life decay,

"Lest the wise world should look into your moan
"And mock you with me after I am gone."

Edward sealed it up and had the sonnet delivered to Mistress Elizabeth Trentham. *Her response was to come in person and utter a one-syllable reply: "Yes! O - yes, yes! And more yes - forever yes! O, o , o, o."*
They married after July 4, 1591, the queen allowing and not objecting. Priests no longer performed the ceremony, but ministers of the church, who began with, "Dearly beloved, we are gathered here in the sight of God."
The bride assured her husband that now they could together rely on the wealth of her father, a squire of Stoke-on-Trent in Staffordshire, north of Birmingham close to the Scottish border.
Her father gladly assured the groom that he was prepared to be of real support, as the groom had been of real support.
"And how have I helped you, Master Trentham?"
"By the fortune. I'm glad to give you what I acquired from my investments."
"What investments?"
"In estates, my lord, which Sir William Cecil put on the market and sold below value, for immediate cash, cash only."
"He sold estates for cash?"
"For immediate cash, over the years, which depleted the estates of an unnamed knight, as I understand."
"I too understand, Sir Thomas."
"Then we understand each other, Lord Edward. Regarding estates whom no one can identify."
"Thus now these proceeds to their source proceed."
"With a father's love, my lord. My daughter's love, my wife's, and mine."

"Together, father."

"Ay, daughter. And no one else's love, my lord. We're a happy family of three here."

"Though we've a fourth now, husband."

With a smile of bemusement, I slipped into that phase of living in rural modesty and anonymity, the life I long had dreamed of and had finally achieved, in Hackney.

It was in Stoke Newington, in the parish of Stratford-att-Bow, across the first bridge built over the river Lea, on the Shoreditch road north of his old haunts in the artist's quarter, still reasonably close to The Theater and The Curtain.

There are no words to describe what can only be portrayed as bliss - utter bliss, total bliss, eternal bliss - as though the language was made for lowly things by a God indifferent to speech, that when the heavens are reached, all quantity of words must fail us, for we are in the presence (I know not how else to describe it) of that thing divine.

Elizabeth set about making their home, "the very foundation of our commonwealth." There was a hiring of servants in four ranks: land steward, menial, porter (who would also be the watchman), and marshall (who would be in charge of the cooks and buttery).

Edward had his wardrober who nightly heated the bed, put a rug beside it, dressed him with tunic, doublet, stomacher, short and long hose and shoes. A new man was interviewed for the porter:

"You know our custom in a fine home, then?"

"Ay, my lady. I come from the country."

"You will claw not your head or back for a flea, stroke your head for a louse, pick your nose or let it drip, puff your chest, pick your ears, spit too far, laugh too loud, or let your lips drivel, and you shall be for a servant suitable."

268

"Ay, my lady."

"Know you ought else?"

"I know that birch sap drawn in March will serve in summer to remove freckles, my lady."

"And what other country knowledge?"

"Why, we can eat snakes to restore lost youth, my lady. If his lordship requires it."

"You have a store of knowledge, John."

"Ravens' eggs are good for ague, me thinks."

"We expect neither fever or chills, John, but I'll take you on as porter."

There is a bodily change that comes to each when a couple is united. The flowers bloom. The birds sing only for our ear their tune. How strange. How strange. And all the time it was there in reach, unnoticed like a blade of grass, as common as a pebble on the beach. What a miracle was this!

"But do thy worst to steal thyself away,

"For term of life thou art assured mine,

"And life no longer than thy love will stay,

"For it depends upon that love of thine.

"Then need I not to fear the worst of wrongs

"When in the least of them my life hath end;

"I see a better state to me belongs

"Than that which on thy humor doth depend.

"Thou canst not vex me with inconstant mind,

"Since that my life on thy revolt doth lie.

"O, what a happy title do I find,

"Happy to have thy love, happy to die!

"But what's so blessed-fair that fears no blot?

"Thou mayst be false, and yet I know it not."

A girl from the neighbors offered her service as a goose girl.

"Dost thou have feather beds?"

"We do."

"Then thou needst a flock of geese."

"We do."

"And to tend the geese, a girl."

"True."

"For feather beds from flocks of geese need tending, caring and plucking by a proper goose girl, my lady."

The storerooms were provisioned with smoked and cured hams and bacon, fish and salted meat. Apples were pealed and cut in slices, dried in baking ovens and kept on trays for winter eating.

"My lady, I go to market with a gally pot and know where two shillings can fetch a pound of musk sugar."

"You are a good girl, Ursula."

"I'll find parsley for toothache and mint for colic and I'll not complain at pounding garden snails into poltices, if need be."

"Then we shall have thee."

"God bless you, my lady, and your worship," the girl curtsied and her red cheeks like apples glowed.

"So shall I love, supposing thou are true,
"Like a deceived husband; so love's face
"May still seem love to me though altered new,
"Thy looks with me, thy heart in other place.
"For there can live no hatred in thine eye;
"Therefore in that I can not know thy change;
"In many's looks the false heart's history
"Is writ in moods and frowns and wrinkles strange:
"But heaven in thy creation did decree
"That in thy face sweet love should ever dwell;
"Whate'er thy thoughts or thy heart's workings be,
"Thy looks should nothing thence but sweetness tell.

270

"How like Eve's apple doth thy beauty grow
"If thy sweet virtue answer not thy show!"

Elizabeth Trentham deVere, 2nd Countess of Oxford, established King's Place for her lord and king near The Theatre and The Curtain by Bow Bridge across the Lea he crossed so many times, not far outside Bishop's Gate and Old London Wall, in a spirit of peace and bliss. Their home in Hackney on the north side of London, a neighborhood known as one of the city's first suburbs, "the Court end of town", was a short walk from a home belonging to the queen.

Here Edward was seen often in the company of show folk under the assumed name of "Willie", much to the chagrin of his puritanical foster father, who had been his father-in-law, and, as grandfather to his three daughters, remained most visibly in charge of all that could be visible, forever declaring how responsible he was in raising them, and implying how less attentive Edward was to paternal duty. The daughters were not allowed to visit their father's new home. *How he could damn me with faint praise for all eternity's disgrace.*

But Sir William had a grief, for his beloved wife of forty-two years died, and he could not imagine proceeding without her. Walter Raleigh and many others who had dealings with him wrote him, encouraged him, urged him to resume his life, at least the appearance of his life, knowing that in such semblance a habit might return.

King's Place was the site of court held by Henry VIII in 1546, Edward VI in 1549 and Her Majesty Queen Elizabeth in 1583. It had a great balconied corridor one hundred sixty feet long, a parlor, chapel and library, all made of brick that stood four hundred eighty five years, which none of the chancellor's spies could penetrate. Indeed, there were none at court now welcome to this estate.

Burghley was so upset by his son-in-law's remarriage and new-found financial independence that he sued Lord Edward for title to the Oxford ancestral property, Castle Hedingham, in the name of his grand-daughters. It was a fitting possession for a fox who started with nothing but the desire to stand by a king. When Edward conceded it to him without a struggle, the righteous Puritan celebrated with his son, and grand daughters, at an otherwise empty table.

The Cecils had almost become noble - strange outcome for a career that was begun in disdain of the nobility. *They placed their clogs upon the instep of civility, tipping toes toward royal consanguinity.*

In their garden at King's Place, seated together under an apple tree, Edward told his new Elizabeth, "I am betrayed by all but you. My father-in-law, his family, their acquaintance, the court. I'm even forgotten by the queen at her convenience."

Said she: "Though usurpers sway the rule awhile, yet heav'ns are just and time suppresseth wrongs," and she touched his trembling hand. Her fingers, "long, small, white as milk" stitched designs "the shape of bud, bird, branch or berry" as she sat beneath the pear tree with her sewing, and sang "the night bird mute."

The time had come to declare his faith, not in life, but art, and commit his works to the public store, by printing and showing them to all.

"I will be heard. I must be heard. My voice is all I have that's left. And yet I'm silenced by authority."

Elizabeth Trentham stood before her husband in the garden of apricots, almonds, peaches, figs, oranges, lemons and olive trees, where the Antwerp rose with its one hundred

272

eighty petals blossomed under the spreading branches. She gazed with absolute devotion on him.

"Edward, let's live, delighting in obscurity, by truth made whole to give each other courage, of none wanting but love's purity, set free in honor, the joy of every age. Let's turn our backs on all who wished you ill, who took your gifts and bent them to their needs, thankless of your part, while keeping still with lies and edicts, bondaging your deeds. Let's give our faith in all degrees to time and close the door on winter, trusting spring when all that's living blooms in joyous rhyme and truth gives truth the voice in which to sing. Let's trust in truth for which alone you've yearned, by time set free of all your tears have earned."

He asked, "And what about my name?"

"And what about your soul?"

"I've been disgraced in fame."

"You are the father of your Tudor rose, forever true and never lost in shame," she said. Henry Wriothesley was a young man he could take pride in, and did take a lifelong interest in.

"Some glory in their birth, some in their skill,
"Some in their wealth, some in their body's force,
"Some in their garments, though newfangled ill,
"Some in their hawks and hounds, some in their horse;
"And every humor hath his adjunct pleasure,
"Wherein it finds a joy above the rest,
"But these particulars are not my measure;
"All these I better in one general best.
"Thy love is better than high birth to me,
"Richer than wealth, prouder than garments' cost,
"Of more delight than hawks or horses be;
"And having thee, of all men's pride I boast:

273

"Wretched in this alone, that thou mayst take
"All this away and me most wretched make."

    He nodded in his twilight act as the twilight evening
set. She bent and embraced him. This much he knew. "Its
scent's the same despite the truth it knows. A rose by any
name would smell as sweet."

    The girl came running through the garden. "The
house is covered in St. John's wort and fennel, orpin, white
lilies and rue, my lady, to ward off evil spirits."

    "Good girl, Ursula. Now see to the spiced pastes;
light pastilles for burning in every room to sweeten the
scents."

    The girl returned to the house still running.

    "Forget the past, the earldom, pomp and pageant,"
Elizabeth said. "The only kingdom is your word's creation.
Publish to the world. Let all men know it, not just the queen
and court. Assign it any name. No one cares who authors
are and no one cares about them. Whatever name you chose
will do. Like both your sons already orphaned from their
titles, yet living, thriving, safe, alive to be themselves, to
make in honor what was always in them, ignore the name
you use. A name is but a ruse. No matter, as you've said, a
rose by any other smells as sweet. I'd let the world enjoy
your works alone and damned be he who claims them for his
own!"

    It was as though a miracle occurred. From that day
on, he was no longer Edward, nor she Elizabeth Trentham,
but bound by a faith in each other together. They were as
one, and new.

    So, in the village of Stoke Newington, on February
24, 1593, the Countess of Oxford was delivered of a son, and
the serving girl ran from the library with her lordship's copy
of the Geneva Bible to slip under the toes of her countess,

that the child be blessed with holiness, and an old shirt of the earl's was brought to wrap the baby in, that he might inherit all his father's properties and virtues.

"A name - a name - we have to name him!" Edward cried. He was supported in his pacing to and fro by his teenage son Henry Wriothesley, who came to quiet his father and comfort him during the countess' labor. "Henry, the son I love so much, you are my miracle."

"You are mine, father."

"E. Vere is Everyman. We'll name him after you, then, your little brother, Henry, and I'll be twice blessed in my heartfelt joy. Henry, my beloved boy."

Thus was it recorded, on March 31, that Henry deVere was baptised in the parish church, destined to be the 18th Earl of Oxford, Lord Great Chamberlain of England.

"And the sun also rises - even on Everyman!"

XXVIII

In the sweet silence of his final years, as he was clouded by growing deafness, unable to hear the song of birds he could see or brooks he could watch, occurred what presumptively is believed to be the greatest work he ever imagined, coming together in the garden of Edward deVere, in that simple existence outside the circle of the court and its power, living in the country in domestic peace and bliss.

His ancestor Aubrey deVere, the 3rd Earl of Oxford, had become a monk three centuries before and lived in a priory, building churches and leaving monuments to his good name, the first in the family to recuse himself from public life.

Now in his last years, Edward's work was the creation of a device to advance the Protestant Tudor cause against the superior forces of both domestic and European Catholics. It was a final tribute to the queen to whom he was Ever Faithful, and achieved a secret code name.

"Edward, turn your back on the court and queen; they can not serve you now. Leave them to their misery and soar to the heights you've earned. Trust me to be your only Elizabeth and give me all you have. Your words are swords. You are much greater than anyone with whom you only wished to be equal. I shall give you all you need for heaven, glory and eternity!" said his devoted wife. "Let none know, not even her majesty's inner circle, that yours is the creation of this secretive age, a sensation of an invention that becomes our nation's greatest star of all the stars of England, the supreme achievement beside which school children will whine and family dogs wag tails and howl - and the means by which your one true Elizabeth shall transform not just an age, but all men and ladies, great and common, of every type and station, Protestant and Catholic, supporter and dissenter, for Elizabeth Tudor and your own true Elizabeth Trentham - Forever."

"Then shall I stand united with my greatest treasure?"

"Your consort is eternity, Edward."

But he did not willingly publish his poem anonymously. He sent it to the printer's unsigned, with every intent that those who knew would know and those who did not, in time might.

I'll give her majesty the most renowned common man without learning in Protestant English history ever to live to pull the wool over the public's eyes. I'll make everyman feel that 'if he can do it so can I'. He'll do a job unparalleled. He'll serve his Virgin Queen and country and give everyman a chance at a dream where ignorance can reign supreme, reaching the sky without effort, education or anything. He'll make the sweat and solitude of writing seem easy like a piece of cake. I'll invest him with creation itself.

Why, he'll be a miracle child for the Virgin monarch, lit by divine inspiration, the savior of her literature, a holy union well-suited - a virgin for a virgin - where all that I have been is suffering and learning. Who would live only as a man, happy to succeed as a dealer in wool and grain? I'll bring him from the most foul and unlearned village in England. I'll bring him from my grandmother's barn. I'll make him Master William Shakespeare, Gentleman, of Stratford-upon-Avon, Warwickshire! From his Stratford to mine. There's a jest to make this England merry and all her courtiers yammer! I erred when I named Eliza the Virgin

277

Queen. I never treated of her virginity and no man living ever knew it.

So Edward scrambled to substitute another name for the acting job of author just a month before the first publication of somebody's name that was designated to be made by the poem 'Venus and Adonis', which all of London discussed, known to the knowing insiders who lived outside and above it all as "the true and intimate love story of Her Majesty the Queen and his fallen grace, the earl who dreamed he might be King, but awoke", as written by himself.

He thought of his son denied his ancestry, his changeling boy with her majesty, Henry Wriothesley, and yearned to share with him their story, so he wrote a dedication which he dedicated to his royal heir, the Tudor rose, revealing the gift of his mother's and father's love - 'Venus & Adonis' - and signed the dedication, for the first time, by his nom de plume.

TO THE RIGHT HONORABLE
HENRY WRIOTHESLEY
EARL OF SOUTHAMPTON, AND BARON OF
TITCHFIELD

Right Honorable,

I know not how I shall offend in dedicating my unpolished lines to your Lordship, nor how the world will censure me for choosing so strong a prop to support so weak a burden; only, if your Honor seem but pleased, I account myself highly praised, and vow to take advantage of all idle hours, till I have honored you with some graver labor. But if the first heir of my invention prove deformed, I shall be sorry it had so noble a godfather, and never after ear so barren a land, for fear it yield me still so bad a harvest. I leave it to

278

your honorable survey, and your Honor to your heart's content, which I wish may always answer your own wish and the world's hopeful expectation.

Your Honor's in all duty.
WILLIAM SHAKESPEARE

"Wherever did you find that name?" Edward's countess Elizabeth asked him.

"O, it was given me once, long ago, when I was young. How is of no importance now."

At first he planned for Christopher Marlowe, one of the university wits occupying rooms in his literary stable, the Savoy in London, to take credit for the work which he'd sent to the printer's on April 18, 1593, but only four weeks later, in May, Marlowe was murdered in a barroom at Deptford, which brought an end to that plan before its publication.

Besides, he might have been believed the author, given his mighty line. I'd rather a straw man in my place, who never wrote or read a word, whose learning all but fools would decline, and skill in wit left not a trace.

Edward had no other author in mind for such a personal, poetic, and pointed work. This was not just the tale of his love with the queen, it was their kingdom and destiny and his tribute to Titian's masterpiece he gave. Also, it was a challenge, just as he'd done in 'Dan Bartholomew of Bathe', daring her majesty to admit what was, to accept what is, to honor the truth they lived, and celebrate what might be.

The printer of 'Venus' was Richard Field. He'd done books for Lord Oxford for some years, starting as an apprentice in 1579 with a book of John Calvin's sermons translated by Edward's Uncle Arthur, and in 1589 reprints of the anthology, 'The Arte of English Poesy'. Field was a Stratford man.

Now we see in the smoky, two hundred thousand population of London, the arrival of another Stratford lad, by name of Will. This wasn't the countryside that Will of Stratford knew, where English was spoken with such an accent that those from Warwickshire needed translators to make themselves understood. And where does Will find a job sweeping out as he wanders the central marketplace of Saint Paul's Churchyard in London? He hears a Warwickshire voice and accent calling out, "Printed books for sale!" under a sign he recognizes. Where in the coming summer of 1593, in that mad scramble to name anyone with a name to be the name that's named, does this lad find work? Right there in the print shop, leaning on his broom. And with a little stretch of the imagination, the lord whose "will shakes speares" finds William Shax-pyre burning to glory in new spelling.

Toward the print shop with Edward comes Audrey, the young lady who for many years has carried his foul scripts to her father, the scrivener Ralph Crane, for copying, and then taken his neatly transcribed texts to the printer. She has learned a lot of banter and nervy answers to outrageous voices in the streets and fancies herself somewhat of a chatty lass herself, whom no man dares overcome. Many times Audrey ran for Lord Edward. She is lively and bawdy, much inclined to talk when she ought better to listen, to going out when she ought better to stay in, to laughing loudly when she ought better to smile quietly, and even inclined to lifting her skirts when it is better advised that she lower them. (The texts Audrey delivered for Lord Edward to her father and then to the printer in recent times included 'Twelfth Night', 'The Merry Wives of Windsor', 'Hamlet' and three other plays copied by Master Crane, so she knew her duty.) As they near the print shop in Paul's Churchyard, Audrey says to Lord Edward:

"Here comes the man you mean."

"It is meat and drink to me," says Edward, "to see a clown by my troth." Edward is sanguine and jolly, a very Falstaff of merriment. "We that have good wits have much to answer for. We shall be flouting, we can not hold."

"Good ev'n, Audrey," says William.

"And good ev'n, William," says Audrey.

"And good ev'n to you sir," says William.

"Good even gentle friend. Cover thy head, cover thy head. Nay, prithee be covered." For Will is at a loss to remove his cap and bow to the Lord Great Chamberlain. "How old are you, friend?"

"Five and twenty, sir."

"A ripe age. Is thy name William?"

"William, sir."

"A fair name. Wast born i' th' forest here?" (Of Arden in Warwickshire, which name is on the printer's sign outside Field's shop, telling prospective customers what region he hails from).

"Ay, sir, I thank god."

"'Thank god'? A good answer. Art rich?"

"Fair, sir, so so."

"'So so' is good, very good, very excellent good; and yet it is not, it is but so so. Art thou wise?" asks the merry earl.

"Ay, sir, I have a pretty wit."

"Why thou sayst well. I do now remember a saying, 'The fool doth think he is wise, but the wise man knows himself to be a fool.' The heathen philosopher, when he had a desire to eat a grape, would open his lips when he put it into his mouth, meaning thereby that grapes were made to eat and lips to open. You do love this maid?"

"I do, sir."

"And trust her?"

281

"Aye, sir."

"And this work you do?"

"Indeed."

"Give me your hand. Art thou learned?"

"No, sir."

"Then learn this of love: to have is to love; for it is a figure in rhetoric that drink, being poured out of a cup into a glass, by filling the one doeth empty the other; for all your writers do consent that *ipse* is he. Now, you are not *ipse*, for I am he."

"Which he, sir?"

"Come hither, William. Hold up your head; come," says the earl.

"Come on, sirrah," says his lady companion. "Hold up your head; answer your master, be not afraid."

"William," says the earl. "How many numbers is in nouns?"

"Two," William answers.

"Truly, I thought there had been one number more," says the would-be lady. "Because they say, 'od's nouns.'"

"Peace your tattlings," the earl admonishes. "What is 'fair', William?"

"Pulcher," gulps William.

"Polecats!" cries Audrey. "There are fairer things than polecats, sure."

"You are a very simplicity, 'oman," the earl declares to the wordy girl. "I pray you peace. What is 'lapis' William?"

"A stone," he answers.

"And what is 'a stone', William?"

"A pebble."

"No," says the earl. "It is 'lapis'. I pray you remember in your prain."

"Lapis."

"That is a good William," the earl declares. "What is he, William, that does lend articles?" Now the earl grows red-cheeked.

"Articles are borrowed of the pronoun, and be thus declined: 'Singulareter, nominativo, hic, haec, hoc.'"

The earl lectures: "'Nominativo, hig, hag, hog.' Pray you mark: 'Genitivo, hujus.' Well, what is your accusative case?"

William labors to find his answer, wrinkling his nose up with his cap. "Accusativo, hinc."

The earl is pushed to the fringe of patience. "I pray you, have your remembrance, child: 'accusativo, hung, hang, hog.'"

Audrey flashes enlightenment and leaps in: "'Hang-hog' is Latin for bacon, I warrant you."

The earl endeavors to stifle her: "Leave your prables, 'oman. What is the focative case, William?"

William positively croons like a crow and rolls his eyes at this one. "'O, vocativo, O.'"

The earl says: "Remember, William, focativo is 'caret'."

Audrey blushes on all these focatives and declares: "And that's a good root."

The earl orders her: "'Oman, forbear."

She lowers her head in disgraced submission and mumbles, "Peace."

Now the earl draws himself up, proud: "What is your genitive case plural, William?"

But William has no idea of the answer. "Genitive case?" he asks, lost.

"Ay," the earl replies.

William takes a shot at the answer: "Genitivo, 'horum, harum, horum.'"

283

The bawdy girl is wise to that answer, looks up and takes it personally: "Vengeance of Jenny's case! fie on her! Never name her, child, if she be a whore."

The earl attempts to silence Audrey. "For shame, 'oman."

But she is on her high horse lecturing now: "You do ill to teach the child such words." She looks around for an audience of lectors: "He teaches him to hick and to hack, which they'll do fast enough of themselves, and to call 'horum'. Fie upon you!"

The earl beats her back like a swarm of hornets. Now he chimes to all around them: "He sir, that must marry this woman (which is to say, have this work which she has brought you here a hundred times - a thousand times a thousand lines of which she is the bearer that I begot, brought forth and gave to her, that she must give to you! Thus is she midwife to a bastard if she be not married, but mother to an heir if she be wed to these words, these texts, that are mine brought to you for setting into print that all the world receives! By which I am eclipsed. As in eclipse is *ipse*, so in *ipse* am I.) Therefore, you clown, abandon (which is in the vulgar, leave) the society (which in the boorish is, company) of this female (which on the common is, woman), which together is, abandon the society of this female (of this printer, this world, this most vile text!), or, clown, thou perishest; or, to thy better understanding diest, or, to wit, I kill thee, make thee away, translate thy life into death, thy liberty into bondage. I will deal in poison with thee, or in bastinado, or in steel; I will bandy with thee in faction; I will o'er run thee with policy; I will kill thee a hundred fifty ways. Therefore, tremble and depart." So changed the voice of the earl from quiet to riot, from pensive to offensive, that he doubled over in coughing and his arms shook.

"Do, good William," says Audrey to hush things up.

284

"God rest you, merry sir," says William, and flees the wrathful earl, leaving him alone with Audrey before the printer's shop, recovering from his coughing spasm and rage. Between cough and laugh, the earl is shouting, "What is the focative case, William?"

Later, recovered: "Be ever mindful, Audrey, of this mystery I created by my disappearance from history, that it was meant to be an illusion, just as any theatrical work, more living than Hamlet or Falstaff. The thesis has grown great that I gave the stage a human being to encompass the ages, to whom I gave the power of creation itself, and spelled that figure from an unknown countryman with unrecorded allegiances, to take the role of a talent in the service of the queen, of England, of the Protestant movement, my greatest literary device. Surely I valued my creation more than life for myself. I was a veritable Prospero at giving the Church of England one of its greatest names and, in the process, becoming one of its first to die for the cause unknown. That cause was to defeat the Catholics. No wonder the great deception deceives: unquestioned by the world at large; that is to say, the vast and vastly ignorant. Forget what I've told you, Audrey. I can not but bring you ill."

The pleasure of this spiritual act of personal sacrifice was humility. For it is written that nothing fails like success. Also suggested: that nothing succeeds like failure. What greater validation than to be a philosopher of reality. As time for me ran out, I replaced a material world of great estates with an even greater world of the spirit, an estate of the mind: Ideas, declared our English lord in his private book. And his estates included ownership of Covent Garden.

This note is entered in the golden book, dated, *May, 1593: Now take a copy of our tale of love since lost, our 'Venus & Adonis' to her majesty. Report that I have given her the child she desired, the miracle invention of our wills.*

It's our creation that creates, though I've no gift to make him live, a player on my stage; I give him life itself to make for others. Of all we can possess, here hold the key, the fire and the fabric of her grace's dreams. So he is me, and what I am is he. Mark this: the sun sets on her hapless earl but rises on her new-born will. Now see her will shake spears and, so, too, does his. Speak nevermore of mine for he's for her forever divine.

The poem was published four months later. Beside it in the golden book Edward wrote, *Autumn, 1593: Leaves fell. I too.* And then: *I am what I am. It remained important in the ruling vision that any fool be foolish, or that those in the know seem knowing. Hence, the greatest hero's obscurity was a starting point and essential to the power with which he rallied, something no noble could achieve without being deemed as just - more privileged, static, ungiving, grabbing, dynastic, lord of fluff and stuff under which the people lived in Catholic times. I found a monkey and made an Ape.*

I found a fool to play the fool and all he fooled were fools - of which more frolicked than I fathomed. He has to be unknown and unknowing in the deed he is to do.

Some go knowing into their grave unknown.

How much the stage distracted, amused, instructed, persuaded and moved her majesty's subjects to a felicity she most devoutly wished, and how mighty it could be, more than her right arm to lead them. The stage was her greatest battlefield. Her soldiers were its words.

Because it was safer to disguise the truth for the unknowing than to risk it exposed entirely in the hands of the unwilling, all the soldiers I had were words. Words. And they did not serve to save me. For I had found my place in the garden of true delights - antiquity.

286

So Edward wrote of kings and queens and courts, of lords and ladies and intrigue, from his place of writing under a tree in the garden of his home, an ordinary, common tree of the sun, seeing a wood for sure which he named "a Ver" (to claim).

Then he wrote himself out and lay his pen down on the desk brought to him from Castle Hedingham by the old retainer of his youth, Robin Christmas, who placed the table in the garden for him beneath his apple tree, and reminded him of those days of innocent childhood when he had written and studied upon it.

"We made this table for you from an oak taken at the Forest of Essex, your lordship, upon your father's command."

"Yes, yes, I recall it."

"Your father, the good earl, said it would be with you always. As Lord Burghley has ordered the old furnishings removed, we undertook to bring you this piece, from all of us who served your father in the days of your time at Hedingham, to remember your father, and those of us."

"I remember," said Edward, and stood straight, though his bad leg denied him perfection. "I remember, good Robin." His finger brushed the surface of the table. "See where that boy of times gone by has marked his initials with his pen knife, my friend, here on the edge of the surface?"

"I see it, your lordship," said the dear servant.

A tear seeped from Edward's eye to his cheek which he could not conceal, so he allowed the tear to be part of him.

"We thank your lordship for all you have done for us," the old retainer bowed.

"It was my honor," said Edward.

287

Now, alone in his garden, he put his quill down. A silence filled him, and the song of the birds was gone, and the movement of the breeze in the leaves was stilled as a hush fell upon everything he saw, and for a moment in the elegant melancholy of twilight, he was embraced by the silence and breathless.

"My fathers, the earls of Oxford, for five centuries stood. . shadows and stillness made their mark. 'Someday,' my father said, 'When you lay down your sword on Essex wood, you'll smile at death, and meet this shade of truth in ghostly hood.'"

He laid his hands upon the table and wept, but did not take up his pen.

XXIX

"What do you write, my lord?"
"Just O's. Just O's."
"I think they are not round, my lord."
"They're round. O, round."
"I think they're tears, my lord. Just tears."
"Can you be sure they're just?"
"O, tears, O, dear."
"Now I die, killed by my enemy, the lie."

Robert Cecil, brother-in-law, with whom Edward was raised as a foster-brother, since grown great as Principal Secretary to the queen and soon to be elevated to the nobility as Lord Salisbury, sat in his study with his feet raised on a pillow and his hunch back wedged against the corner, reading a letter from E.Ver, the Earl of Oxford, seeking support for his interests, which he was not destined to receive despite his attempt at goodwill between them. First Edward sought the governorship of Jersey. Then he asked for the Presidency of the Isle of Wright. Finally, he solicited an interest in some tin mines, ever hungry to attain his own fortune in metal, to be on his own feet, stable, secure, to stand tall and proud by his own hand and metal.

"Though I am not splenetive and rash, yet have I in me something dangerous, which let thy wisdom fear. Hold off thy hand. I loved you ever," Edward wrote.

But true to the shadows, Robert Cecil did not even bother to answer this letter. He threw all record of it away, into the fire, a busy minister at the royal court, and gave it no more thought. But another letter did survive:

"For truth is truth, though never so old, and time can not make that false which once was true."

Robert pictured the Countess of Oxford, his sister walking through the Palace of Hampton Court from the three-room apartment generously granted her husband due to his position, seeking her husband who was with the queen, decked out in her newest finery with rosemary in her hair (to remember her state), pansies in her hands (to help her think), and fennel (to give her the strength to see), as she offered all the men columbines at court (the flower of cuckolds), while under the hem of her long skirt, she was barefoot and lost.

Be funny, be witty, be nimble, be quick, always jump over the candlestick, and never be sure you can't lose your head, because there are others all around (with high stakes at risk losing theirs) who are dead.

Thundering hooves were heard on the Hackney road, crossing the Bow Bridge, then in the yard at King's Place, and boots on the entry floors and striding the length of the long hall to the library where the Earl of Oxford was beside a fireplace reading. His legs were covered by a blanket. A cane leaned against his chair. He looked up and recognized the young man with the blue gray eyes wrapped in a soldier's coat with buff leather and gabardine over the cloak lined with fur and a brimless Monmouth cap. The young man was breathless.

"Father!"

"There, there now, take off your cap, Henry," the earl said, and smiled at the Earl of Southampton, who did as bid and pushed back his long hair with his fingers. "Be seated."

"Why did you name me, father, in your book?"

"In 'Venus'? A rousing tale to heat the blood, Henry." Edward smiled.

290

"But you identified me."

"I cherish you."

"To what end, father?"

"To move the queen, to keep her promise - "

"I don't care about her promise, old witch!"

" - to make you heir and king."

"Father, you still trust her. I don't. None do. No one trusts her."

"I have no choice but to trust. That trust I keep, son."

"Is she inclined?"

"If any can persuade her."

"Father, surely you know reason doesn't move her, nor sound argument. She's the laughingstock of everyone at court, thinking herself young and beautiful - the crow! She hears the wind, the nag."

"Now curb yourself. Remember whom you serve. There's little mercy but in loving eyes."

"She loved none but herself and lost that too. A hag, a leafless branch who scratches 'gainst the windowpane. I have no reason to attend her mumblings."

"I'd have her know the truth, Henry. That's all there is to know and do - the truth."

"She honors nothing more than nothing, father. What a crow she is, weighed down in silken finery and jewels enough to sink a ship. Her face's become a mask of paste. That smile, that hideous, evil grimace foretells death. I'll bet she dreams of all the men she's killed. How many is it, father? The hag slept with everyone before she ordered them off with their heads, I'll swear. To press her endangers all."

"Do you desire the crown?"

"What I desire counts for little. What I can do to serve the good is everything. I'd wear the crown in honor if it was gained through honor. Now Lord Burghley wants my faith in marriage to - "

"Elizabeth deVere, his grand daughter."

"My sister! Father, is he daft?"

"More cunning than you dream, son."

"But he knows who my father is, who her father is - "

"He knows much more than apples on the tree, Henry. Who your father is you know, and he knows well who I am. Who her father is you don't know."

"She is my sister!"

"Lord Burghley is her father. In my absence on the continent Sir William Cecil feared for the sanity of his daughter, Anne, with whom I'd never slept. He was and is a vulpine man. So, to secure his progeny in a high estate, he got his own child with child, and she is my daughter Elizabeth, whom I cherish as though she were my own. I have come by love the hard way, and learned more of her and life in knowing her than all the rumors could provide. Elizabeth is my daughter as much as if she were my flesh. We are not any of us whom we seem to be."

"I want no part of this. Ugly, feckless, twisted, iniquitous spirits. Father, there's an evil in these alliances."

"In what we do the force of love is present. If love was life, we would live forever. I bid you, follow love. That is more than life."

"I confess, I don't love Elizabeth, father, as a man should love, though I honor her. I respect her. I think of her as my sister."

"Let that be your answer then."

"Why would Lord Burghley engineer this? Place me in such conflict?"

"Because he knows, if you accept, his daughter's daughter will be married to our sovereign's heir, and he would press your coronation. Failing that, if you decline, the law entitles him five thousand pounds repair, for breach of promise, and he'll move on that."

"I'm not afraid of him."

"But caution, Henry. Be cautious or be dead."

"You look for truth, you talk of truth, but who dies for truth? None die for truth but truth's ambassadors. Truth dies, and gives life up to lies."

"Be wary of him, Henry. Fear is not the measure of valor, but sober rectitude."

"I have met someone else I love, father. She's greater than the crown. That's all I know. She is a kingdom in a glance."

"Does she love you?"

"More than the sweetest day of spring, she does, though she was born a Catholic, my Earl of Essex's cousin and maid of honor to her majesty."

"But not yet baptized."

"What do you mean? Of course she is."

"Still, has no name yet."

"Why, it's Elizabeth Vernon, father."

"Ay! A maid, a name, a kingdom next. Now she's christened 'beloved'."

"She's sanctified in our devotion. Her majesty wouldn't give a fig for us."

"Then I encourage you, for Catholics and Protestants have no differences that politics can't decide, and politics will pass. A love of Jesus unites all in the end. Remember who your mother is, and honor her. But be wary of her. You do not need look farther than the 2nd Earl of Southampton to make the name for caution. Who involved himself against her, in the Ridolfi Plot, and was beheaded for it? You want a better fate. I trust you, Henry, with good judgment, stamp of honor."

"Thank you, father."

The porter brought wood for the fire in. He laid it on and waited with a muttering, "M'lord?"

They turned their attention to him and he inquired of Henry's horse, if he intended to stay the night.

"No, my horse will leave tonight, and I on him!"

The porter continued in his stammer. Did he require accompaniment on the road to defend against its dangers, then?

"God forbid! I am a soldier!"

The porter nodded and muttered something about directing his link boys to their beds. They would have carried torches to light the road.

"Father, I've attended the theater often of late."

"I'm satisfied."

"And other matters. My friends, Sir Henry and Sir Charles Danvers fought a man named Long. Sir Henry shot him when he was fighting Sir Charles, then leapt between them and finished Long off with a dagger."

"Your part in this?"

"I hid them, Sir Henry and Sir Charles and, under cover of a hunting party, helped them flee to the port of Southampton where they made their escape to France. John Florio, my tutor, and my barber kept the sheriff at bay with his search warrant and threatened to drown him till all was safe."

"And you?"

"It was nothing. Safe too."

"It was dangerous."

"Am I afraid of danger? You were a soldier, and how many generations before you? Now I'm a soldier like you!"

Edward changed to a subject more to his liking. "Look what I'm writing, Henry. Would you care to hear?"

"Yes, father, proudly yes."

"I'm making old plays new and summing thoughts up. Where before I dealt in shadows, now I know their substance. You, together, are my living voice, and what you do are my words. The only price to pay is my own. To make dreams real, I must transcend myself and take on such a form as some might think transparent, of a likelihood, a truth."

"That's how you live, like a ghost?"

"I've found the secret of true happiness. My body is not able. I am wracked with pain, but joy is not transferred, only shared. In having this, I've come to pity everyone who's lived, who went to court, who clawed or hacked or grasped for greed or gain, the untrained torrents of ambition. They have not learned that sharing's everything. Go be my agent to the court and queen. There is a season and a time to every purpose under heaven. Look, here: 'If music be the food of love, play on.'"

"I honor you more than all people, father."

"And I you, son."

"Your counsel is a calmant," said Henry.

"'He seeks wisdom but is unwise.'" Edward laughed, but continued. "One thing more I have to tell you. The queen your mother is my mother too."

"Her body?"

"In the flesh."

"Most foul. What abomination!"

"'Tis a ghostly malice paid for by all the acts of life."

"How can you countenance it?"

"In shame. It came with the night and unawares of danger I allowed my innocence to guide me. Desire lead where reason was not heard."

"O, poor father, what pity I have for you."

"That's pity's gain. So even from this wanton act, some benefit in pain."

"How sad she is, truly, the mother of us all."

"Our fate rides as a ship upon her sea."

Within the year, the Earl of Oxford published again, this time a poem called 'The Rape of Lucrece':

TO THE RIGHT HONORABLE
HENRY WRIOTHESLEY
EARL OF SOUTHAMPTON, AND BARON OF
TITCHFIELD

The love I dedicate to your Lordship is without end; whereof this pamphlet without beginning is but a superfluous moiety. The warrant I have of your honorable disposition, not the worth of my untutored lines, makes it assured of acceptance. What I have done is yours; what I have to do is yours; being part in all I have, devoted yours. Were my worth greater, my duty would show greater; meantime, as it is, it is bound to your Lordship, to whom I wish long life still lengthened with all happiness.

Your Lordship's in all duty.
WILLIAM SHAKESPEARE

The Earl of Southampton then married without the queen's approval, and she banished him from court, and her maid of honor forever, refusing him the ceremonies intended to invest him with such honors as the Knight of the Garter, which were befitting an heir and future king, and were reserved only to the family and most favored of her majesty.

Henry Wriothesley joined his friend Robert Devereux, Earl of Essex, in military service in Ireland, then Cadiz, Spain, determined to be a soldier to the credit of England, a husband and a father. His wife remained devoted and faithful to him only, writing him almost daily, "My dear lord and only joy." She never looked back on her days at court in regret, but forward to long life with her husband, two daughters and a son.

296

Picture, in 1595, a writer so positioned that he can carry out numerous commissions. He is "crammed with obligations".

Now, his oldest daughter, Elizabeth, is approached and courted by England's richest man, William Stanley, 6th Earl of Derby; who's also known to write plays for the common public, and for his utter devotion to Edward's oldest daughter. Indeed, theirs is a love of the heart. He came by his title and riches when his elder brother, Fernando, died suddenly. He came by Elizabeth deVere as luckily.

Will Stanley was able unopposed to press his suit to the only one he ever loved, Elizabeth deVere, who as truly loved him, for all the world so knew it. Hence she became on January 26, 1595, the wealthiest countess in the kingdom, much blessed by "I her father".

And Pondous could do nothing!

The wedding at Greenwich was one of pomp in the presence of the queen and court, "with great solemnity and triumph." From an old book of Edward's, rewritten and performed for the occasion, the two Wills laughed as they worked on its revision.

"Will Stanley and Sweet Will, a willing pair of S's!" laughed Edward. They both laughed. "The lunatic, the lover and the poet are of imagination all compact: One sees more devils than vast hell can hold; that is the madman: the lover, all as frantic, sees Helen's beauty in a brow of Egypt: the poet's eye, in a fine frenzy rolling, doth glance from heaven to earth, from earth to heaven and, as imagination bodies forth the forms of things unknown, the poet's pen turns them to shapes, and gives to airy nothing a local habitation and a name. Such tricks hath strong imagination, that, if it would but apprehend some joy, it comprehends some bringer of that joy; or in the night, imagining some fear, how easy is a bush supposed a bear?"

      "Let's write that in. Here, write that in, Ned."

      "What?"

      "What you said."

      "What did I say?"

      "You said it. Here, now, write it."

      "I wasn't listening. Did you catch it?"

      "Yes, yes!"

      "Then you write it."

      "Truly, what a foolishness this is."

      "It has its place."

      Finished in time, cast assembled and rehearsed, with Will Kemp engaged to provide a comic presence, it was presented as 'A Midsummer Night's Dream'.

      As to Henry Wriothesley, 3rd Earl of Southampton, in 1595, he took his father Edward's advice, looking for an heir to an heir.

      "When forty winters shall besiege thy brow

      "And dig deep trenches in thy beauty's field,

      "Thy youth's proud livery, so gazed on now,

      "Will be a tottered weed of small worth held:

      "Then being asked where all thy beauty lies,

      "Where all the treasure of thy lusty days,

      "To say within thine own deep-sunken eyes

      "Were an all-eating shame and thriftless praise.

      "How much more praise deserved thy beauty's use

      "If thou couldst answer, 'This fair child of mine

      "Shall sum my court and make my old excuse,'

      "Proving his beauty by succession thine.

      "This were to be new made when thou art old

      "And see thy blood warm when thou feel'st it cold."

Henry was tall, and the epitome of 'The Courtier', like his father, which gave the queen even more reason to reject him, a reminder of her own youth's passage, which none can ever reclaim.

When he offered to assist her in mounting a horse she spurned him for the last time. It was clear that Elizabeth would recognize no love or heir of her own doing ever again in her life.

By ignoring what she had done, she could claim she had not done it, and thus anticipate someday doing again, as though for the first time, what could never be undone.

It was Colonel Sir William Stanley "at camp" who received this letter: "Lord Southampton has married Mistress Vernon, whom he has got with child. Maids of the Court go scarce twenty weeks with child after they are married, and every man has liberty of conscience to play the knave."

But this Elizabeth was so loyal to her Henry that even when the queen banished her from court forever, he proved devoted and faithful to her for life, and she bore their family proudly. The queen, his mother, forgave him eventually for marrying her maid of honor without permission, but she never forgave him for his love.

"I know the best land is the land well-tilled. I know the best mate is the mate well-stilled," the saying went.

But Edward was not silenced. In his golden book, said he, *Her majesty could not forgive who loved, who could not love herself. She could not love what she most loved. To love would be to lose, and losing, love no more, and so forgiving was not given. She was, of all who live a lonely life, the loneliest of all.*

I grieve that your natural sisters do not know you, that your natural mother will not grace you, that you are denied all family that by birth and blood are yours, and yet I celebrate that you, on your own, a family made, a man most gracious and a state most brave. My son, my son, what I have lost, and yet have won!

In the spring of 1598, Sir William Cecil, Lord Burghley, Chancellor of the Exchequer, achieved his triumphant apogee of policy and career. He moved the Privy Council to vote to "pluck down" every theater in London, to end the reign of the low and licentious acting rabble who entertained the crowds and diverted her majesty from great affairs of state.

At issue was mockery, and derisive declarations describing Puritans as monkeys. Also, there were other offenses.

In this one great vote, Burghley saw to the condemnation of a play called 'Isle of Dogs', confiscation of every copy existent, destruction and burning of the same, including all other works by its author, Thomas Nashe. In this he achieved complete success. That Nashe was a boonfellow of Oxford's he noted.

For 'Isle of Dogs' was a play about playwrights and politicos, and foremost among its representations was that tale it told of a most connected figure in the governing world who also wrote of his experiences at court, and portrayed all other contemporary creatures of their regal world, in acid and spice, as Apes with Apish ways, the queen and her maids as nymphs and fairies, making Diana into Titania, featuring such personages as the Earl of Leicester, Sir Christopher Hatton, Sir Philip Sidney, the Duc of Alencon, brother to the King of France, as a creature named Bottom, and even himself, Lord Burghley, including his renowned precepts, to the amusement and laughter of some, and the profit of strangers who went to the theater pits without baths or clothes or anything, to hear that it "is better to have a full purse than a fine frock," which precept he preferred to keep to himself, and share with his family only. Theatre goers

300

were the unlearned rabble whom Cecil despised, preferring to keep them ignorant and ruled as he advised.

But more dangerous to the realm was that 'Isle of Dogs' insinuated a scandal concerning a monarch, a courtier and a bastard child born to the realm which gave the lie to a policy of state, that a queen could be a virgin.

And so the play was destroyed.

With this decision, the Privy Council concluded that not only would its author, Thomas Nashe, be prevented ever again from exhibiting his writing, but that his patron, also, would be silenced. Sir William at last had the goods he sought so long against his son-in-law whom now he could bring to a crashing silence and defeat. While Edward was not locked up, Nashe was enprisoned in the Fleet.

Said the queen's principal secretary of his son-in-law: "He has a thousand pounds per annum. His work's well-known. His hand shall be undone and that shall go unknown."

And others of his council concurred. Once they condemned him, they talked like him.

"For who can sign the sunrise but the clouds that turn the gold to gray?"

"A clear light has no shade. A bright day has no cloud. A true word is the orphan of a phrase."

"Well-known are his words, then."

"The better for not knowing who has said them. Let this specter be a ghost henceforth to walk the earth until he ends his days."

"Authority's a fist best gloved."

"He speaks for England, not one man, so now let England speak for him, and speak as him, not as himself, and he will be a phantom for eternity."

Sir William, aghast, amazed and aflutter, could not write it down fast enough. "My precepts - O! my ducats!"

Then Robert Cecil, Sir William's son, said, "and thus I clothe my naked villainy with odds and ends stolen forth of holy writ, and seem a saint when most I play the devil."

On hearing this verdict of his father-in-law, the Privy Council and the government against him, Lord Edward bowed his head. "Here I stand, your slave, a poor, infirm, weak and despised old man. I am Oxford no more, nor any other, an O without a figure, a man more sinned against than sinning."

The council rose and was dismissed. Members stood in the hall outside and chatted. The Earl of Oxford walked silently past them. He nodded to them.

"Good even', my lord."

"Good even', friend. Some say I knew you once. And so I believed I did. But some in time will say, I never knew you once."

They nodded in agreement, "Not ever."

In the time of both the Cecils, father and son, as Francis Bacon revealed: "able men were by design and on purpose suppressed."

"Yes, yes, 'tis true."

"'Tis sad, 'tis true, but sadly truly is."

"That's true."

"That's sad."

So the courtly caterpillars chatted, evolving the language of bureaucracy, in the corridors where Edward passed.

Lord Burghley went home and wrote his will, eighteen pages of detail, without another mention of the lord whose name and nobility and family estates and father's death had served to provide him with a title and fortune of his own, and heirs to the House of Cecil. He left fifteen thousand pounds worth of silver plate, and no debt.

Then even he, the Great Burghley, pulled the curtain in his bed and died.

But the "Ruling of Silence" by the Privy Council stood, controlled by Cecil's son Robert, who replaced his father as the queen's Principal Secretary, against the likes of Edward for good.

Sir William was buried. "No trophy, sword or armorial hatchments were placed over his bones. No noble rite nor formal ostentation was observed at his internment." Though he had his name on the monument in Westminster Abbey; his corpse was hauled up river to be buried alone.

Now picture Elizabeth deVere Stanley, Countess of Derby, wearing a locket portrait round her neck of her Uncle Robert Cecil who raised her, and of the things about her father which she was wordless to say, and speechless with feeling before her father, quivering to betray. Picture her uttering nothing, for she knows not where to begin, or how, or to whom, knowing what her father knows, and who her father is, and whom her father hates, which father that is, and what her uncle knows, and whom he loathes.

As Edward assures the Stanleys at their home in London's Cannon Row, after a sumptuous meal and seated before the fire, raising his glass for the last sip of claret before they turn in, his daughter (in name only) listens but hesitates.

"With you I have found comfort, Will, and my daughter has found love," Edward says and turns to her.

"Whoever hath her wish, thou has thy Will,

"And Will to boot, and Will in overplus.

"More than enough am I that vex thee still,

"To thy sweet will making addition thus.

"Wilt thou, whose will is large and spacious,

"Not once vouchsafe to hide my will in thine?

"Shall will in others seem right gracious,

303

"And in my will no fair acceptance shine?
"The sea, all water, yet receives rain still
"And in abundance addeth to his store;
"So thou, being rich in Will, add to thy Will
"One will of mine to make thy large Will more.
"Let no unkind, no fair beseechers kill;
"Think all but one, and me in that one Will."

Then to his daughter, Edward says: "Will will fulfill the treasure of thy love? Ay, fill it full with wills, and my will one."

Each of them laughs at this amusement. Everyone refills their glasses for yet one more, but Elizabeth is not confident.

Lord and Lady Oxford enjoy the company of his oldest daughter, the two earls talking of their stage business, laughing and enjoying the nonsense of Edward's silly word games, while their ladies recall their days together as maids at court, when Elizabeth Trentham befriended the shy and retiring teenage Elizabeth deVere her first day curtsying before the queen.

That was a day not unlike the day when Penelope Rich, sister of the Earl of Essex, was deemed by the queen to have misbehaved and obliged by the queen to crawl on her hands and knees across the great oak floor of her majesty's throne room, a hundred fifty feet beneath Elizabeth's scornful eyes, before two hundred disdaining courtiers.

In her first marriage Penelope Devereux became Lady Rich and bore her husband two children, but tiring of him she became the mistress of Lord Mountjoy and bore him a second set of two children. She managed to live with both men equally and serve each of them dutifully, to their admitted satisfaction though they knew of her double life.

"To Mountjoy becomes Rich," Edward punned unmercifully. They grinned.

304

The queen would not allow Lady Penelope to divorce, preferring she suffer publicly for her infidelity, and thus serve as an example of the shame of adultery, a scandal which only enhanced the absence of scandal effecting her majesty.

"Maids want nothing but husbands; and when they have them, they want everything," whispered the courtiers.

"Honest men marry soon; wise men not at all."

Then, "Swine, women, and bees cannot be turned."

And, "Wedlock is a padlock."

Now Lady Oxford and her step-daughter-in-law, the Countess of Derby, look at their husbands in the firelight, the father not feeling his daughter's anguished state, the husband of the daughter unable to broach her painful subject of family hate.

The Earl of Derby had recently given his wife, age twenty three, an allowance of a thousand pounds (a quarter million dollars) a year. No wonder Queen Elizabeth called the Stanleys the richest family in England - and found no way to annex them.

Edward smiled at this. "All I hear is sweetness."

What fine times were those to be had, seated around the Earl of Derby's chimney, joined by his "cousin" poet, Edmund Spenser, as talk of words and plays prevailed, and such discussions as only earls would shape. It was of a future they could not even speculate.

In one of his earliest poems, Edward already was revealing a love of word play, making puns on his name and beginning a life-long game of spelling it into the text, something which had nothing to do with his real purpose.

As Edward deVere he became E.Ver, then EVER. Other combinations emerged, across English, French and Latin with "never" as NeVer (born truly true), N.eVer (Name: E Ver) and NeeVer (Formerly Known as Ver), but

305

these word games, acrostics and puns were only for recreation, done as an afterthought, to amuse, making a barb and bearding it.

"O! Here is a wit of cheverell, that stretches from an inche narrow to an ell broad," says Romeo, something that seems to say nothing and mean less. But "narrow" that "inche" by taking out the "in" and what is left of the inche is "che". Stretch that "che" to an "ell" the "broad" way across that middle syllable and what appears? "Che-ver-ell" - a play again on the name "ver". By no other means does Romeo make sense of his meaning.

As Oedipus executed his personal fate, so Oxford assumed responsibility, not only for his beginnings in glory, but the precise terms of his end, giving life in a gesture and taking it away at will. For him, all was will, his work to be seen or not to be seen, resting in the final words, standing in plain sight as evidence that all was written from behind a curtain, everyone seen as an actor on a stage, shown only by "A NEVER WRITER, TO AN EVER READER. NEWS."

Every man who would dare to reveal the scandals of his own house would do honor to honor if he obliged himself to keep quiet on the sins of another's. Or cut off his name and become anonymous rather than use his hand in such an invasion of privacy.

Every soul who ever lived believes in his heart of hearts that what words he has to say are special, a treasure for the world, if only he could see his way clear to voice them. But he lives beneath the shadow of a censor, in fear and trepidation and loathing, even when the censor's himself,

From the royals to the pits, what I saw were the commoners, sloshing about a London unpaved, with no plumbing, in mist and rain and muck, where wagon wheels stuck in the bog and the streets stank of the odor of horse dung and urine tossed from bedpans out the second floor windows of houses, the air hanging heavy with the smoke of burning peat moss and wood hauled in from the countryside. Everyone who was no one coughed and wheezed and spat and rubbed and itched and scratched, they were so foul from the weather and no niceties. A bath was considered a luxury. A proper meal was a thing of conjecture, for who could cook anything properly on an open fire? While her majesty's love was to love herself in love, Edward's golden book declared.

Soon after Edward and Elizabeth Trentham's marriage, the plays and poems of Shakespeare began to be published. And that went on with seventeen quartos by 1604 when (to the mystification of Shakespearean followers) the author stopped editing his work and overseeing the publication of good and clean editions (perhaps explained by the fact that the Earl of Oxford died). Only four more plays and his personal sonnets appeared before Lady Oxford's death in 1612, when there was cause on the part of some enemies to believe that perhaps this alias, "Master William Shakespeare", could be revealed as a literary hoax. How better to embarrass the Protestants who had taken their charge from the infamous earl than for Catholics to reveal the lie!

In 1612 this dehoaxing was attempted in a book called 'Minerva Britannia'. But history and the momentum of their cause was not on the side of truth or revelation - or the Catholics. The hoax was not exposed, though there are hoaxes that survive and hoaxes that perish, and some who hoax become hoaxed, if they marry themselves to a hoax, for a starter. But word games continue. Some ask, and some tell, so read how.

307

XXX

Now came a bricklayer who'd served time for murder and bore the thumb print of a convict forever branded into his flesh, a grim reminder of his brutal past, self-taught in the ways of literature, eager to make friends with Robert Cecil. As this aspiring author would say, Cecil "never cared for any man longer nor he could make use of him" (something he did not declare right away, but waited almost twenty-five years after Robert was dead and gone to admit he could say).

So the murderer established a need for himself in the colorful, fashionable, worldly domain of the court. About him it was said, Ben Jonson never spoke well of a person if he could speak ill, an avoidance well made, for he spoke ill of everyone, and when he spoke ill he was well, a mean and mongrel man at best, a silent and surly sort at worst, but recognized by all, for the way he spoke was well, being ill. He called his wife, "A shrew but true."

He began by writing a play.

His effort was called 'Every Man In His Humour' and he showed it to the greatest theatrical benefactor of the day. Edward deVere read it, liked it and sponsored it for a performance. Artful Ben's name was launched.

He found many friends in the theater world after that, among them a fellow named Shax-paw who sometimes worked as an interpreter of dumb shows put on by puppeteers, as well as a prompter and manager whose job was to muster companies on the road now and then.

"Haven't I seen you in Paul's Churchyard, Shackey?" asked Ben.

"Ay, sir."

"Weren't you hired by Richard Fields, the printer, to sweep his shop here a year or two back?"

"Ay, and I was."

Ben had a good time with his new-found friend. In fact, when they first met, Shackey was trying to convince an actor who had played the part of Marcellus in a production of 'Hamlet' to transcribe the play onto paper so they together could sell it to a printer he knew.

The idea was for the actor to write down all the parts, only the actor couldn't write and told Shackey he'd have to do that, but Shackey said he had a pain in his hand and couldn't write, either, which is when they met canny Ben who had strong mason's hands and could write, he said, over a tankard of grog.

"These hands were used to murder a man once. They'll serve to write for a man," Ben laughed.

His comrades were duly impressed and also laughed. Everyone laughed at that.

Shackey's idea was simple enough. These plays were circulating which were very popular and printers were willing to pay money to have them, only the writer of some of the most popular plays was unwilling to part with his work, in fact was unwilling even to discuss his work.

"And I know about printers. I was a good sweep for one."

"And writers too?"

"I know a thing or two about writers. Especially this one. His lordship is easy, that's what I know. I used to sweep his grandmother's barn at Bilton when I was a lad in Stratford. He talks a lot and shouts a bit. He likes to have the last word, he does. If you let him have his words, he's easy, that's what I know about his lordship. He'll talk more than you'll listen, I'll wager. Doesn't mind what broom you use either, just sweep."

"Then he'll be pleased you sweep this up," said Ben.

"Ay, sir. Mighty pleased."

Shackey's scheme was applied to that author's 'Hamlet' and sold to a printer at once for a shilling. Shackey and the actor met in the tavern soon after to split the change and drink to their prosperity, and raise a jar with tricky Ben for his hand in it. They were so high of spirits that Shack thought he ought to become a proper gent, and Ben wrote down every word of it.

Said Shack, "I am pointed out for a poet in Paul's Churchyard, and in the tiltyard for a champion."

Ben laughed at that, at the nerve of his friend, for even he knew who was pointed out for poet and tilting champion. He decided to introduce Shackey to his patron, the sponsor of his first play, whom he warned Shackey in advance was an earl, so be careful, be proper, least he find his wit stretched on the rack of a greater champion than he'd see fit.

When presented to the august figure, Shackey performed at his best: "And how does my sweet lady? in health? Bona roba!"

Ben took notes as they walked together, joined by the noble earl who was pretending to be just a regular gent - "Call me Willie!" - to which Shackey exclaimed: "You can call me Will, too! That's my name! Blimme what a sauce!" And the earl smiled, amused at the rustic's language.

Shackey was so impressed with himself and his own success on meeting the august earl that he decided he should become a gentleman, apply for a coat of arms and really have a go at this noble gentry stuff, betraying no recollection of having previously met the earl.

Ben had just explained to the earl about his friend Shack, "I came from him but now, he is in the herald's office yonder."

The earl asked, "What, has he purchased arms, then?"

"Ay," answered Ben. "And rare ones too; of as many colours as e'er you saw any fool's coat in your life."

Said Shack, coming from the office in a heat: "By this parchment, gentlemen, I have been so toiled among the harrots yonder, you will not believe! they do speak in the strangest language and give a man the hardest terms for his money, that ever you knew."

Ben asked, "But have you arms, have you arms?" all impatience to see what Shack had got for his silver.

"I' faith, I thank them; I can write myself gentleman now; here's my patent; it cost me thirty pound, by this breath."

"A very fair coat, well charged, and full of armoury," approved the earl admiringly.

"Nay, it has as much variety of colours in it, as you have seen a coat have; how like you the crest, sir?"

The earl frowned a little. "I understand it not well, what is't?"

"Marry, sir, it is your boar without a head, rampant. A boar without a head, that's very rare."

Ben tossed a word in. "Ay, and rampant too! I commend the herald's wit, he has deciphered him well; a swine without a head, without a brain, wit, anything indeed, ramping to gentility. You can blazon the rest, signior, can you not?"

"O, ay," said Shack. "I have it in writing here of purpose; it cost me two shillings the tricking."

Ben was eager for more. "Let's hear. Let's hear."

311

The nobleman who called himself Willie muttered, to himself and Ben, "It is the most vile, foolish, absurd, palpable, and ridiculous escutcheon that ever this eye survised."

But Ben cut him off. "Silence, good knight: go on."

And Shack read from his paper: "Gyrony of eight pieces; azure and gules; between three plates, a chevron engrailed checquy, or, vert, and ermines; on a chief argent, between two ann'lets sable, a boar's head proper!"

Ben was incredulous. "How's that! On a chief argent?"

Shack pointed to the paper with his nose and finger: "On a chief argent, a boar's head proper, between two ann'lets sable."

Ben couldn't believe this. "'Slud, it's a hog's cheek and puddings in a pewter field, this."

To which Shack was all smiles at his success. "How like you them, signior?"

To which the benevolent earl smiled his tenderest. "Let the word be, 'Not without Mustard'; your crest is very rare, sir."

For they noted in the margin of the paper that it was first denied with the Latin rejection, Non, Sans Droict, which meant No, Without Right. To which Shack became so enamored that he dropped the comma and called his family motto, Non Sans Droict, meaning Not Without Rights, acquiring a right where none before had been. Hence the earl's modest jest, Not Without Malice.

They soon parted company, though not for long. The nobleman often walked in Paul's Churchyard and made the acquaintance of everyone. Shack also walked in Paul's Churchyard and made the acquaintance of anyone.

Though at a later encounter the earl, a toothpick jutting from his jaw, his manner sanguine and content in white cassock and pump shoes, bountiful, kind and looking cheerful, inclining to be fat and prone to laughter, loving music, mirth, and yet not caring what came after, did tell Ben what he really thought, to which Ben addressed his lordship as Ovid:

"A college of wit-crackers can not flout me out of my humour, Ben. Dost think I care for a satire or an epigram?"

They were jostled by the crowd in Paul's Churchyard, it being market day. "All the world's a stage, Ben, and all the men and women merely players; they have their exits and their entrances, and one man in his time plays many parts, his acts being seven ages." They could see about them all the pageant, the whole bazaar.

"At first, the infant, mewling and puking in the nurse's arms. Then the whining schoolboy, with his satchel and shining morning face, creeping like snail unwilling to school. And then the lover, sighing like furnace, with a woeful ballad made to his mistress' eyebrow. Then a soldier full of strange oaths and bearded like the pard, jealous in honor, sudden and quick in quarrel, seeking the bubble reputation even in the canon's mouth. And then the justice, in fair round belly with good capon lined, with eyes severe and beard of formal cut, full of wise saws and modern instances; and so he plays his part.

"The sixth age shifts into the lean and slippered pantaloon, with spectacles on nose and pouch on side; his youthful hose, well saved, a world too wide for his shrunk shank, and his big manly voice, turning again toward childish treble, pipes and whistles in his sound. Last scene of all, that ends this strange and eventful history, is second childishness, a mere oblivion, sans teeth, sans eyes, sans taste, sans everything."

Ben listened, silenced in utter awe, and the earl removed the toothpick from his stubbled jaw. It was a

313

gentleman's toothpick, not cut from the twig of an ash bough, but as white as bone. It was a dried bird's leg.

XXXI

Henry Wriothesley's very existence of course would have been a deadly political blow to the reign, so long as he could claim to be the bastard heir to the throne, her majesty's royal stain.

That he grew up to become a national hero in the Protestant cause, for which he gave his life with his brother Henry, the 18th Earl of Oxford, would only have made his father proud, could he have lived to see it.

Who was this orphan of the throne? Henry Wriothesley, 3rd Earl of Southampton, whose youth was spent so addicted to theater, and turned away from the royal court, was known to jump in and play a part himself, even on the public stage, disguised. Nobles were forbidden by custom to take part in any public performances, but when Henry did it he won the crowd. His interest was such that he saw plays, read plays and staged plays with the guidance of his father, ceaselessly, and avoided the royal court.

"This is the only court I know. The theater's the court of life and feeling, persuasion and ideas!"

"But the other court will rule you. That is the court of law and authority."

"Then we shall rule it with wit!"

But the queen would have none of that, let it be known, and shut her door against the young Turks of her court, the Earls of Southampton and Essex. Essex had returned from Cadiz reformed in spirit and faithful, devoted to his wife, and never again inclined to court the queen.

315

Henry Wriothesley sponsored his father's plays most passionately, until the Saturday night of February 7, 1601, when he hired The Theater in Shoreditch to perform his father's old work, 'Richard II'. For the purpose of inspiring a revolution in the populace, a riot in the streets of London, an uprising against Robert Cecil's control of the queen, Henry conspired with his friend Essex, having tired of the aging monarchy and the undetermined fate of who would wear the crown succeeding his cold-headed mother.

In a world where truth was true and right was right, where fair was fair and what should be was what became, the crown his mother wore was Henry Wriothesley's claim. Only no such world exists. No truth - no right - no fair - no just. That is a world of dreams. And he who pays by the loss of dreams gives up the most of what life seems. Outside is a world of death.

Essex and Southampton were arrested after Essex burst into the palace alone, muscled past the guards and entered the queen's private chamber where he startled her majesty who was receiving a layer of facial paste meant to conceal her wrinkles.

Hell had no fury like a woman unveiled!

He was removed to The Tower, and Henry Wriothesley with him.

"Your Lord Southampton hired the players last night to excite the public with 'Richard II'!" Robert Cecil reported to the queen, and made sure she understood its implications, that her boys were conspiring to end her rule, which he was determined to protect.

She cut Cecil off. "But I am Richard II, know ye not that?"

"He used the play to make the people rise against us," Secretary Cecil replied.

316

She cut in again, and came to Southampton's defense. "This tragedy was played forty times in open streets and houses." She gazed at Cecil incredulously. "Know ye not that? For traitors, it plays like a toothless dog."

"To no effect, I know, your grace, to cause rebellion. Still, they have rebelled," said Robert Cecil. "And it has its price."

"Then out - get out!" she wailed.

Robert Cecil saw her boys were brought to trial. The charge was treason. The queen refused to discuss the matter and did not intercede to save them.

"Your majesty could, of course, if your majesty would, of course, dispose herself to mercy," Robert Cecil suggested. "Which disposition would support another insurrection."

"You needn't lecture princes on disposition," the queen replied.

"Nor would I try," said Cecil.

"We are not disposed," said the queen.

"Then they will be tried," said Cecil. "Is that correct?"

"As you like it," said the queen. "Only put Lord Oxford at the head of their jury. Let him sit in judgment of his peers."

The lives of Essex and her son would rest in Oxford's hands.

Robert Cecil rubbed his hands at that. He confided to his attentive secretary: "We have Lord Oxford in charge. Seniority reigns, you know. Long live seniority! He sits at the head of the legal committee in parliament. All the lesser lords defer to him. Now let his lordship sit. Put an earl to judge an earl, an old one to hobble a young one. That'll fix our sabled nobles."

317

"Yes," said the deferential secretary. "That will. That must. That is. Most quick. Like putting a father to judge a son."

"Indeed," Robert replied. "Indeed." He looked at himself in a mirror to wink, and let his man see nothing, though he marveled at the intuitive perception of his man and wondered if his man knew more than he let on, then eyed him shrewdly before he eyed him kindly. "That is quick. Must be. Will be. A father for a son."

The secret of the court he kept.

The final verdict was woeful on February 19, 1601. In the trial, the Earl of Essex was condemned to death. Only by Oxford's persuasion, and his return to the court of his queen to plead for the life of their son, promising anything, even silence, was he able to win amnesty for the Earl of Southampton's life.

"I'll not write of this! I'll not write of anything! I'll not write again! Never EVER!"

"Aren't you a little late to plead your case for silence, Edward?"

"I have no other voice."

"Then take your silence with you, and listen," said her majesty.

Nothing spared Essex, though it was said that the queen had once given him a secret ring which he was to give back to her as a sign of his special need if ever that arose. Then, from The Tower, he gave the ring to his sister to place in the hand of the queen, without telling her what it signified. She failed to deliver it to the queen, admiring and keeping it for herself and never dreaming of its power. The queen wailed in vain for the ring as a sign of Essex's plea for mercy. When it failed to come she let him be executed. Not until after Essex was beheaded did the queen see the ring on the coveting finger.

"Why wearest thou that?" she snapped.

"His lordship gave it me, and I admired it, though he asked me to deliver it to you," replied Penelope.

"And why didn't you?"

"Her majesty already has rings," answered the guilty Lady Rich.

Courtiers in her hearing tittered.

The queen turned pale, retreated to her chapel, and remained alone to pray until the offender left. But Penelope was replaced by the widowed Lady Essex, clad in mourning rags.

She whispered: "They say he wore a black velvet suit embroidered, and a bright red waistcoat pulled over his head as he went to his execution, my Lord of Essex did. It was his favorite waistcoat, red. He said he kept it for a festive occasion and hoped he'd never stain it, red."

The queen saw her and screamed: "Is every lady clad in rags before me?"

To spare the Earl of Southampton, the queen required much of Lord Oxford. To let Essex die and Southampton live could mean the return of gossip and scandal about her preference and her heir's inheritance.

"If one lives, both live. If one dies - you'll have to pay dearly, Ned, if what you'd save is his life."

Paying court to her majesty was dear enough. "I stand before you broken," was what Edward said.

The queen asked Edward to raise his head, to look her in the eye. "We have known each other so many years, Ned. What has it come to?"

We hadn't known each other at all, if what it came to was this - a nothing.

"We were never so real as when we were little. Children we will always be. As I grow older, I grow younger. To be with me you must a child be," said the queen.

Edward inclined his head. "As always, yours is the last word, majesty."

And how did Edward end his years with her? It was just such a display of spontaneity, as he had always enjoyed, that engraved history's farewell portrait of Oxford as a frivolous courtier, an Osric, for the next four centuries to bear his name.

But to follow it, we must first study the Elizabethan piano, a musical instrument called the virginal. It had keys, called "jacks", which hit the strings to sound the notes with felt-covered tips, called "heads". Thus was music made by the queen herself seated at the virginal when news was brought that her much-vaunted protégé-turned-traitor Robert Devereux, Earl of Essex, thirty-four years her junior, had been executed by the ax.

In the silence that followed this news in the room, the queen refrained as if frozen from touching her keys, and the first earl of the land uttered his forever-famous double stroke pun on the dead insurgent upstart "jack" Essex - a warning to Walter Raleigh and every man who would trust the queen with his destiny, and loose his head over the crown.

Said the Earl of Oxford: "When jacks rise up, heads go down."

And only then did the music play on under her majesty's tiny fingers, accompanied by cittern and harpsichord.

"I can not tell; the world is grown so bad that wrens make prey where eagles dare not perch: Since every Jack became a gentleman there's many a gentle person made a Jack."

"Edward, you are the only noble to know me my entire reign, and survive - truly a proof of family."

"You paint a picture, your majesty. I have heard of your paintings too, well enough. God hath given you one face, and you make yourself another. You jig, you amble, and you lisp; you nickname God's creatures and make your wantonness your ignorance."

"And we have managed to save our son from beheading."

While Henry Wriothesley hired actors to perform one of his father's plays, 'Richard II', in the belief that public discontent with their fading queen, for falling under the spell of Cecil, would lead to open rebellion, they saw only his political innocence, for they knew what power the people possessed - none. He and young Essex could then foment, they hoped and believed, an insurgence ending with Henry putting on his mother's crown. Only they did not plan so well. Within hours of the Essex rebellion, there was no rebellion at all, and the young discontents were locked in The Tower, fomenting nothing but rage.

Henry's father, the Earl of Oxford, pre-eminent jurist, president of the legal council in the House of Lords, was seated as senior judge at the head of a jury of twenty five nobles. His verdict for his son's rash, youthful act of insurgency in his attempt to seize the throne, which his fading queen mother was allowing to go unassigned, was profound.

Southampton was sentenced to spend his life in The Tower.

Robert Cecil in secret had begun his work to convey Elizabeth's crown onto the head of the son of the Catholic Mary, Queen of Scots. James the Sixth of Scotland would become King James the First of England, not by conquest or virtue, but because his ascension would confirm the hidden power of the Cecils, to whom he would remain beholden: not the best choice of king for England, but the best choice for

321

the Cecils, who could rule that King of England as they could rule no other. So England would be ruled.

There was nothing the Earl of Oxford could do to save that crown, or his crown, his work, his family. Indeed, there was little left that anyone could do about the indecisive queen, or the deceptive Cecil.

That ogre sat in Theobalds like a spider in a web.

"Winter in the garden of my home. I break a twig. I break a man. I break my word. I break a life. I break the truth with truths of my own, and all about me scatter, for I never break myself. What a man am I, strong in other's weaknesses, brave before cowards, decisive before doubt, and those who showed me no mercy will fear the mercy I offer. What a man am I, whom no one calls a man, but a worm, a caterpillar, a slug, while they are twigs on whom I crawl, and eat them one by one, and live. They call me broken with my back deformed. But who is broken? Winter in my garden and all is well. All is broken but me. Even the king! Who is he? I am the king of the king, I see!"

Henry Wriothesley was hidden away in The Tower to live out his mother's reign in safety. Popularity attended him always. His father wrote him poetry. Even his cat, Tawny, was said to have crossed half of London to find and stay with his master in The Tower. And 'Richard II' was played many more times, to crowds of sleepy subjects who heard no call to treason in its vaunted lines, but applauded beauty, truth and authority, for it presented a monarch as a poet, with no other poet in sight.

Truth is truth. Beauty is beauty. Power is power. Duty is duty. Separate are these beneath authority.

Edward called his porter. "Here, John! Send the boy to the stationer's for two shillings of white Spilman paper and a half pound of sealing wax. And give him eight pence more for two ounces of gum, two ounces of copperas and four ounces of gall. I need to make ink. Hurry now!"

John said, "Yes my lord," several times, and fingered a snake head he wore round his neck for his "quinsy" which was a swollen throat.

In 1603 occurred the passing, legendary:

"Come, come, you paraquito, answer me directly unto the question that I ask! In faith, I'll break thy little finger - " screamed her majesty, and then lapsed into silence, exhausted. She had raged and battled her life through. For three weeks she refused to sleep, not eating so much as a single foul cake, not even a jumbold or marchpan, and claimed that her throat was bound up as in a corset.

"Who strangles me? I can not speak. I can not breathe!"

"Who would you have us call, your majesty?" asked her doctor, William Gilbert.

'I have no voice! I can't tell you! My words! My words!"

Her godson, Sir James Harrington, came to read her amusing verses and be humorous. She did not smile at this peacock who only recently had invented a new device for plumbing, called the Ajax by those who spoke Greek, and A Jacques by those who spoke French, but a Water Closet in English.

"When thou dost feel creeping time at thy gate, these fooleries will please thee less," she told him. "I am past my relish for such matters."

The queen's bath was mirrored on all sides including the ceiling and was heated by steam, but she had no inclination.

"So you are more yourself now, godmother."

"I am no lover of pompous titles, but only desire that my name may be recorded in a line or two, which shall briefly express my name, my virginity, the years of my reign, the reformation of religion under it, and my preservation of peace," she told her maids.

Then she saw Edward somewhere beyond them in the chamber. "I care nothing for epitaphs, Edward. For me a simple memorial - Elizabeth Tudor, a good and virgin queen, who kept the peace in her reign. Will you see to that, Ned?"

Lord Edward bowed his head and displayed in his smile the "grim-grinning ghost, earth's worm." He had only silence to answer her. A slight deafness, a limp, a certain frailty of bearing made his movements slower and less sure, and he leaned on a stick picked up from a garden path and well-worn into a cane. What remained between them was memory.

She was the mother to our son whom now she denied she bore. She had doomed him as surely as her father, King Henry VIII, in the infected and vile throes of his final evil, executed my innocent uncle, the Earl of Surrey, but twenty six years old and already the creator of our greatest and most enduring literary form - the sonnet. Henry VIII executed him on a rumor, without further discussion, because as the monarch it pleased him. Now it pleased her. Like father, like daughter, imperious, denying, extracting more than giving, nothing faithful admitted. O foul - O most foul fealty!

The dogs of death pursued her like mongrels snapping at her heels for blood, that were not fed, and circled her and bit and barked the more they were unsatisfied. And to their snarling tune she danced, and let them wail, and did not hide or sit out intrigues of opposing sorts, but bathed herself in all the flatteries of her court, those that obeyed her equally with those that wished to kill her. Often warned of Catholic plots, she tolerated and

324

ignored them, declaring herself as queen invulnerable. None could frighten her any more than they had her father.

But I am not the source of this history to tell it. I am the cause of its misery.

Edward gazed at Elizabeth the queen who walked in her nightgown from chamber to chamber. Her hair was unstrung and hung down to her waist. It was no longer reddish blonde in color, but white: *Love - so easy to recognize, so hard to find. She was a virgin, and I - a fool.*

"What I think I utter, and spend my malice with my breath," Edward said.

Now her majesty's new principle minister, Robert Cecil, cool with anticipation, urged: "To content the people, you must go to bed."

Said the queen: "The word 'must' is not to be used to princes. Little man, little man, if your father had lived, ye durst not have said so much; but ye know that I must die and that makes you so presumptuous."

To Lord Admiral Charles Howard of Effingham, Earl of Nottingham, she gasped: "If you were in the habit of seeing things in your bed as I do when in mine, you would not persuade me to go there."

But persuade he did, by the gentlest importunement. In the last week of her decline, silence pervaded the city and not a bell rang out, not a bugle sounded over London, though dogs roved the streets under a gentle rain; they stared at beggars with malevolent eyes.

She spoke her final words to Edward: "Come dance, my Turk!"

On Thursday, March 24, 1603, the relentless queen died in bed.

Her last wish was her nearest heir by blood should wear her crown. She never said who that was but her eyes were fixed on Edward. Cecil knew who that would be.

325

Cried Edward: "You go not till I set you up a glass where you may see the inmost part of you!" And then she whispered and was not heard. He turned to leave and found himself with Robert Cecil, face to face. "She hath left me to try my fortune. . either without sail whereby to take advantage of any prosperous gale, or with anchor to ride till the storm be past," Edward said.

The hunch back minister in his turn listened, smiled, remained silent, a model of infinite patience with his eyes half closed, and nodded, as though he knew the answer, and knew all the words before the answer, and yet allowed that the words could be spoken, and was counting the time, for he had so much time, now he was in charge of the answers.

His was the silent answer. No one remained to challenge him.

As Edward walked from the palace he limped, and to the retainer, Hercules, the queen's porter who stood eight feet six inches and had hands seventeen inches long, who held his horse, with whom he was over a lifetime familiar, Lord Edward sighed: "The end is near. O, the end is here."

To the streets Sir Robert went, and from the steps of the palace read from a paper of the death of the queen, and of her majesty's final declaration, which he announced that she had spoken to him directly on her death bed in her final hour, by the words, "I declare King James the Sixth of Scotland to be King James the First of England - God Save the King!"

And the people shouted and some cursed (the name of Cecil) and wept (for her majesty) and carried their burdens through the muddy streets to wherever they had been going. It was another night without the Moon.

Said the solitary earl, humming a tune to himself and stumbling home across Bow Bridge: "My high-blown pride at length broke under me, and now has left me, weary and old with service, to the mercy of a rude stream that must forever hide me."

Ben Jonson stood beside him gazing down in the black, still water, where glimpses of the moon from behind the clouds were reflected. "The Lea runs deep. King Lea, that's me." Ben hemmed and hawed and stammered at his interruption of so pregnant a silence, then pushed ahead and volunteered to finish Edward's final play for him, the end of 'The Tragical History of King Henry VIII'.

"Why not? Go at it." Edward let him.

So Ben became his censor.

He told Ben: "I give you my large kingdom for a little grave, a little, little grave, an obscure grave."

"It will be as a treasure in a leather purse," Ben assured him, but was so amazed at his appointment that he was almost speechless.

Edward went to court no more. But his sons grew to devote themselves to his causes in religion, politics, and soldiering for life. Only his daughters dabbled in theater and publishing literature. This with less persuasion.

Said his eldest daughter, Elizabeth deVere Stanley: "It is unspeakable, unbearable, unutterable, what our father did." Said she: "He caused our poor dear dead mother such a life of grief that death itself became her sole relief."

The perfume of the moment, the nectar of infinity: I loved four times, the goddesses of hearth, of forest, altar and of caring virtue at the center of my life; two Anne's, two Elizabeth's, each a mirror of the other, alike and opposite. I had three daughters and three sons and loved them all, though none alike. To tell of their amenities would take from now till night, but they have been the filling of my soul, the shaping of my flesh, the depth and breadth of every ocean's roll, and I am all they are and all they are is me. Contentment fills this universe, good feeling to be free. I love you my son to whom I write. I love you this side of idolatry.

When clever Ben asked what Edward was scribbling, reminding him of his promise to the queen to write no more, Edward closed the golden book and put it away without answering.

"A letter to my son," he said, and said no more.

"Whom you love 'this side of idolatry' - a good phrase, good indeed, O most good," muttered Ben, and noted it.

His nephew, his sister Mary's son, wrote him:

"My Lord, I wish infinitely to convey to you in some manner the honor I bear you, having always been well looked upon by you; but aside from the fact that I have not yet found a subject worthy to take you from your more serious affairs, I should not make so bold as to write you, for fear of being too ill-advised to importune you with letters which would not even deserve to be opened, if not in that they would assure you of the eternal service which I have sworn to you and to all your house; praying you very humbly, sir, to take this kindly and to consider me one who is ready to receive your commands with such devotion that I shall be all my life your very humble servant and nephew, Robert Bertie."

The son of Lord and Lady Willoughby would one day become the 19th Earl of Oxford. He would be serious and attentive to business and not unlike his father, a man of depth and width, of vision and grasp, of force and feeling, a citizen on a stage of the world whom his uncle Edward adored as a man of infinite jest, and whom he could only admire and treasure, as he did his uncle.

A closing section of the golden book is in another hand, the same as Robert Bertie's, and reads under date of 1630:

I, Edward deVere engaged in one of England's towering creations, the common man, by celebrating a faith, my death, and doing battle with its flower.

On completing 'The Tempest', as the sun went down through the pear trees in his garden at King's Place, Hackney, Edward, clothed with a long white shirt to his ankles like a monk, his feet slipped comfortably into pantofles which were like high slippers or mules, lay at the end of his gravel path, seeing himself as the Duke of Milan and his daughter, Susan deVere as the duke's daughter Miranda, remembering a sad event they shared when she was little.

He called his beloved countess to his side. "Elizabeth, listen here!"

She came to the garden and sat beside him. Her smile was glowing. Such was the gravel on the path that it crunched as she approached the fruit tree and he rose.

"You are the only audience I ever cherished," he whispered, and read: "'Canst thou remember a time before we came unto this cell? I do not think thou canst, for then thou wast not out three years old. Twelve year since, Miranda, twelve year since, thy father was duke of Milan and a prince of power.'" So he referred to his past. "And she asks, 'Sire, are you not my father?' and he says, 'Thy mother was a piece of virtue and she said thou wast my daughter.'"

The play was written and rewritten and written over again, in the endless years of a lifetime's revision, in 1603, recalling December 2, 1591, when Castle Hedingham was taken from him by fine and given to his father-in-law, Lord Burghley, when Susan was three years old.

"Edward, I would that we could buy it back, now Lord Burghley is dead. I'd give more than my father left us, if I could give you back your childhood home, and see you

329

there again. You woke again last night from a dream and I asked you what caused you such a fright. All you whispered was 'Hedingham'."

Such power-grabbing stripped me one more time. I've been stripped and picked over by the Cecils a thousand times, and by their pious, righteous, upstanding, low-blowing class of rising vultures, ever since I lost my father - my dear, my sad, my ghost of a father, the great earl, when I was a boy. I see my father often now as I become my father: in the mirror when I shave, (and Edward never let his beard grow according to the custom, but kept clean-shaved with mustache trimmed except now in the garden, where he was abristle with stubble and new phrases.) *I see him in my hair which has turned from auburn, gray; and in my words and voice, sometimes the very phrases that my father used once, long ago to say, which I can not forget since boyhood though I supplant this manhood.*

His father's ghost alone comes to him in the garden now, and speaks: "Let me sit heavy on thy soul tomorrow. When I was mortal, my anointed body by them was poisoned! - I that was washed to death with fulsome wine - Edward, thy wife, that wretched Anne thy wife that never slept a quiet hour with thee now fills thy sleep with perturbations - thou quiet soul, sleep thou a quiet sleep. Dream of success and happy victory! Dream on, dream on, of bloody deeds and death fainting, despair, despairing, yield thy breath. I died for hope ere I could lend thee aid but cheer thy heart and be thou not dismayed."

Edward starts out of his slumber. The ghost continues in his waking state, at the end of the path beneath the tree.

"I am forbid to tell the secrets of my prison house. I could a tale unfold whose lightest word would harrow up thy soul, freeze thy young blood, make thy two eyes like stars

330

start from their spheres, thy knotted and combined locks to part, and each particular hair to stand on end like quills."

"O my prophetic soul!" mourns Edward as the vision fades.

"Mark me," its voice repeats.

Remember him - his father dead since he was twelve? "I will. While memory holds a seat in this distracted globe" he would remember him. How could he forget his father, the poisoned earl? He could not, not ever.

"Within be fed, without be rich no more."

I see you, father, in the twilight of my years, in all I am and dreamed to be, in every wince and utterance, a match so mirror-made I can not tell myself apart from you. Yet who would wish what I've seen on your eyes, or heard upon your ears? What treasons not yet told were plagues to you? I'd not wish you to mine for any reason. Damn! But this much I have known - the glory of a woman's love. She sits beside me now and she is all there is. Forgive a sane man who attempts imposing sanity on a world insane; forgive the madmen who would no more deal with madness, for such a wish is maddening. There is no more to be, nor could I ever see.

He turned his page. "Teach me how to curse mine enemies!"

On the day of King James' coronation, the first acts of the new king were to honor that king who never was, Edward the Seventh, Lord Great Chamberlain, the Earl of Oxford, by renewing his lifetime annuity from the treasury, for his ministry of propaganda and theatrical production, reappointing him to the Royal Privy Council, and granting him custody of the Forest of Essex and keepership of Havering-atte-Bowre, Cymbeline's Castle at Colchester and the Ewer, which in one stroke of his pen restored what had been denied to Edward by Cecil greed and the queen's

331

indifference for thirty years, securing his status and some measure of his estate to its dreamed of, former magnificence forever.

Though Edward's son and heir, Henry deVere, someday to be the 18th Earl of Oxford, would spend a wanton youth, perturbing his mother with dissolute conduct and dubious friends, he would be noted as the most impoverished earl, until he attained maturity, and rode to war with his friend, his hero, the 3rd Earl of Southampton, who treated him as only a brother could. It was remarked but unsuspected.

The king's second gesture of magnanimity was in releasing that noble, "Great Oxford's" son, Henry Wriothesley, 3rd Earl of Southampton, from The Tower.

"In sleep a king, waking, no such matter."

The only bargain struck was that Henry renounce all claim to the crown, maternity of the queen, and any championing of those works - those dreaded works once written in such shadows that they deserved to be hidden forever.

"What do you think now of those written works, Lord Henry?"

"I do not think of them at all, Sir Robert."

"Then they are worthless?"

"I have said I will not discuss them."

"Then what claim have you to anything?"

"None, Sir Robert."

"No claim to your father's disgrace or his vile version of history?"

"None."

However, the new king ordered that 'Hamlet' be published under his personal patronage, signed with the author's pseudonym, and that seven plays be performed at court by his personal troupe of actors at once, and another thirteen when Lady Oxford died nine years later, retrospectives in tribute to the greatest artist of the age, the voice who was silenced by all but truth.

"Does His Majesty believe this wise?" asked Sir Robert Cecil of his new King.

"Of course," answered the monarch, seconded by his wife Queen Anne, who was utterly enthralled by the famous Oxford's great plays. "It is wise because I say it is wise. It will be done because I say so, and you will become a king in your own home, Sir Robert, not mine. I will give you a title for your kingdom. In future, you may call yourself Lord Salisbury - and you will call the most noble playwright of our times or ever - 'Great Oxford'. Do you hear that name? 'Great Oxford'. He of the Great spear. He who shakes spears. Say it, Cecil, loudly." The king's voice echoed in the palace hall but the only other sound was Robert Cecil's shoes retreating from the royal audience.

In his study at King's Place, Edward watched Ben Jonson sitting at the table which was sent from Hedingham.

"How is the writing, Ben?"

"Smoothly advancing, sire. Do you have a coin?"

"What for?"

"The money. I want money. I need money. Just a coin for now."

"Ben, you shame yourself. Learn to be a poet. They are not born. They're made."

"I'd rather make a coin. Just a coin for now."

"Make this note fit in a speech somewhere, Ben. I'll toss you an angel of a coin for it. Pen ready? I'll work with anyone, Ben, even you. Now write: 'What paradigm of shifting faiths assumes possession of the mind, to be or not to be remains the answer truth must find.'"

"Very good, m'lord. May I have the coin now?"

"To be or not to be, that's the question, Ben."

333

"But what about my coin?"

"I can't win with you or without you. I remember when we all were crowded in a room: Grievous Greene and kidding Kyd, nasty Nashe and mighty Marlowe, fiddlestick Lyly and forever Munday, turning plays and poems out like a watermill. Remember that, Munday?" No answer. "Now alone," said Edward. "With begging Ben. A sorry ending to a jolly tale. Oedipus plucks out his eyes; Oxford plucks out his name."

Part Five

"The fable of the world"

"I will not blaze or publish until it please me."

XXXII

June, 1604: "Come hither, Henry." His little boy is eleven, same age as he was when his own father, the good earl called him to his side in the Forests of Essex. "Sit thou by my bed and hear, I think, the very latest counsel that ever I shall breathe." It is a feather mattress on a litter in the garden under an apple tree, sun shining where he rests. It is hard now, drawing breath. He rasps as loudly as a wheel turned gravely. "God knows, my son. . it seemed in me but as an honor snatched with a boisterous hand - to write, to tell a tale, to turn a word in two - and I had many living to upbraid my gain of it by their assistance's: which daily grew to quarrel and to bloodshed, wounding supposed peace. . All my writing hath been but as a scene acting that argument." He is sweating beads.

They have prepared the rooms at King's Place, Hackney. Sliced onions on plates in every room sit by red rose leaves in candle wax.

Lady Oxford rubs her husband's chest with powdered animal horn mixed with angelica root to bring on sweats.

He nibbles at fine white wheat bread, called manchet, which he dips in a broth and then forgets to swallow.

On May Day the servant girl threw open the windows and smelled the warm, sweet air of spring, then squealed to her lady that she would run to the fields and woods to gather dew.

As Midsummer, Saint John's Eve, the longest day of the year approached, June 24th, the air was sultry. In the

337

streets was merrymaking, the local folk dancing around bonfires, brave servant lads and farm hands still in their teens leaping over the wild flames while maids admired their skill and courage, and old women wearing mourning shawls warned little boys not to walk in the churchyard of Saint Augustine, "for the souls of those to die this year are said to wander forth to their burial site this night!"

Boys with faces died black to imitate devils vied with morris dancers as peddlers with birch boughs made their rounds of gates to sell their goods to decorate the houses, and maids sewed bunting of buckram, silk and canvas to decorate wagons and stages.

Yellow rush lights, called cressets, made by the candlemaker from cooking fats, which had a foul smell, were placed on tables to ward off darkness as people sat on porches looking for ghosts and wraiths.

Now Lady Oxford, clad in dark red murrey, the color worn to ward off the plague, returned from her duties at the private girls' boarding school adjoining King's Place, where she taught French, Italian and book keeping. Here she had hired Emilia Bassano Lanier at one shilling per week, a guaranteed forty shillings per year, to give instruction in verse making, and Emilia with her husband moved to Hackney. Young ladies of the school read Lyly's popular 'Euphues, the Anatomy of Wit' and 'Euphues and His England' as well as Robert Greene's venerable, 'The Mirror of Modesty' with their favorite tale, the Susanna story. Also, they made notes from Angel Day's book on the tone of writing and methods of argument and rhetorical figures. All these writers had worked for Lady Oxford's husband once.

When Edward's sonnets were published, the scandal of the "dark lady" so embarrassed Emilia that the following year she registered and published her own response to restore her honor in the eyes of those at court who knew her, knew

Edward, and recognized their affair. Her book of poetry and prose, called 'Salve Deus Rex Judeorum', made history. It was "the first genuine feminist tract ever published in the English language. It would be the only one for almost two hundred years." She dedicated her work to a dozen women, also a publishing first, and fought the first battle in the great struggle for women's equal rights and honors in a man's world, "boldly and in the first person" under her own name, yet another first. She also created a new genre, the country house poem, which would soon be appropriated by that artist of all others' work, shifty Ben Jonson. Emilia's immortality rested on her style so clearly influenced by Edward, of easy, rapid flow as though thinking in verse aloud, and it was the court community that read her, knew her and saved her classic for posterity, when all the rest lost trace of it.

Waiting for Lady Oxford's return home was her physician wearing black, with a muff to keep his hands soft and a cane with pomander box on top, filled with the scent of orange. He peered at the countess over his spectacles.

"Wives are believed best to nurse all ills, even a servants' ills, my lady," he urged her to hear him. "I can offer concoctions, wormwood, juniper berries and red nettle juices, but as to a cure, I have only an opinion. Rhubarb and senna for physics is common. Rhubarb syrup is common. I would suggest your laundry be washed in lye at least every three months."

"Don't you offend me!" said Lady Oxford.

When the physician had gone she went about filling a wooden tub before the fire with scented warm water, and then marched into Edward's room.

"It's bath time, Edward. John went to the fountain for nine buckets of water and I believe he's started selling water to houses that have no water carriers, the old rascal. And we have something new for your supper, my lord. It's called a potato just sent from Ireland and is said to have amazing benefits."

"Where is my Flanders gown with the ruff collar?" Edward asked her. "I want to put on my Dutch round gown this evening and feel like a newborn baby wrapped in an old garment to start life well."

"And so you shall, my lord," said the countess, and helped him to the tub.

Children in the yard were playing shuttlecock and troll madame, which was badminton and bowling, with their son Henry, and laughing. The servants were seated in the yard at a table of dominoes and draughts, which was checkers, and a pair of servant girls played cards on the steps.

Down the street danced men with bells on their legs, costumed up as a hobbyhorse, and children were skipping about them.

Now we are beside the water and before us, a pale and sickly man of fifty four, leaning on a hand-carved cane, watching his young son of eleven throwing rocks in the stream, the River Lea, who does not hear a word his father says, who would not understand, had he listened. With Edward are his cousin, who is thirty nine, and his old retainer, fifty one. This is what he says.

"I am dead, Horatio. Things standing thus unknown shall live behind me."

His cousin responds. "But you can make them known. All things are yours to tell."

"Cousin, I've gone here and there and made myself a spectacle, a motley to the crowd, sold cheap what is most dear, but never made a truth from what was false. I beg you with my love: Forget yourself awhile and draw one breath of grief for me. Then tell my story truly to the unsatisfied, if you will."

340

Edward reminds Horatio that many years ago, when they were young, he had made his Will to the benefit of his cousin.

Says Horatio: "You grieve but are not dead."

Says Edward: "And when I'm dead I'll be unfit to grieve."

The old retainer, Anthony Munday, laughs. "I'll note that down your lordship. 'Grief'."

Edward says: "Look at my son. He skips his rocks upon the water and little dreams what's deep. Protect him, Horatio, from the fangs of courtiers. Beware that Pondous clan of politicians. They're grown fat on me."

"And to be feared."

"I dread the thought of yet another son their ward, to feed their greed by giving them my father's blood as their tuition. They feast on scars that never felt my wounds. Dear, kind Horatio. Take my Henry. Raise him proud. I give you the future Earl of Oxford. The past one is his prologue."

"Those love you best who say your humor is your sword."

"And there's the kindest cut," adds Munday.

"I would have laughed but laughing's dying in the only voice I have. All that's changed is everything. Have yourself a laugh, Horatio. O God, what a wounded name. Lord Burghley's dead and he destroyed me. The queen more beautiful when we were young, more glorious than the sun, uncontained by all that's come, eclipsed me. You see me as I am, Horatio. What remains is nothing but remembrance. And I beside myself before I fell behind."

"Papa, Papa," little Henry squealed. "I saw a fish jump in the stream. Can I catch it?"

Edward looked in silence at his son, tears at the corners of his eyes.

341

Horatio touched his sleeve. "Edward, do you hear him? Edward?"

There was no answer.

June 24, 1604, fifteen months to the day following his queen, "Great Oxford", as King James called him, expired, six days after giving his keepership of the Forest of Essex to his cousin, but leaving no will.

"Someone go to the library." said Lady Oxford, "and tell Mr. Jonson he can stop the writing now. My lordship has no further use for him."

On the north side of the chancel in the Church of Saint Augustine at Hackney, on July 6, the Earl of Oxford was buried. Next to the record of his death, the clerk noted, "Plague."

His wife, the Countess of Oxford, placed a bid to purchase Castle Hedingham from his three daughters for her son, the 18th Earl of Oxford, and, after five years of negotiations conducted through Sir Robert Cecil, Lord Salisbury, they sold it to her. She emptied her wardrobe of the white and golden gowns and all the others, more beautiful than most women ever had worn, and chose widow's black for the remainder of her life. She was laid to rest beside her husband, upon her death, in 1612. She left this testament to her eternal love, on November 25: "I joyfully commit my body to the earth from whence it was taken, desiring to be buried in the Church of Hackney, within the County of Middlesex, as near unto the body of my late dear and noble Lord and husband as may be, and that to be done as privately and with as little pomp and ceremony as possible may be. Only I will that there be in the said Church erected for us a tomb fitting our degree, and of such charge as shall seem good to mine executors."

She also added payment of a few pounds quarterly, "to my dombe man". These things were carried out by her executors.

A few weeks later in the quiet of an evening, a gentleman of Stratford came to London and purchased the Blackfriars gatehouse as an investment, but only as an investment, and kept dumb, after that. He was called, while in town, to the trial of a wig maker's father, to give a deposition as a witness for a marriage dowry that was never paid, and for back taxes that went ignored by him from the last time he lived in London. Silence was his best role and he slipped out of town without breaking it. His chums from the Mermaid Tavern called that the greatest performance in acting history. Or, as friends of shifty Ben noted, "that Stratford man is truly Hamlet's ghost."

"So all the world's kept dumb," said Ben.

After the death of Lady Oxford, who willed that she be buried beside her most beloved lord, a decade passed before Oxford's third daughter by his first marriage, and her husband, together with her husband's brother, known always as "The Most Noble and Incomparable Pair of Brethren", took up publishing in one great collection, the Complete Works of Edward deVere, at a time when the Catholics were again threatening the Protestant throne.

This First Folio was done hastily and would be sold for two shillings. The work was undertaken by a printer who had gone blind and balanced on bankruptcy, William Jaggard. He already had worked for Lord Oxford's daughter, the Countess of Montgomery, Susan deVere. In fact, he'd been nibbling at the treasure of Lord Oxford's manuscripts for two decades.

Edward's oldest and youngest daughters had made friends with the newest playwright to hit London in 1598, Ben Jonson. Only because he was turned down by theaters until his first play, 'Every Man In His Humour' was read by their father, and he was given the go ahead for a start on the boards and in literary circles, did he prosper. Oxford's oldest and youngest daughters acted for Jonson in this first play's first production. They were excited to be part of their father's world. The year after his death, Edward's youngest daughter, Susan, married Philip Herbert, Earl of Montgomery, the son of her father's oldest and dearest friend, Mary Sidney, the Countess of Pembroke. It made her instrumental in the patronage of the publication of the Complete Plays of her father.

In 16th Century England, Protestants knew who he was, that his fight was in shaking his speare - a crusade that concluded The Crusades by crowning the Church of England triumphant.

"They fight best who do not admit to fighting."

Now Henry Wriothesley together with his younger brother, Henry deVere, and after correspondence with their brother, Sir Edward Vere who was a Captain in service in the Low Countries, met at Wilton Manor, near the great and mysterious pillars of Stonehenge, in the octagonal room where the Countess of Pembroke was supervising a cowering, submissive scrivener named Ben Jonson, editing play scripts. Lady Mary informed them that some texts would be too controversial for publication.

"Besides, they were already published by Lady Oxford. I am referring in the main to 'Pericles, Prince of Tyre'. They need not be included. Nor 'The History of Henry VIII'."

Ben Jonson objected. "I completed that."

"I know, Ben. It's finished. Also we'll exclude 'Arden of Feversham', and other early drafts, like 'The Spanish Tragedy' since 'Hamlet' treats of that subject more fully. We'll make it in three parts: twelve comedies, twelve histories, twelve tragedies. That's enough."

The discussion turned to a frontispiece. "Who can draw our father's likeness?"

"Let someone who did not know him. We'll find a young engraver. He can work from father's full-length portrait in robe with book and skull."

"What book?"

"His little golden notebook which he kept always by."

"Where's that gone?" Ben Jonson asked, sitting up.

Henry Wriothesley examined the beautiful ornature of the ceiling and kicked Henry deVere under the table, who fell silent in the middle of finding his voice, which he never found, so settled on whistling.

"And might I propose," said Elizabeth deVere Stanley, the Countess of Derby, speaking for herself and two younger sisters, "that we retain our father's anonym, which I believe he used?"

"Then we'll alter father's portrait?"

"I don't think that necessary. How can the engraver get it right, afterall? Father's dead almost twenty years. We hardly recall what he looked like ourselves, except when we see a painting."

"I grew up with his portrait," said Henry Wriothesley. "He had it done and sent to me at Welbeck Abbey, when I was a child. I see his eyes wherever I go. His look is never far from me."

"Then there is nothing more for discussion?"

"Nothing."

So Edward deVere vanished. So effective did his disguise become as a front for a cause to which he had been so closely affiliated, like his father before him, and his grandfather, that the deVere family made even bolder steps in securing immortality for their creation.

His full-length oil portraits were retouched and all identifying marks were painted out.

I am a man who knew what was true, and what the price was for truth - it was lies.

Who needs the roar of the crowd, "clapper-clawed with the palms of the vulgar", when the glory of his vigorous - modest - exuberant - humble - noble - private life kept private, sets a model for any age and enlightens all with a cautionary tale who would bask in the fickle flame of fame and miss the fruits of private contemplation, "especially this author's comedies, that are so framed to the life that they serve for the most common commentaries of all the actions of our lives."

Who asked nothing for himself from "the smokey breath of the multitude", but trusting to "the grand possessors" for whom every author knows how to pray, "that will not praise it", the wise do not even cry.

It is rather an author's choice, and a glory to his theater, to know when it is timely to exit, and do it well, leaving the stage to others more suited to the lines yet unspoken, where grief need never dwell.

Here is the gift of a cautionary tale. Not only is there a beard for a barb of a bard, but there are others out there who would tell the truth and perish unknown, or else later be exposed, for their service. Who wants to know who? Again, so read how: The more deVere, the more Shakespeare.

If he would know an author, let him ask: "**How'r odes made**?" There is at least one more to be unknown - with the censor hot in pursuit.

He changes history best who does not seem to change anything, but remains like a virgin in the dark while the light shines. Better to be known in the silence of heaven for

346

greatness or modesty or anything at all than in the noise of earth's brawling ditch of bistros and playhouses for self-aggrandizement and celebrity.

There are more who must hide in plain sight, agree to change their identity and enter the anonymous gardens, where the musk-rose intoxicates dreams. That is the price of their glory - infamy, being in posterity. Where anonyms are found will truths abound.

First son, Henry Wriothesley, 3rd Earl of Southampton, lived to prevent King James from negotiating away the American colonies to Spain. Third son, Henry, the 18th Earl of Oxford, fought and was jailed and died at Henry Wriothesley's side, opposing the corruption and dishonor of the monarch and the disgrace into which England fell with the passage of two decades under James I.

Through the years, Henry Wriothesley strayed from the court, denounced King James' policies of reconciliation and marriage with the Catholic Spanish throne, for the king was proposing that his son, Charles, marry the daughter of the Spanish king, thus burying forever the old conflict between Protestant and Catholic. It was a marriage proposal conceived in hell, according to the Earl of Southampton and Protestants everywhere, who cared not at all about returning, even halfway, to the Church of Rome. Henry Wriothesley's leadership was pivotal in abolishing that marriage proposal. When Charles I became king, it was with a Protestant English queen.

Henry Wriothesley died at war on the continent in service to his country, having fought to save the American colonies, and leaving descendants in the Dukes of Portland, Devonshire and Northumberland. They were devoted defenders in the House of Lords, during future generations, of that most prized of English ideas - American liberty. His brother, Henry deVere, 18th Earl of Oxford, Lord Great

347

Chamberlain of England, died at his side. He was thirty two. They were famous as "The Two Henrys".

William Jones preached the Earl of Southampton's burial, for "this glory of his country", his "ladyship's wonderful joy and honor." It was "no small joy" for Jones to "stand in the presence of that mirror of nobility," to "hear his wisdom and behold his gracious conversation." Through thirty years of married devotion, Henry Wriothesley's "gracious countenance" had "dispelled all ill weather."

The process toward publication of The First Folio began on orders from London, in the last hours of the life of Robert Cecil, Lord Salisbury, who lay in his bed being eaten alive by a stomach cancer, and whose last wish was to ease his pain, whose wish was his family's command: under cover of night, that a pair of messengers were dispatched to the church at Hackney. "Do it - do it!" Cecil told them, shouting at them. "May doing that relieve this constant agony! Go do it!" He rolled toward the wall in his bed, turning his back to them. "Worms! I'm eaten alive by worms. They're everywhere I turn - in my service, in my house, in my stomach, devouring!"

The messengers arrived by horse-drawn cart at Hackney with their orders and a lantern, lighted by the moon. The arms and seals were ripped from Lord and Lady Oxford's burial place. The ruffians did as commanded so that Edward could be removed anonymously and stashed, to be hidden forever without a trace. What the Cecil family knew their Oxford daughters would make true.

"The lion will shake spears nevermore!"

Two grave diggers came in with their shovels and did some work, effacing all sign of those once interred, their station and degree, and with their plunder on the cart returned, covered in dirt, begrimed in sweat, by the same

348

route young Edward as the new-made first earl of the kingdom had taken fifty years before, to the city.

Said one of these two shoveling clowns: "Come, my spade. There is no ancient gentleman but gard'ners, ditchers and grave-makers."

Said the other: "Was he a gentleman?"

"'A was the first that ever bore arms."

"Why, he had none."

"What art a heathen? How dost thou understand the Scripture? The Scripture says Adam digged. Could he dig without arms?" asked the clown.

"Go to," said the other, who would not be a clown, but would be serious and take all seriously, to be taken so.

"What is he that builds stronger than either the mason, the shipwright, or the carpenter?" the digging clown asked, leaning on his shovel and wiping his brow.

"The gallows-maker, for that frame outlives a thousand tenants," spat the other.

So they laughed and started as their cart squeaked into the night from the church in Hackney, over the stones of the unfinished road.

When they reached Westminster Abbey, the unmarked box was buried in the Vere family crypt, under a stone on which three words were chiseled without a name or date: "Stone Coffin Beneath".

"Thus patience wins the day and those most persevering turn those, born nobles who were towering, into common clay."

The agents of Robert Cecil completed the mandate of his father Sir William, Prime Minister to Her Majesty the Queen, Lord Great Treasurer, Chancellor of the Exchequer, first Lord Burghley and founder of the House of Cecil, which continues to this day, all at the whim of a queen. While there remains a grave in the abbey in which Lord Burghley

349

buried those he ruled in his family, he did not place himself there. The Cecilian Rule reigned for eternity: Touching all, touched by none. Only his name was on the monument.

How right Mr. Ben Jonson (of foul temper) was later to say, being a man who never said anything kind if there was something more mean he could find:

"I, therefore will begin. Soule of the Age! The applause! delight! the wonder of our Stage! My Shakespeare, rise; I will not lodge thee by Chaucer, or Spenser, or bid Beaumont lye a little further, to make thee a room: Thou art a Moniment, without a tombe. . . For a good poet's made, as well as born, and such wert thou."

And he was forgotten, but did come within a stone's throw of Poet's Corner, as the clever Ben made clear.

"No pity, no friends, no hope: no kindred weep for me: Almost no grave allow'd me. Like the lily, that once was mistress of the field and flourish'd, I'll hang my head and perish."

An epitaph was written later by someone anonymously, first found three hundred fifty years afterwards, in a manuscript accidentally saved by the nephew of Arthur Golding, Edward's uncle and first tutor: "Edward deVere, only son of John, born the 12th day of April, 1550, Earl of Oxenford, High Chamberlain, Lord Bulbec, Sanforth, and Badlesmere, Steward of the Forest of Essex, and of the Privy Council to the King's Majesty that now is. Of whom I will only speak what all men's voices confirm: he was a man in mind and body absolutely accomplished with honourable endowments."

When the writer of the sonnets discussed who bore the canopy over his ruler, as he walked backward with his rear forward toward the crowd, he was not referring to an actor but to himself, the Earl of Oxford, at his queen's

350

triumphal, and funereal, processions, and King James' coronation in Sonnet 125.

Now Ben Jonson proposed that most curious of schemes.

"Let the plays live, Sir Robert. But give them another name. Let the words sing, the deeds blaze, the glories shine on England's pastoral claims, by a simple act of substitution, of a simpleton for a saint."

"You call my foster brother a saint, Ben?"

"Well, Sir Robert, not really, your lordship. Only in a manner of speaking. No, in fact. Not at all. No saint, no soldier, no statesman, no scholar, Lord Robert, nothing in the least, in fact. Not even a poet worth saving. Forget him. Forget that. Forget everything. I've said nothing. I only meant that you might save the words, and assign them to a simpleton's name, declare them the words of a common fool, and that would be England's saving, don't you think?"

"Are they still worth saving?"

"Well, not for me of course, or for your lordship. We've come beyond them. But her late majesty found their points amusing. Would it not be something for her memory? Especially as the names were changed?"

"So they leave no trace."

"That's right, Sir Robert. No trace at all. Vanished. Gone. Erased, as though they never were. And yet they'd be, assigned to the most lowly of gulls, a bubble, a jay, a mere laughingstock, his name a disgrace to the lowborn who were amused by him. Let his name rest with those who are no great shakes."

"Then, let it be, Ben, if it benefits you and me."

"True, Sir Robert. Then it is to be."

"Just so. To be. I have answered the question."

"O most truly, Sir Robert. Thank you. Thank you."

And so was the Earl of Oxford forgotten, and a butcher's apprentice remembered, by all who knew not and knew not what they knew, for who would believe a grain dealer from Warwickshire could give the lie to a kingdom's honor and a queen's virginity?

He was to be unknown as some go knowing into their grave unknown, unknowing in the deed they are to do. By simple substitution the truth I made to hide in plain sight. It is still the best policy to tell the truth, only there aren't so many policy holders. Common sense could prevail, of course, but it's not so common anymore.

Cunning Ben made sure of the scheme. After he cozened Robert Cecil for approval, then the author's friend Mary Sidney, Countess of Pembroke, then the author's three daughters, Grand Possessors of the play books themselves, and their husbands, nobles all, one a playwright, another the chief censor and the third eventually prime publisher of the collected works. But not until shrewd Ben published his own collected works first to demonstrate how it was done.

For this work with Edward's lifelong friend, Mary Sidney, in the double cube room at her estate, Wilton House, crafty Ben was paid a stipend of two hundred pounds a year ($50,000) while he edited the project and wrote its prime deceits, being one never to turn away from turning up a coin.

He made sure to stage a masque with the Earl of Oxford's daughter, Susan, who was married to the censor. And he covered that other base, deadly Ben did. He printed the name of his simpleton substitute, the country actor, in the cast lists of two of his own published plays, though the fellow performed no specific role in them, except to be mentioned.

Finally Ben made a trip to Stratford-upon-Avon. There he drank his substitute actor into a stupor, leaving him to die under a tree, a death most renowned down through the annals of history, a poetic death made legendary. But was it murder? A murder most foul? Ben did his best to appease the family who wondered what he was up to, coming in and drinking with their Will.

"We're friends, just friends. The lights burn blue. It is now dead midnight. Cold fearful drops stand on my trembling flesh. What do I fear? Myself? There's none else by. Ben loves Ben: that is, I am I. Is there a murderer here? No, yes, I am. Then fly. What, from myself? Great reason why - lest I revenge. What, myself upon myself? Alack, I love myself. Wherefore? For any good that I myself have done unto myself? I am a villain. Yet I lie. I am not. Fool, of thyself speak well. Fool, do not flatter. My conscience hath a thousand several tongues, and every tongue brings in a several tale, and every tale condemns me for a villain. Perjury, perjury, in the highest degree. Murder, stern murder, in the direst degree. All several sins, all used in each degree, throng to the bar, crying all, 'Guilty! guilty!' I shall despair. There is no creature loves me; and if I die, no soul will pity me and, wherefore should they, since that I myself find in myself no pity to myself? Me thought the souls of all that I had murdered came to my tent, and everyone did threat tomorrow's vengeance on the head of Ben. Just friends, just friends!" he told his Stratford hosts, and left them and their Will well buried by a monument.

Ben saw to the monument raised in the Stratford church, which featured a bust of his substitute player resting his hands on a sack of grain, a fit figure for a dealer in chaff, much to the satisfaction of his family - a widow, two daughters, one son-in-law, and a sister, plus another lad hanging about.

Now cold Ben could concentrate on the real mask, noting: "Thou art a Moniment, without a tombe" -

353

"Wherein the Graver had a strife
"with Nature, to out-doo the life:
"O, could he but have drawne his wit
"as well in brasse, as he hath hit
"His face, the Print would then surpasse
"All, that was ever writ in brasse.
"But, since he can not, Reader, looke
"Not on his Picture, but his Booke."

'Tis a shame the fate of an earl is left to be executed by a murderer. But then, who has not murdered once? And who would judge who is to judge what judgment be?

What matter was it, whether the author be known as Shakespeare or deVere?

Only so long as truth matters, simple, gentle, humble truth, on which all meaning is based, on which all knowledge is shared, on which all trust is evinced in the community of souls, is there reason to know. From the rooftops truth shouts truth, and none deny its source. Let the flowers tell what secrets men can not:

"A rose by any other name would smell as sweet."

So to repeat the truth and because it's true, it's nectar and forever youth: He did it, he did it, he did it, and was glad! Damned for breaking the code of silence, but damned glad.

"He did it! He did it! He didn't dare to do it but he did it. Damned if he would do it, he done did it and damned glad! Indubitably delighted, actually."

Imagine monkeys, apes and sprites alive in trees and speaking, leaves and flowers and water fountains singing.

"Bad is the world and all will come to nought
"When such ill-dealing must be seen in thought."
End story.

XXXIII

They would argue amongst themselves, shrewd Ben Jonson and his patrons, the family of the earl, as they prepared The First Folio for William Jaggard, the printer who was now blind, in bankruptcy and tied up in several lawsuits over money, but whom they were using as their publisher.

One such argument would be the order in which they presented the texts.

Because one patron of the Folio, Philip Herbert, Earl of Montgomery, saw 'The Tempest' first performed for him on his wedding day, and then had it performed again before King James I, when it succeeded in persuading the monarch to commute the death sentences of Herbert's friends, he was indeed most proud of its powers and put 'The Tempest' first. Not to mention that the wedding day was when he married Susan deVere, the third and youngest daughter of the Earl of Oxford. She handled sharp Ben personally and with him became the Folio's patroness, over the objections of her oldest sister, Elizabeth Stanley, Countess of Derby, who could not resolve her objections. She knew she was in her heart a laughing, loving, liberal deVere, but she was raised a stern and serious Cecil from which she knew she could not escape.

The sisters argued for not including 'Pericles, the Prince of Tyre' in the Folio at all. This play was about a ruler who committed incest with his daughter. It was a subject too delicate and too close to home to be discussed,

355

for its potential to rake through the coals of dormant Tudor gossip, awakening yet again those embers of disgusting whispers regarding the Tudors, the Cecils and deVeres.

Elizabeth wanted nothing recalling her father Edward's birth, or her brother Henry Wriothesley's birth, or her own conception, all of which were plagued with talk of incest. So 'Pericles' the play, with Susan's agreement, was excluded from the Folio, abandoned as publishing discard, verbal trash, out of respect for the family's privacy and good name.

The deVere's were relieved to censor all use of their name in connection with this Folio, and thus, through obscurity and disuse, to allay such hints of disgrace and family abuse as might dishonor them.

Crafty Ben Jonson had his hands full, fighting for publication, but when he answered them that the world would never know, that he had a fellow in Stratford who was set to assume responsibility, and blame, for having written everything, and the deVere family honor would not be compromised by so much as a hint of suspicion, not by a whit, they decided to push forward and allow him to construct his forgery, being repeatedly assured by sly Ben that their secret was well-kept and their identity would remain hidden. They were glad to be done with it, finally.

But to be remembered most is that final, glorious love in which their passions and pains were resolved and their suffering washed away.

The 2nd Countess of Oxford, Elizabeth, Edward's true and ever-reigning queen, allowed her copy of her late husband's sonnets to fall into the hands of a printer named Thorpe, when she was moving from her home at King's Place, Hackney, and a dealer named William Hall snatched it, in 1608. So they were brought out, under the title of "Shake-speare's Sonnets", together with the last three play books on which Edward worked, 'King Lear', 'Troilus & Cressida', and 'Pericles, the Prince of Tyre', ten years before the Folio ever was started.

On the publication of The First Folio of 'Mr. William Shakespeares Comedies, Histories, & Tragedies, Published according to the True Original Copies', November 15, 1623, in the vicinity of Blackfriars, London, at a secret Catholic service held on the third floor of a private house, the floor mysteriously gave way, plunging ninety five people to their inexplicable deaths.

All who knew the man who lived at the center of a controversy as deVere, lived on to recall an angel who neither challenged nor offended, who was baptized by all as Shakespeare.

His book is found under another cover.

XXXIV

A WORD FROM MUNDAY written in 1633 to the son of
Henry Wriothesley upon learning of the deaths of the 18th
Earl of Oxford and of the 3rd Earl of Southampton, who died
together in 1625, folded and enclosed in the last pages of the
golden book:

From A. Munday in his 80th year:
Most Illustrious Lord:
I am here set down of things once lived. Of your
grandfather, the 17th Earl of Oxford, most beloved, whom I
knew from youth, for whom I was want to transcribe all
matters of words he wrote, which from him like a river
flowed, from earliest times until after his death, being whole
volumes of 'Hamlets', and for that most faithful Lady
Oxford, I also served, and did myself a small partition of one
rising mountain build, as I have been a maker of story
structures in a battle for words that would to every writer
honor, these few remembrances of things past I give, that
you may be forever in glory with the knowledge of what he
did, before all is forgot. He was wont to write with others,
and by secretary transcribe once spoke; at night by light
made notes that were his guide from which contrived now
some thirty six works deemed fitting examples to survive as
one in his memory. We did at least two hundred then! No
hand was greater than his own amongst us. No day was done
until his words had come, nor satisfied unless he moved the
ears of others. But what was done by some for bread, by him

was done for dreams, as the quality of joy was everything. What it brought him in its gain was worthless, though it profited his minions much. He was of spirit gentle and of humor passing great, more generous than the sun, affording every man his time and all nature his generosity. As he urged us each, and was himself the most: Prosper-O! The finest candle ever lit, a shame his name will not be writ.

Yours Ever True,
Anthony Munday

This, Included with Munday's Letter:
Hackney, June 19, 1604.
To My Son, Henry Wriothesley:
I will have you understand of utmost importance - that I have always been proud, but never pleased, my name being greater before me and after me than it has ever been with me. I am of human parts and their sum makes less than I admire in others. As a man who would farm a field but harvests a single plant, I have fallen short of my best, and found myself where my interest took me and conscience warned me against. My name and station were a burden I could not comfortably bear, as I believed myself to be the worst of sinners. My father died but never left; cherished of me above all men, yet when he trusted me the most, I failed. He called me to a skill I lacked. And I often dreamed of this. He held his head in both his hands. He begged me for relief while I, a boy, stood helpless by, and could not share his grief. A physic rushed throughout his body. He cried his flesh was burning and his skin like parchment flashed afire. I was alone beside him in the forest when he stirred no more,

359

in the August wind. They said my mother's lover did it doubtless with her complicity. I lived in hate, which means alone, too hurt to feel at all. I have borne it, a mistake. Seek absolution in others, by service to them as I have done, by concern for them, by sharing with them. Thus did I move in this life from wealth to abject despair, from glory to poverty, from the greatness which was promised to the misery delivered. Yet joy ensued. You will remember me as a life forgotten, and your humble father. If others argue down my book, objecting obscuritie against it, I bid you answer that, above all names in the world I hated most was Lucifer, and all open writers are Luciferi. I will not blaze or publish till it please me. With lips sealed, and book closed, I remain your loving father, and commend you to eternitie,

Edward Oxenforde

XXXV

A FORWARD AFTERWORD
(end of the novel)

From 1661 to the 1700's, professors heretofore wed to Will Shaxpere of Stratford, about whom the only record of writing consisted of liens, leases, licenses, bills, and debts for tax evasion, came nightmarishly awake. Their man wrote nothing! And took no part or interest either. But a pay-off for an acting job well-done, doing nothing.

Just forty five years after the death of their prime citizen, the Rev. John Ward, of Stratford-upon-Avon, made a note in his journal to learn all he could of him, but all he learned was nothing, except that the man was of genial wit and no learning. Everyone who knew him testified to his swiftness, which is perhaps just the sort of character to be found playing comic relief.

Doubts about the Stratford man continued into another century with another warning in a paper to the Ipswich Philosophical Society given by James Corton Cowell, professing great consternation at having met in Stratford an "ingenious gentleman of the neighborhood who goes so far as to suggest that the reason for the non-existence of the manuscripts is that they were the work of some other person who had good reason for concealing his connection with them."

We have no argument with the Stratford man. He did a magnificent job at what he did.

361

Perhaps we can understand now the following, how, for the tongue that stung, where all who were described so sharply felt revealed, their only chance was by removing the author if they were going to remain concealed. Take his sources, from every record or reference, thereby assuring themselves of no place of ridicule in history, a discretion that would reign supreme.

As our historian declares: All who appeared in the plays and poems were agreed "that the author must never, *never* be known for who he was, lest his characters be seen for who they were, if heaven and earth had to be moved to prevent it. And for all we know, the inheritors of their power well into the future would be aware of that necessity and be obedient to it."

Censorship had to be done. In the end, censorship did its work and won.

So I close this golden book, bound richly up in crimson strings, and lock its golden clasp. My thoughts are moved by many things. Indeed, many have loved him, perhaps more than he loved himself. Surely we can know him no less, where all humanity was waged in that struggle alone with himself, not to live as others made him, but as he made himself, only as a man.

Isn't it strange that the Geneva Bible, which belonged to the Earl of Oxford personally, has, notated and underlined in his own hand, the very passages which were inserted into lines in the plays of Shake-speare? Just the way a schoolboy underlines passages and copies them for his own purposes. A discovery made in 1992 at the Folger Shakespeare Library.

Isn't it strange for our age that the two most famous portraits of Shakespeare, owned by the Folger Shakespeare Library in Washington, upon x-ray, show the painted-over crest and seal of the Oxford family and the Earl of Oxford himself under the touch-up?

362

To conclude with the answer to who'd write (heros wo'd!) and who really said, "I'll not trouble thee with words." (Shakespeare could!)

In 'Richard III', Act IV, Scene iv, line 350, the character of Queen Elizabeth asks:

"How long shall that title 'ever' last?"

In 'Third Part of Henry VI', Act V, Scene v, line 5, comes the answer in sweet wistfulness, spoken by a minor, modest character who then went to his execution, having played his part on that stage of old - one whose name for all the rest of history remains, as it just happens to be, in the words of Shakespeare, told:

"The Earl of Oxford speaks:

"For my part, I'll not trouble thee with words."

Thus closes our serpentine tale.

XXXVI

A knock comes at my library door. My friend is announced and I ask he be shown in. From our little Long Island village, looking down the green hill and through the trees over the sound, I can see the distant shore of New England. Then I greet my guest. He is our village magistrate who sits one night a month resolving local summonses issued by our policeman. "Thanks for coming, Judge Florio." At this my boys come in all breathless and asking, as impatience pushes them, if we can go back to Washington for a visit to the Folger Shakespeare Library before next week; they have a paper to write for their English teacher on 'Hamlet'. They must describe its author's intent. "Of course - only, too bad you didn't have time for that on our first visit," I say. They agree. "Then maybe you could learn more by reading here at home. I have a book for you, after all." They grumble but go. My friend and I sit down.

"You know," he says, "I'm very interested in the Elizabethan Age. I have an ancestor, a scholar who was rather well-known back then."

"By name of John Florio, I presume."

He answers: "Right."

"There's something I'd like you to look at, if you have the time."

He agrees.

I bring my golden book out. It is most beautiful. Its leather cover with golden borders encloses 194 parchment

364

pages, about five-eighths of an inch thick, measuring six and seven eighths by four and a quarter inches in dimension, four faded ribbons of silk to bind it with one golden clasp, the exquisite script of a clarity so simple, so steady, that each word is outstanding and read easily. I will hold this book before me as of a purity so moving, the penmanship possesses a power in every line, the heart is tempted to argue, that here was the very hand of God made manifest. The beauty of each word transformed our dark to day.

By 6AM my friend and I had earned the night. I knew I could not part with it.

"How do you suppose it was saved?"

"Oxford's son. I believe his widow gave it to the 19th Earl of Oxford who eventually took it to France and there it was kept by the unsuspecting, in some aristocrat's library, unread through the centuries."

My friend smiled. "The French are wonderful in treasuring all things beautiful."

"I venture to say there are more English secrets in French libraries than all the world can gather."

Now we come to our times. The 20th Century's revolution in truth continues. These marvelous discoveries - George Mallory, King Tut, Lucy (at seventy five thousand years the first humanoid), the five thousand year old Alpine Iceman with blue eyes, the sacrificed five-hundred-year-old Peruvian maiden in her golden regalia, even the twenty-thousand-year-old woolly mammoth in his block of ice, Caiaphas' bones, two thousand years in his sarcophagus after Jesus lived and died and was judged by those bones; the discoveries this century past in science, math - the astronauts on the moon - provide a litany of revelations where all was mystery before, unknown, now true, now unmasked, now transforming. We stand on the doorstep of infinity, witness to the Eternal Being, and lift our eyes to the stars, asking:

365

will the heavens ever be ours? How many further truths will be known in our time, the jewels in our national crown? Here in our land in our age all is truth and true. Damned be death for the risk of telling.

We stand in the pathway to my front door. My friend is walking toward his car which long ago fell still in the night, as the sunlight from the east peeks through the old oak tree to my left. He stops as his hand falls on the car door.

"If the world sees this - smoking gun - it's a *coup d'etat.*"

I go back inside after the sound of his engine is replaced by the song of early birds.

In the winter of the year 2000, the Folger Shakespeare Library and George Washington University, in *The Shakespeare Quarterly*, admitted that orthodox establishment academics are "losing the public debate over the authorship question." The editor added, it is "infuriating". But only for those who must have Authority, that stubborn bear.

Thus can some maintain: the Earl of Oxford, without my help, began winning the battle for recognition as the ghost of William Shakespeare - only four hundred years into his reign.

In every life there is a golden book
That takes true reading with the eyes to look.

On his final page, in his perfect, flowing, measured hand, Edward penned these four short lines, following which he left a space:

> *God hath rendered verdict here:*
> *I came and parted life deVere.*
> *Though what I offered will shake spears,*
> *None but my ghost in that appears.*

THE END

FINIS CORONAT OPUS

WHO HAS A BOOK OF ALL THAT
MONARCHS DO
HE'S MORE SECURE TO KEEP IT SHUT THAN
VIEW.

-- from Pericles, I.1.94-5

WRITERS MINT AS FICTION
WHAT THEY DARE NOT PRINT AS FACT

-- the Author

368

DEDICATION TO

"The Author of Waverly" (Sir Walter Scott), Stendhal (Henri Marie Beyle) Honore de Balzac (Honore Balssa), Boz (Charles Dickens), Currer Bell, Ellis Bell and Acton Bell (Charlotte Bronte, Emily Bronte and Anne Bronte), George Eliot (Mary Ann Evans), George Sand (Amandine Aurore Lucie Dupin, Baroness Dudevant), Lewis Carroll (Charles Dodgson), Mark Twain (Samuel Langhorn Clemens), O. Henry (William Sidney Porter), Joseph Conrad (Joseph Korzeniowski), Max Brand (Frederick Faust), George Orwell (Eric Blair), Henry Green (Henry Yorke), Josephine Tey (Elizabeth MacKintosh), Jean Plaidy (Victoria Holt), John LeCarre (David Cornwall), Patrick Dennis, (Edward Everrett Tanner), John Jakes, (Lyle Kenyon Engel), and more to come. To the myriad unknown: It is an obligation of the faithful and the devout who wish to belong and at the same time can not, to take an alias as did Aesop (an unknown slave), Terence (Scipio), Moliere (Jean Baptiste Poquelin), Voltaire (Jean Marie Arouet), Cyrano de Bergerac (Savinien), Nathaniel West (Nathan Weinstein), "Deep Throat" (still Anonymous of Watergate) and Anonymous of 'Primary Colors' (Joe Klein) - to undo the censors who would do them in or up or out. Joking is no joke. To those glorious behind the pen names of Ellery Queen and yours truly: May it not be forgotten who is forgotten in writing this. So read how! The author answers to none but the name given him by God. Just as "heros wo'd". Nothing is Perfect, friend.   -- Owen D. Rhodes

ACKNOWLEDGMENTS

To Robert Ostenberg Lindig, who noticed this manuscript handy, took it, vanished, returned and declared it a page turner, and has called often since to pronounce the wittiest earlicisms.

To Mildred B. Sexton, author of the series, 'What Shakespeare's Audience Knew', who took this, nursed it, called for more and got that too, being most precise in fact and spirit, then declared this book, by any name, welcome to the world.

To Richard F. Whalen, president-emeritus of the Shakespeare Oxford Society and author of 'Shakespeare: Who was He?' for his wise counsel and warm support.

To Barbara Burris, mystery author and scholar who found more answers than questions, and more help than hindrance in solving this crime.

To William Boyle, Editor of the *Shakespeare Oxford Newsletter*, who made the argument of the Pearl: an oyster is strong, but the pearl is made from friction; what's worst in the rub is best in the gem.

To Dr. Ren Draya, professor of literature, Blackburn College, who read and gave in warmth, wisdom and acuity.

For those books that form the gospel texts of this documented history: John Thomas Looney, 'Shakespeare Identified'; Bernard M. Ward, 'The Life of the Earl of Oxford'; Eva Turner Clark, 'Hidden Allusions in Shakespeare's Plays'; William Plumer Fowler, 'Shakespeare Revealed in Oxford's Letters'; Dorothy & Charlton Ogburn, 'This Star of England'; Charlton Ogburn, Jr., 'The Mysterious William Shakespeare'; Joseph Sobran, 'Alias, Shakespeare'; Elisabeth Sears, 'The Tudor Rose'; Lu Emily

Pearson, 'Elizabethans at Home'; and Roger A. Stritmatter, 'Edward deVere's Geneva Bible'.

To contributing members of the Shakespeare Oxford Society (US), and the deVere Society (UK); and to Darren Charlton for acute documentation. May the Earl of Rutland come forth from the womb of time.

To Karyn L. Sherwood, who corrected, grammartized, plotted, puzzled, researched, spell-checked, printed, copied, edited, encouraged, enthused, supported, published, frowned at, smiled with, advised, facilitated, represented, managed, comforted, believed - alas, much more! - and through all loved because she is the wife, friend, partner and very life, first, last and always, of this work and author (only).

Also Available
Published by OPUS BOOKS New York
www.opusbooks.com
fax: 516/365-8331

Opus 1 *SOME SONNETS OF FLAME & FLOWER*
By JAMES WEBSTER SHERWOOD
ISBN: 0-9661961-0-4 (Pbk) $12.00
Gathered from the Original 1959 Underground
101 Sonnets of Sex, God, the Circus & Love –
praised and collected by the peerless for its
classic sonnet structure and language –
for lovers of poetry, *this is enduring!*

Opus 3 *STRADELLA*
By JAMES WEBSTER SHERWOOD
ISBN: 0-9661961-2-0 (Pbk) $25.00
Reissued Classic Olympia Press/Grove Press
1960's Bestseller – "The Sunset Strip novel *par
excellence*, a very nearly perfect rendition of the
people and places of that unlikely community. A
geography of the grotesque" – *Los Angeles Times*
Banned in England by Act of Parliament –
Denounced by critics for its sexual content –
Its quality of beauty prevails in undimming prose-
poetry and "outrageous comedy" *(Rod McKuen)*
"The best Hollywood novel since *Day of the
Locust*" and "the most important Channel
Crossing since 1066" (Foyle's). The novel
Spawned *THE HOLLYWOOD OPERA* Sextet.

Collect
OPUS BOOKS
PRESERVING THE RECORD
Of the unspoken, unknown, unashamed